MOLECULAR BIOPHYSICS

Proceedings of an International Summer School held in Squaw Valley, California
August 17–28, 1964, sponsored jointly by the North Atlantic
Treaty Organization and the United States
Office of Naval Research

Edited by

BERNARD PULLMAN

INSTITUT DE BIOLOGIE PHYSICO-CHIMIQUE
UNIVERSITÉ DE PARIS
PARIS, FRANCE

and

MITCHEL WEISSBLUTH

BIOPHYSICS LABORATORY
STANFORD UNIVERSITY
STANFORD, CALIFORNIA

1965

ACADEMIC PRESS   New York and London

ACADEMIC PRESS INC.
111 Fifth Avenue, New York, New York 10003

United Kingdom Edition published by
ACADEMIC PRESS INC. (LONDON) LTD.
Berkeley Square House, London W.1

LIBRARY OF CONGRESS CATALOG CARD NUMBER: 65–23843

PRINTED IN THE UNITED STATES OF AMERICA

Contributors

Numbers in parentheses indicate the pages on which the authors' contributions begin.

PIERRE DOUZOU, *Laboratoire de Biophysique du Muséum National d'Histoire Naturelle, Paris, France* (239)

J. S. GRIFFITH,* *Department of Mathematics, Manchester College of Science and Technology, Manchester, England* (191, 411)

F. GROS, *Institut de Biologie Physico-Chimique, Université de Paris, Paris, France* (1)

JOSEPH O. HIRSCHFELDER, *Theoretical Chemistry Institute, University of Wisconsin, Madison, Wisconsin* (325)

MICHAEL L. INGERMAN, *Physics Department, The George Washington University, Washington, D. C.* (343)

HERBERT JEHLE, *Physics Department, The George Washington University, Washington, D. C.* (343, 359)

HARDEN M. McCONNELL, *Department of Chemistry, Stanford University, Stanford, California* (311)

CARLA G. MESSINA,† *Physics Department, The George Washington University, Washington, D. C.* (343)

MANUEL F. MORALES, *Cardiovascular Research Institute, University of California Medical Center, San Francisco, California* (397)

ALBERTE PULLMAN, *Institut de Biologie Physico-Chimique, Université de Paris, Paris, France* (81)

BERNARD PULLMAN, *Institut de Biologie Physico-Chimique, Université de Paris, Paris, France* (117)

EOLO SCROCCO, *Institute of Chemical Physics, University of Pisa, Pisa, Italy* (293)

* *Present address*: Department of Mathematics, Bedford College, London, England.
† *Present address*: National Bureau of Standards, Equation of State Section, Heat Division, Washington, D. C.

IGNACIO TINOCO, JR., *Chemistry Department and Lawrence Radiation Laboratory, University of California, Berkeley, California* (269)

GREGORIO WEBER, *Division of Biochemistry, Department of Chemistry and Chemical Engineering, University of Illinois, Urbana, Illinois* (369)

MITCHEL WEISSBLUTH, *Biophysics Laboratory, Stanford University, Stanford, California* (205)

Preface

This volume contains the major part of the proceedings of the International Summer School of Molecular Biophysics, held in Squaw Valley, California in August 1964 under the joint sponsorship of the North Atlantic Treaty Organization and the United States Office of Naval Research. The School included general courses and a series of seminars given by invited speakers. It was attended by about 150 participants coming from 13 different countries.

It is the duty and pleasure of the editors of this volume to express their gratitude to the sponsoring agencies for their generous contributions and in particular to H. J. Helms and B. Coleby of the Scientific Bureau of the North Atlantic Treaty Organization in Paris, M. A. Garstens of the Office of Naval Research in Washington, and E. A. Edelsack of the Office of Naval Research in San Francisco for their help in planning the general organization of the meeting. Special thanks are due to E. A. Edelsack, J. C. Breedlove, and R. Breger-Smith for their most efficient handling of the complex local arrangements to the complete satisfaction of all the participants.

Finally, the contributors to this volume are to be thanked for having taken some of their valuable time to record their lectures. The editors regret that some members of the teaching staff were unfortunately prevented, because of other duties, from contributing to this written account of the meeting.

August, 1965

BERNARD PULLMAN
MITCHEL WEISSBLUTH

Contents

ix

The Cell Machinery

F. GROS

Institut de Biologie Physico-Chimique,
Université de Paris,
Paris, France

PART 1. PRINCIPAL STEPS IN PROTEIN SYNTHESIS; STRUCTURE OF THE BACTERIAL CHROMOSOMES

The scope of the following lectures will be to try giving a generalized and over-simplified picture of the machinery involved in the synthesis of one of the most important macromolecules in the cell: the protein. Why is the study of protein synthesis so important? This is, evidently, because it identifies itself with the analysis of the dynamism of life, for proteins are the main supports and catalysts, and also the major constituents, of all cells.

Today, the interrelation of scientific disciplines is such that, to the same extent that it would not be forgivable for a biochemist to ignore the physical properties of macromolecules (if he wants to understand how they function and how they are reproduced), neither would it be forgivable for a biophysicist to ignore how the molecules he is considering pure physical entities are integrated, dynamically and topologically, in the cell architecture.

The principal aspects of the structure and functions of the cell machinery that will receive our attention can be classified as follows:

1. As an introduction, we shall first recall the very general scheme which can account today for the biosynthesis of polypeptide bonds from free amino acids.

2. We shall then examine the components of the protein-forming system, by focusing more, in the first two parts, on the properties of DNA, sRNA, and the ribosomal particles.

3. We shall then devote the third part to the problem of "information transfer" in order to get some hints on how proteins derive their specificities.

4. Finally, our last lecture will try to give a survey of the present status of knowledge regarding the regulation of protein synthesis, a problem which remains one of the most fascinating in modern biology.

Before starting, the following remarks might be worthwhile: The first has to deal with the field of molecular biology, in general. One of the main acquisitions of this discipline, during the last 10 years, is the realization that cells, even when derived from broadly different species, grow and reproduce themselves by mechanisms involving grossly the same enzymatic steps and performed by the same general constituents. Twenty years ago, it would have sounded revolutionary to claim that, despite differences in their morphological aspects or their physiological functions, cells derived from a specialized organ, such as liver, from a yeast, or from a bacterium contain the same protein-forming apparatus, and that, aside from minor details, can synthesize their protein according to the same metabolic patterns. Today this unitary concept of cell behavior not only is admitted, but even, we think, definitively proved. The situation is therefore such that a biochemist can speak about protein synthesis by considering solely the reactivity of the very general macromolecular components of the cell without having to precise the biological origin of these components.

Now, because bacteria constitute, by far, the best analyzed cell material in respect to their biosynthetic pathways and because, among bacteria,

Escherichia coli has received the greatest attention, most of the structures we are going to discuss will refer, in the majority of cases, to structures occurring in *E. coli*. This bacterium will be our *biological standard*.

The second remark deals with the general concept of template action. We shall admit that this concept is self-explanatory: *DNA* is made on a DNA template, *RNA* is very often made on a DNA template, but can also be made on RNA templates. As far as *proteins* are concerned, they are always made on a *RNA* template. This is a rule in nature. Why DNA is never made on an RNA template nor protein directly on a DNA template is probably a result of numerous selective steps in the course of physiological evolution. This is a problem that people interested in the origin of life will have to solve.

I. Principal Steps in Protein Synthesis

If we consider an oversimplified scheme of protein synthesis such as the one depicted in Fig. 1, we can distinguish three levels of increasing complexity: (a) the activation level, (b) the polymerization level, and (c) the "programmation" level.

Very briefly one sees, in this scheme, that free amino acids have first to receive a certain "impulsion" from ATP. This is called *activation*. The ultimate result of this is the formation of a product called "sRNA-amino acid" or "aminoacyl-sRNA." Those aminoacyl-sRNA products serve essentially to "position" or "adapt" each particular amino acid in regard to a specific RNA template also called messenger RNA (mRNA) sitting on cytoplasmic particles, the "ribosomes." Here the process of polycondensation begins: Each ribosome, by moving along on the RNA template, allows for the attachment of more and more aminoacyl-sRNA units; these units react together in forming peptide linkages; a polypeptide chain starts elongating, and, finally, the finished protein falls off from the multiribosome–template-RNA complex (called polysome).

We have to introduce an element of *specification* or programmation in order to account for the fact that each type of protein found in a cell differs from the other by well-defined physicochemical and biological properties. The programmation of the protein-forming machinery lies on the fact that the RNA template results itself from the *copying* of specific territories in DNA, the genetic material.

We see also, incidently, that the ribosomal particles whose role in protein synthesis appears at first glance so decisive contain an RNA moiety which is also a copy of a special region of the DNA. The same remark applies to sRNA, which serve to adapt the amino acids to the template. Thus, all RNA's have a common genetic origin, but we shall temporarily admit that

SCHEMATIC VIEW OF PROTEIN SYNTHESIS

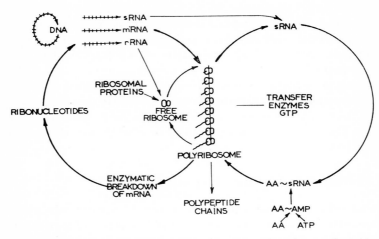

F<small>IG</small>. 1. Schematic view of protein synthesis. For the explanation see the text. sRNA, transfer or soluble RNA; mRNA, messenger RNA; rRNA, ribosomal RNA; AA, amino acids. From Watson (1964).

ribosomal and sRNA are the chemical "images" of much-smaller DNA territories, than what we have defined as template RNA. Finally, our scheme indicates that, after the RNA serving as "assembly line" has catalyzed several rounds of protein synthesis, it is decomposed into smaller fragments. We shall at present examine these different steps with slightly more attention.

A. Activation

Free amino acids are not *directly* incorporated into proteins, and it is largely to the merit of Lipmann (1941, 1949) to have suspected that ATP was providing the energy for this process. This was proved to be correct, for Borsook discovered (Borsook, 1952, 1956) that protein synthesis *in vitro* requires the participation of ATP. The exact mechanism of the activation reaction was finally elucidated by Hoagland and Zamecnik (Hoagland, 1955; Hoagland *et al.*, 1956), who assumed the formation of an intermediary "enzyme-AMP-substrate" complex of the type previously postulated by Maas (1956) and Berg (1956) to account for the activation of pantoate and acetate, respectively.

The reaction accounting for amino acid activation can therefore be formulated as follows (where "aa" stands for free amino acids):

$$aa + E + ATP \rightleftharpoons E\text{—}AMP \sim aa + PP \tag{1}$$

There is formation of a "ternary" complex with liberation of pyrophosphate.

The reaction, being freely reversible, can be studied by measuring isotopic exchange between PP and ATP. Another way lies in the use of hydroxylamine as a "trapping agent." Activated amino acids display a high reactivity toward hydroxylamine and form with it an aminoacyl hydroxamate very easy to titrate chemically or to identify chromatographically on paper.

The intermediate ternary complex has been isolated using substrate amounts of enzyme, and its synthesis has also been proved by O^{18} transfer experiments.

There is one specific activating enzyme for each of the 20 amino acids (Schweet *et al.*, 1957; Acs *et al.*, 1959; Cole *et al.*, 1957; Davie *et al.*, 1956; Berg, 1956). In this way the cell can select the building block that it will ultimately assemble into protein. *One exception* to this specificity rule is known, however: The isoleucine enzyme can activate valine. But the reaction, it is true, does not proceed much further, as the enzyme-AMP-valyl complex thus formed does not react with the sRNA specific for valine attachment (Berg *et al.*, 1962; Norris and Berg, 1964).

We have used the term *activation* to describe the preceding reactions, because there is formation of an "energy-rich" linkage, consisting of a mixed anhydride bond, between the COOH group of the amino acid and the phosphate group of AMP. The ΔF of hydrolysis for this linkage is of the order of -15 to -20 kcal.

An *a priori* reasoning could have easily led one to think that this type of activation was in itself sufficient for allowing the polymerization of aminoacyl residues on RNA. Yet, this is not the case, and it is to the merit of Crick (1956), to have had the remarkable insight that amino acid molecules cannot be sterically recognized by a polynucleotide template, another molecule having to serve as an *adaptor*. This is indeed what has been confirmed by the discovery of the *soluble RNA* (Hoagland *et al.*, 1957, 1958; Ogata *et al.*, 1957): In other words activated amino acids have to react with the adaptor, called soluble RNA (sRNA), before being transferred to the ribosomes-template-RNA complex:

$$E\text{—}AMP \sim aa + sRNA \rightleftharpoons E + AMP + sRNA \sim aa \qquad (2)$$

As can be concluded from reactions (1) and (2), activating enzymes not only join free amino acids to AMP, but they catalyze also the attachment of activated amino acids to sRNA. They have thus two functional sites: one to recognize the specific radical of the amino acid, and the other to recognize a specific sequence on the sRNA (Berg, 1958). A recent confirmation of this dual role has been given by Holley and Goldstein (1959), who showed, with the alanine-activating enzyme from yeast, that the

PP⇌ATP reaction, characteristic of amino acid activation, and the ATP⇌AMP reaction, characteristic of amino acid attachment to sRNA, always exhibit the same *relative* rates in the course of a very extensive purification of the enzyme. In fact, although sRNA's are exceedingly specific in their capacity for binding amino acids, there exist usually from two to three distinct types of sRNA molecules capable of binding one given amino acid (Berg *et al.*, 1962; Weisblum *et al.*, 1962; Sueoka and Yamane, 1962). This redundancy has to do with the degeneracy of the code and will be considered later.

B. General Properties of Soluble RNA

sRNA is a polynucleotide of low molecular weight, containing about 70 nucleotide residues. It has a molecular weight of the order of 30,000 and a sedimentation constant of 4 S (Hoagland *et al.*, 1958; Tissières, 1960; Brown and Zubay, 1960; Luborsky and Cantoni, 1962). It contains not only the four usual bases A, G, U, C, but also a large variety of the so-called odd or rare bases such as *pseudouridine* (ψU), in which the linkage between the ribose moiety and the pyrimidine moiety is a C=C linkage instead of an N=C one (Davis and Allen, 1957; Cohn, 1959). It also includes many methylated purines or pyrimidines (Littlefield and Dunn, 1958; Adler *et al.*, 1958; Amos and Korn, 1958; Dunn, 1959; Smith and Dunn, 1959), such as the compounds: thymine, methyladenine, methylcytosine, or methylguanine. The relative contents in these "rare" bases can differ markedly from species to species (e.g., *E. coli* sRNA contains thymine ribonucleotides liver sRNA does not, but contains methylcytosine that *E. coli* contains only in trace amounts). All sRNA chains, although they have the same average length, probably have different nucleotide sequences. This is proved by the fact that they can be separated by countercurrent distributions as pure biological entities reacting only with *one single* amino acid [cf. the work of Holley (Doctor *et al.*, 1961; Apgar *et al.*, 1962)].

If one compares the general compositions of the specific sRNA's thus purified, appreciable differences can be found. For instance, if we consider the case of three specific sRNA's derived from yeast and reacting, respectively, with the three amino acids alanine, tyrosine, and valine, striking differences can be observed. The alanine-sRNA contains much less adenine than the others; it contains methylated guanine, but no methylated adenine. The valine-sRNA contains methylated adenine but no methylated guanine. Finally the tyrosine-sRNA contains approximately 15% of its total residues in the form of nine minor nucleotide components. Analysis of ribonuclease-digestion products derived from these specific sRNA's also suggests important differences in the arrangement of their nucleotide sequence: It is found that, of the 10 different types of large oligonucleotides obtained after separation on DEAE-Sephadex columns, only one, a trinucleotide, appears to be common to the three RNA components. Therefore the nucleotide sequences of the different sRNA entities probably have little in common (Holley *et al.*, 1963).

Yet, despite their specificity in nucleotide sequence, which might provide a molecular basis for the recognition of activating enzymes and of ribosomes, all the sRNA molecules have at least two common structural features. The chain always starts by a guanylic acid residue at the extremity bearing the 5′-phosphate radical, and it always ends with the trinucleotide sequence C-C-A, in which the adenosine residue represents the 3′-OH terminus:

A general formula of RNA's can thus be written:

After the reaction between amino acids and sRNA's has taken place, there is formation of an ester linkage between the 2′-OH group of the last adenosine residue and the carboxyl group of the activated amino acid (Singer and Cantoni, 1960; Zillig *et al.*, 1960; Ralph *et al.*, 1962).

The C-C-A sequence can thus be regarded as a *cofactor* for amino acid attachment (Hecht *et al.*, 1958a, b, 1959; Zachau *et al.*, 1958; Preiss *et al.*, 1959). Besides, there exist specific enzyme systems (Herbert, 1958, 1959; Canellakis and Herbert, 1960) which are able to specifically add or remove the C-C-A moiety. The building of this terminal sequence involves the sequential attachment of two CMP and one AMP residues from free CTP and ATP.

The molecular structure of sRNA has been studied in great detail. X-Ray diffusion analyses (Brown and Zubay, 1960; Spencer *et al.*, 1962) suggest a helical configuration. Actually, there is a very large body of evidence that most of the nucleotide residues, except ψU and the methylated bases, are engaged in complementary hydrogen-bonded associations, satisfying the Watson–Crick rules for base pairing (Cantoni *et al.*, 1963; Ingram and Sjöquist, 1963; Brown, 1963).

Two models have been proposed to explain the molecular conformation of sRNA, either a single hairpin-like structure (I) or a double hairpin-like

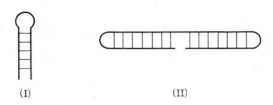

(I)   (II)

structure (II). Certain arguments plead in favor of (I) [e.g., some studies on oligonucleotide frequencies in the nuclease-digestion products (McCully and Cantoni, 1962) or the fact that, upon digestion of 40% of the chain by the snake venom phosphodiesterase (an enzyme attacking RNA sequentially starting at its 5' end), 90% of the hyperchromicity is lost (Cantoni *et al.*, 1963)]. In contrast, Felsenfeld and Sandeen (1962) and also Fresco *et al.* (1963) have concluded from studies on the hyperchromicity of sRNA at different wavelengths that their preparations contain regions rich in GC pairs, which can melt *independently* of AU-rich regions, as the temperature rises. Some other disturbing facts against (I) are that the residue most frequently found in *covalent* association with the second cytosine of the C-C-A sequence (the most internal one) is an adenine (Lagerkvist and Berg, 1962). Yet, Bell and co-workers (1963) have recently observed that, next to the G which forms the predominent 5'-endgroup, there is quite frequently a G or a C, and not a U, as one would expect from the structure predicted by (I).

Whatever the actual structure of sRNA molecules, it is evident from chemical analyses by Ingram and Sjöquist (1963) and by Holley *et al.* (1963) that a certain number of bases (something like 10) cannot find complementary partners for base pairing. This observation plus the fact that the odd bases (ψU, methylated bases) seem to be located in rather unique sequences (Cantoni *et al.*, 1963; Ingram and Sjöquist, 1963) lead to the conclusion that sRNA molecules contain *nonhelical regions* rich in methylated bases, probably clustered at the folding point of the single hairpin, or between the two hairpins in the double hairpin-like model (II). To this *nonhelical* region (or loop) could be devoted the role of containing the specific triplet (*anticodon*) matching the specific codon to which each sRNA has to adapt.[1]

---

[1] Recently (Holley *et al.*, 1965) the *complete nucleotide sequence* of an alanine transfer RNA isolated from yeast has been determined. The anticodon "CGG" seems to be located around the middle of the chain between two dihydrouracils (DiHU). This is the first nucleic acid for which the structure is known.

C. Polymerization

The role of sRNA is clearly to serve as an adaptor for specific amino acids, that is, to put them in front of the appropriate coding unit present in the template RNA.

This has been definitely proved by the experiments of Chapeville and associates (1962). As we shall see later, the synthesizing capacities of ribosomes can be programmed by the addition of specific polyribonucleotides prepared enzymatically. For instance, when the polymer poly U is added, there is formation of a specific homopolypeptide: polyphenylalanine. Similarly, when the appropriate *copolymer*, poly UG, is used, one can observe the selective incorporation of cysteine into a protein product because, if sRNA "charged" with radioactive cysteine is added to the system, radio-

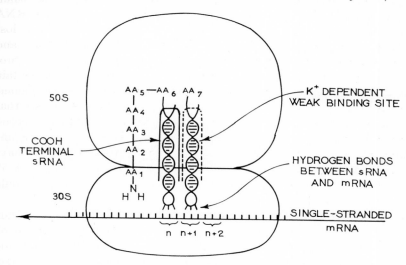

FIG. 2. Binding of aminoacyl-sRNA to the 70-S ribosomes. 30-S ribosomes provide the specific sites for mRNA attachment; aminoacyl-sRNA becomes linked to 70-S particles by cooperative forces. On the one hand, they are placed in a cavity present in the 50-S ribosome; on the other hand they are maintained by base-pairing exchange between a trinucleotide sequence, on the mRNA (codon), and a complementary region located on a loop in each sRNA molecule (the anticodon).

The steric interactions between the nascent polypeptide chain and the ribosomes probably contribute also to the reinforcement of the sRNA-70 S association. From Watson (1964).

active cysteine will be found incorporated into a protein linkage. Now if the "sRNA-bound" cysteinyl residue is *chemically* reduced *in situ* into alanine, this alanine will become incorporated in the place of cysteine, although the naturally occurring alanyl-sRNA intermediary *does not* function as a precursor for polypeptide synthesis under the conditions of programmation imposed in the experiment. In other words, the RNA template can "recognize" the sRNA which carries the specific amino acid but not the attached amino acid itself.

The principle of sRNA amino acid attachment to the "template-ribosome complex" is the following: When the template-RNA and the ribosome meet, they form a site, or "cavity," for the binding of specific aminoacyl-sRNA, the specificity being provided by the particular section (or codon) of the template RNA which comes in the close vicinity of the ribosomes (Spyrides, 1964; Watson, 1964). K^+ ions are required for this binding (Watson, 1964). Part of the binding forces holding the aminoacyl-sRNA involves the formation of complementary base pairs between the specific regions of the RNA in contact with ribosomes, called the *coding unit* (or *codon*), and a portion of the sRNA, called *anticodon*, because it has a sequence complementary to that of the codon (Fig. 2). In this way, each codon determines the exact *order* of amino acid condensation during protein synthesis. Yet, aminoacyl-sRNA's do not *spontaneously* condense when placed on the mRNA-ribosome complexes (called polysomes). Some other factors are also required. These are soluble proteins (also called transfer factors) recently purified by Lipmann (Nathans and Lipmann, 1960; Nakamoto et al., 1963; Hoagland and Comly, 1960) and GTP, the role of which is still unknown. When GTP and the transfer factors are added, peptide bond formation occurs according to Eq. (3).

$$
\begin{array}{ccccc}
R_1 & O & & R_2 & O \\
| & \| & & | & \| \\
HN_2{-}CH{-}C{-}O{-}sRNA_1 & + & HN_2{-}CH{-}C{-}O{-}sRNA_2{\rightarrow}
\end{array}
$$

$$
\begin{array}{ccccc}
R_1 & O & R_2 & O & \\
| & \| & | & \| & \\
HN_2{-}CH{-}C{-}NH{-}CH{-}C{-}O{-}sRNA_2 & + & sRNA_1,\ etc.
\end{array}
\tag{3}
$$

In this way, polypeptide synthesis proceeds by gradual elongation of the chain: The starting point corresponds to the future α-amino group of the finished protein, and the growing point is the carboxyl residue esterified to the last added sRNA of the elongating peptide (Bishop et al., 1960; Dintzis, 1961; Cannon et al., 1963).

The growing polypeptide chain, or *nascent protein*, remains bound to the ribosomes by the terminal sRNA until the relative slippage of RNA and ribosomes brings the ribosome to the distal portion of the template. At this time, the ribosome and the finished protein are released (Rich et al., 1963). There are good reasons to believe that the tertiary structure of the proteins is adopted in the course of polypeptide elongation, or at least before the release of the polypeptide chain (Kihara et al., 1961; Zipser, 1963).

When protein are composed of several protomers, these protomers associate by virtue of a complementation, either between free soluble protomers and ribosome-bound protomers (Zipser and Perrin, 1963) or between several bound protomers (Kiho and Rich, 1964).

D. Programmation

We shall not insist much, at the present state of our lecture, on programmation. We know that the *primary* structure of proteins is determined by the genes. This has been definitively proved by the classical experiments of Ingram and Pauling on the modified hemoglobins (Pauling *et al.*, 1949; Ingram, 1958; Hunt and Ingram, 1958), as well as by a large series of studies on the primary structure of altered bacterial enzymes resulting from a specific mutation in a given gene (Horowitz and Fling, 1953; Maas and Davis, 1955; Suskind *et al.*, 1955; Yanofsky, 1963; Perrin *et al.*, 1959; Garen, 1960; Levinthal, 1959).

If we admit that the assembling process of amino acids has to take place on an RNA template, we are somewhat forced to assume (and this is in fact the case) that this template is a copy of DNA. The statement "DNA makes RNA and RNA makes protein" constitutes the *central dogma hypothesis* in biology.

For a long time, it was admitted that, as ribosomes contain a high-molecular-weight RNA, ribosomal RNA was serving as the hypothetical "assembly line." We shall see later that this view is not correct. It is established today that the *true active template* is a distinct RNA called *messenger RNA* (mRNA), so designated because it carries the genetic information from DNA to the cytoplasmic particles (Jacob and Monod, 1961b (see Fig. 1).

In summary the general scheme for protein synthesis can be depicted by two simple equations:

$$\text{DNA} \longrightarrow \text{mRNA} \tag{4}$$

$$\text{mRNA} \xrightarrow{\text{Ribosomes}} \text{Protein} \tag{5}$$

Reaction (4) is called *transcription*; reaction (5) is called *translation.*

Ribosomes can be regarded as devices which serve to *translate* the code defined by the succession of ribonucleotides into the language proper to the protein molecules.

II. Structure of the Bacterial Chromosome

Before discussing the general properties of ribosomes, it may be appropriate to make a few general remarks about DNA. We do not intend to give any exhaustive description of the physicochemical properties of this nucleic acid; this problem will be covered elsewhere. We shall be concerned with DNA here, to the extent that it represents the *reservoir* of genetic information which determines the primary structure of all proteins.

As there are good reasons to believe that, at least in bacteria, the protein-forming apparatus is closely linked to DNA, we should like to comment on the configuration and molecular size of the genetic apparatus in these microorganisms.

Cytological studies in the past decade show that, as far as the ultra-structure of their genetic apparatus is concerned, cells of bacteria and of blue-green algae are quite different and much simpler in organization than those from plants or animals. Two groups can thus be defined: (1) the *eukaryotes* that possess a characteristic nucleus, and (2) the *prokaryotes* in which the nuclear equivalent does not show a typical chromosome-like structure in the sense that it is not bounded by a nuclear envelope and does not divide by mitosis (Ris and Chandler, 1963). Bacteria, indeed, are prokaryotes: They contain a Feulgen-positive material localized in very discrete vacuoles under the form of one, two, three, or four chromatinic bodies or chromosomes, this number depending upon the state of the division.

Several questions can be asked about these bacterial chromosomes: (1) Can they be studied in their native state, that is, without fixation by strong chemical reagents, and under the absence of shearing? (2) What is the form of the bacterial chromosomes (linear or circular)? (3) How are chromosomes cytologically related to the other cell components?

Considerable progress has been made in the course of the last four years for treating viruses or micororganisms in order to observe the native shape of their chromosomes. These techniques have been particularly developed by Kellenberger's group (Ryter *et al.*, 1958) and by Kleinschmidt and Zahn (1959), who discovered that, by mixing DNA with a protein such as cytochrome c in an ammonium acetate buffer, DNA spreads in a mono-layer at an air-water interface. One can, for instance, prepare protoplasts of bacteria (that is, suspensions of bacterial cells devoid of their wall) or a suspension of phages, and burst them in a protein monolayer. One then sees very long fibers with very few free ends.

In some instances, this technique has permitted measurement of the length of the fibers with great precision. Thus T2-DNA is about 50 μ long, T4-DNA 76 μ, while the DNA from phage λ is only 16 μ long (Ris and Chandler, 1963).

However, it is only recently that, in using a method somewhat different, Cairns (1963) has been able to study autoradiographically unbroken chromosomes of *E. coli*. The strain from which the chromosomes are studied is first labeled with tritiated thymidine. The cells are then lysed in the presence of lysozyme and a chelating agent; the lyzate is then extensively dialyzed, and finally drained on membranes that are submitted to auto-radiography. It is found that up to 1% of the chromosomes are unbroken and appear like a more or less tangled circle with a circumference of 1100 μ, corresponding to about 52 T2-DNA equivalents, which represents a molecular weight of 2.9×10^9 daltons.

That *E. coli* chromosomes appear like circular structures was not so much of a surprise, since Jacob and Wollman (1957, 1958a, b, 1961), as well as Adelberg (Taylor and Adelberg, 1960), had to postulate that the genetic apparatus of this bacterium is a continuous structure, in order to account for their results on transfer experiments.

It is worth recalling that, in certain strains of *E. coli*, there are individuals containing a DNA factor *distinct* from the chromosome and apparently not connected with it. It is called the *fertility* factor. We shall designate by F+ the individuals who have the factor and by F− those who do not. We shall use the general term of *episome* to designate fragments of DNA such as the fertility factor which can exist *free* in the cell or eventually inserted inside the circular chromosome. In certain strains (called Hfr), the episome can become inserted at any point on the chromosome, and the cell in which this happens can transfer very efficiently its chromosome inside the cyto-plasm of an F− recipient. (Eventually, the sex factor can be transferred itself from a male to a female by a process called sexduction; Jacob *et al.*, 1960b.) Both the Hfr and F− cells conjugate by a sort of protoplasmic bridge, and the chromosome is inserted by passage through the bridge.

Jacob and Wollman (1961) have observed that, if strong shearing forces are applied to bacteria in the course of conjugation, the bridge itself can be broken, and the zygote will express only the phenotypic characters corre-sponding to the portion of the chromosome already injected. It is evident that, by using such a technique, one can determine the order in which genes are transferred. When this is done, one observes that, although the order of transfer is always the same, the first genes to be transferred or, if one prefers, the starting point, might differ from one Hfr strain to another. This situation can of course be best explained by assuming that the bac-terial chromosome is originally a *circular* structure, which becomes broken by the insertion of the "fertility" (or sex) episome, as is the case in Hfr strains. Those cells with a broken chromosome can transfer it into a female. The transfer always begins at the point adjacent to the sex factor, the sex factor itself always being the *last* to be transferred (Fig. 3). It is assumed that the insertion point can vary from one strain to another, to explain why the genes first transferred vary from strain to strain. Besides, certain strains can transfer the chromosomes clockwise and others counterclockwise.

Finally, there are strains of Hfr which have an exceptionally high fre-quency of transfer (VHf). Those strains are able to transfer the entire

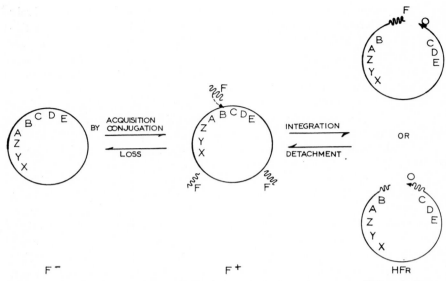

F_{IG}. 3. Diagrammatic representation of sexual types in *E. coli*. An F⁻ strain has a closed genetic apparatus but no sex factor (episome F). An F⁺ donor has outside its circular chromosome (and not integrated into it) several episomic elements called F or fertility factors. During the conversion F⁺ → Hfr, an F factor becomes attached at any given point of the chromosome. From Jacob and Wollman (1961).

male chromosome in 110 min. By using different VHf strains, one can demonstrate the *continuous* linkage of all known markers and construct a circular map (Jacob and Wollman, 1961; Taylor and Adelberg, 1960) (Fig. 4).

Circularity does not seem to be a character restricted to bacterial genomes. The genetic apparatus from bacteriophages of the T series, and from many viruses seems also to exist as a closed ring. This is the case for polyoma or papilloma viruses (Weil and Vinograd, 1963; Dulbecco and Vogt, 1963; Crawford, 1964) or for the replicative form of the bacteriophage $\phi \times 174$, a virus which contains a single-stranded DNA molecule.

Certain DNA molecules when extracted with great care exist as linear structures that can reversibly form a closed ring under appropriate conditions such as a suitable ionic environment. Most remarkable is the case of the DNA from phage λ, which when extracted exists as extended fibers 16 μ long that can form rings in the presence of certain divalent cations or when kept for some time at low temperature in a medium of high ionic strength (Hershey *et al.*, 1963).

This capacity of taking a ring configuration depends upon the presence of so-called "sticky ends" at both extremities of the DNA fibers. Those

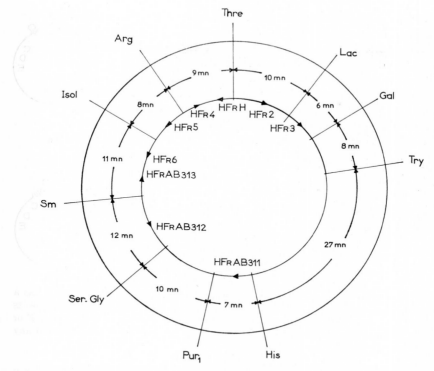

FIG. 4. Simplified circular map of an *E. coli* chromosome. The arrows in the inner circle indicate the origins for the penetration of the chromosome among different Hfr strains. The times in the middle circle correspond to the periods elapsed between the penetration of two specific adjacent determinants in the course of a sexual transfer.

sticky ends can be seen in electron micrographs (Ris and Chandler, 1963). Recent studies from Kayser (1964) show that sticky ends correspond to single-stranded regions, about ten nucleotides long. Their integrity is required for the maintenance of the DNA-transforming activity or for infectivity, since replication of these ends by the enzyme DNA polymerase abolishes the biological activities of λ-DNA preparations, whereas digestion of the replicated portion by an endonuclease acting at the 3′-OH end can restore this activity.

Circularity of DNA, we shall see, can be a very good index of nativeness of a preparation, because it restricts the transcription of certain DNA's by the RNA polymerase to only one of the two complementary strands (Chandler *et al.*, 1964).

Another important question dealing with the structure of native DNA molecules concerns the possible presence of protein or amino acid "linkers" covalently inserted inside the DNA chain. It has been proposed a few years ago (Freese, 1958; Taylor, 1962; Kellenberger, 1960) that the DNA molecule, instead of being continuous, is composed of subunits joined by linkers. The reason for such a speculation was the necessity for packing or folding a tremendously long chromosomal structure inside a nucleus. The essential feature of the linkers model is a DNA duplex with a regular sequence of linkers alternating in two chains, and located opposite a gap in the complementary chains (Fig. 5).

The only evidence as yet in favor of linkers can be listed as follows:

1. Amino acids are always found to be present even in the purest DNA preparations. For instance, according to Bendich and Rosenkranz (1963), there is one molecule of phosphoserine for 1000 nucleotides in sperm DNA and in calf thymus DNA, and one for 500 nucleotides in T4-DNA.

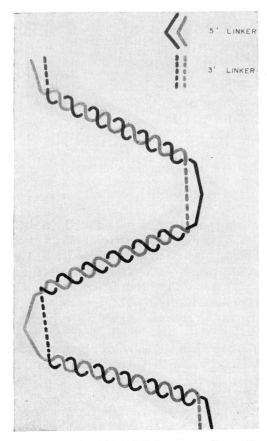

FIG. 5. Schematic representation of DNA linkers (according to Taylor, 1963).

2. Certain agents, such as hydroxylamine or some reducing agents, can convert even circular DNA molecules to large fragments (of molecular weight approximately 500,000) still dispalying normal melting behavior (Vinograd, 1964; Bendich and Borenfreund, 1963). This suggests that the site of cleavage could be at an amino-ester bond of the type found in aminoacyl-sRNA.

It might also be worth speculating a moment about the presence of *preexisting breaks* located at some points in the DNA duplex. These breaks could indeed provide punctuation points for the starting or ending of the transcription of genetic operons by the RNA polymerase. Their existence has been postulated several times by different schools. In fact, it remains highly controversial.

On the one hand, making equilibrium sedimentation analyses of unbroken DNA molecules or of the polynucleotide fragments obtained by treating these molecules with formaldehyde, Thomas and his colleagues (Thomas and Berns, 1961; Berns and Thomas, 1961; Thomas, 1963) have come to the conclusion that there are no pre-existing breaks or "weak points" in the molecules of T2- and T4-DNA. The method used should be able to detect even a single interruption if it occurred in the middle third of the molecule. Burgie and Hershey (1961) concluded similarly in studying chromatographically the size distributions of the breakage products obtained by short or prolonged stirring of DNA molecules. The probability of breakage seems to be governed by hydrodynamic factors in the region of the stirring blade rather than at weak points.

On the other hand, Marmur (1964), by comparing the width of the bands obtained in sedimenting at equilibrium density denatured DNA from phage α (a DNA which upon denaturation can separate into two bands of different buoyant densities), finds that one of these bands is clearly *wider* than the other, a result suggesting that it could contain pre-existing interruptions.

The last comment we want to make about bacterial chromosomes concerns their topological relationship with the other structures of the cell: Are chromosomes dispersed freely in the cytoplasm, or do they form an association with certain components of the cell?

Recent experiments due to Jacob and co-workers (1963) about the regulation of DNA replication have led these authors to propose a general theory, an implicit part of which is the prediction that chromosomes or episomes are not free in the cytoplasm but are closely attached to the cell membrane. When cell bipartition has just finished, there is a signal "triggering" the activation of the insertion point (called initiator). *The DNA begins to be replicated at this point and always at this point* (Sueoka and Yoshikawa, 1963; Nagata, 1963).

When the chromosomal structure has finished its duplication, a new signal triggers the growth of the cell surface in an equatorial plane of the cell. The formation of a new septum is initiated. According to Jacob and his colleagues, it is precisely the elongation process of the surface which would allow the separation of the parental and replicated chromosomes and their distribution among the two daughters cells.

This scheme is not a purely abstract view. Recently, it has received some direct support from electron-micrographic studies on cells of *B. subtilis* or of *E. coli* placed in hypertonic media (2*M* sucrose). Ryter (1963) has been able to observe that retroaction of the mesosomal structure toward the cell surface attracts the chromatinic body toward the bacterial membrane. This treatment allows us to see clearly the attachment of chromosomes to a limited section of the membrane as postulated in the model of Jacob *et al.* (1963).

PART 2. RIBOSOMES[2]

As we have seen in Part 1, ribosomes constitute the cell device for translating the RNA code—which is composed of a succession of triplets—into the language proper to the protein grammar. They do so by attaching aminoacyl-sRNA in front of each "coding triplet" present in mRNA. Because ribosomes have such a fundamental role, and because 80–90% of the RNA of the cell exists in the form of ribosomal particles (Roberts *et al.*, 1963), the rest being sRNA and mRNA, it is of prime importance to analyze what are the chemical, physical, and three-dimensional structures of ribosomes.

As pointed out by Watson in a recent review (Watson, 1964): "In this respect, the attitude of Biochemists has an obvious parallel with the experiments on enzyme function. Here many people work on how molecules act without knowing their exact chemical structure." In fact, although we know interesting facts about ribosomes, we still do not understand their ultrastructure, nor their functioning.

The definition of ribosomes is relatively recent. Twenty years ago, Claude (1943) first observed particles of about 200 Å in diameter among the microsomal fractions from animal cells. Analysis of the microsome fraction released from the membrane by deoxycholate treatment showed the presence of objects with sedimentation coefficient values between 20 and 100 S (Peterman and Hamilton, 1957).

In bacteria, the situation has been thought to be completely different for some time. The first real recognition of ribonucleoprotein particles in these organisms is due to the work of Schachman, Ts'o and their co-

---

[2] Many developments in this section have been inspired by the reading of the articles by Watson (1964) and by Roberts *et al.* (1963).

workers (Schachman *et al.*, 1952; Chao and Schachman, 1956; Ts'o *et al.*, 1956), who demonstrated that particles similar to those found in higher organisms also exist in the cytoplasm from several microorganisms. This is a rather good illustration of our previous statements about the similarities in the ultrastructure of the cell components from widely different species.

The term *ribosome* was introduced by Roberts (1958) in opposition to the older term of *microsome*, in order to distinguish the true particulate material from the remainder of the microsome fraction, composed mostly of lipoproteins.

As we pointed out already, ribonucleoprotein particles are currently regarded as one of the principal machines of the cell for protein synthesis, a belief which has gradually emerged from Cassperson's (1950) and Brachet's (1950) hypothesis according to which cells rich in RNA are those where protein synthesis is the most active. Soon after (Borsook *et al.*, 1950; Littlefield *et al.*, 1955), several workers succeeded in showing that, when radioactive amino acids are added as protein precursors to tissue slices, the radioactivity appears to be located in the particulate fraction before accumulating in the soluble fraction. A symmetrical demonstration of the role of ribosomes was finally provided by the use of *in vitro* systems, since it was found that in extracts from animal tissues (Littlefield and Keller, 1957), as well as from bacteria (Lamborg and Zamecnik, 1960; Tissières

TABLE I

INCORPORATION OF C^{14}-ALANINE INTO CRUDE EXTRACT, SUPERNATANT, AND RIBOSOME FRACTIONS[a,b]

Composition	dpm	dpm/mg dry weight
Crude extract (0.5 ml, 3 mg ribosomes)	8300	1080
Same without ATP, PEP, and PK	100	13
Same without PEP and PK	139	18
Same with 1×10^{-4} M Mg^{2+}	116	15
Supernatant (0.1 ml)	41	51
Ribosomes (3.2 mg)	423	132
Ribosomes (3.2 mg) + supernatant (0.1 ml)	2900	725

[a] From Tissières *et al.* (1960, p. 1453).

[b] The complete reaction mixture consisted of 1 μmole ATP, 5 μmoles phosphoenolpyruvate (PEP), 40 μg pyruvate kinase (PK), 0.022 M KCl, 0.01 M magnesium acetate, 1 μmole C^{14}-alanine (3×10^5 dpm), and the cell fraction in a total volume of 0.85 ml. Incubation was at 37°C for 45 min. Radioactivity was measured in precipitate from hot trichloroacetic acid. Note that the supernatant which contains all the soluble proteins is inactive unless supplemented with ribosomes.

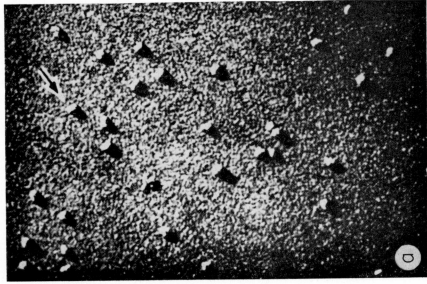

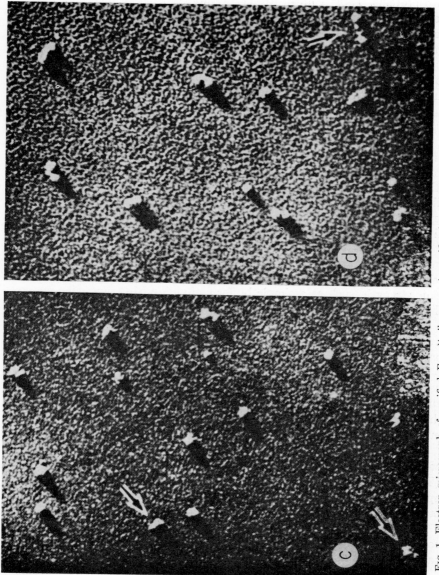

Fig. 1. Electron micrograph of purified *E. coli* ribosomes (magnification ×100,000). (a) 30-S preparation; (b) 50-S preparation; (c) 70-S preparation; (d) 100-S preparation (Hall and Slayter, 1959).

et al., 1960), ribosomes are essential for incorporating C[14]-amino acids into proteins. Table I illustrates an example of such an incorporation experiment. We shall see later how crude extracts are obtained. We can compare here the relative incorporating efficiencies, of (1) a total extract from *E. coli*, (2) the purified ribosomes or supernatant fractions, and (3) a mixture of both. Although the supernatant contains almost all the soluble proteins of the cell, its protein-forming ability is weak, if it is not supplemented with ribosomal particles.

I. Preparation of Ribosomes

First, how can ribosomes be purified in order to become suitable for further analysis? In Fig. 1, we see an electron micrograph of *E. coli* ribosomes showing that the cytoplasm is full of very refringent bodies rich in RNA which are nothing but ribosomes. There are of the order of 10,000 ribosomes per cell in *E. coli* (Roberts *et al.*, 1963). Ribosomes can be separated quite simply from the rest of the cell components by proper differential centrifugation of bacterial lyzates.

These bacterial lyzates are easy to prepare. One way consists of treating cells with an enzyme that destroys the external wall and then bursting the cellular structures so obtained (called protoplasts) into a medium of low ionic strength, such as a simple buffer containing Mg^{2+} ions (for reasons that we shall see later).

As a result of centrifuging such a lyzate at a relatively low acceleration, we separate a pellet, made of cell membranes and containing most of the bacterial cytochromes, and a soluble extract containing the bulk of the cellular RNA. When this extract is submitted to further centrifugation at very high speed, we obtain a supernatant fraction in which all the sRNA and most of the soluble proteins are present, plus a sediment, which has the composition of a ribonucleoprotein. This sediment is made up of almost pure ribosomes.

Another method for breaking open bacteria in order to prepare ribosomes consists of a grinding in the presence of a very fine alumina powder (Tissières and Watson, 1958). The mixture is then submitted to the same operations as before to purify the particulate matter from the soluble matter.

Indeed, the ribosomes thus obtained are usually not pure; they are still contaminated with many soluble proteins and with some sRNA, which can be eliminated by repeated washings in Mg^{2+}-containing buffers, or by centrifuging the ribosome suspension through a linear sucrose gradient.

II. Dissociability of Ribosomes; Effect of Mg^{2+} Ions

The most striking property of ribosomal particles is that, in their true functional state, they appear to be composed of two different subunits which can be defined by their sedimentation constants, 50-S and 30-S particles, respectively; the first one has twice the size of the other (Figs. 2, 3, and 4).

Furthermore, these subunits can be dissociated or reaggregated depending upon the ionic environment. Generally speaking, the principal ions affecting the dissociation equilibrium are Mg^{2+}, K^+, and polyamines (principally the compound spermidine, which exists in large concentration inside bacteria or phage systems). The following equilibria can be observed (Tissières and Watson, 1958; Roberts et al., 1963; Watson, 1964):

$$30\ S + 50\ S \xrightleftharpoons[K^+]{Mg^{2+} \text{ or spermidine}} 70\ S \qquad (6)$$

$$2 \times 70\ S \xrightleftharpoons[K^+]{Mg^{2+} \text{ or spermidine}} 100\ S \qquad (7)$$

The question is now: Which of these four types of particles constitutes the functional unit in protein synthesis?

It results from Eq. (7) that, if the concentration in K^+ is low or the Mg^{2+} concentration high (around $10^{-2}M$), 70-S and 100-S particles will predominate. Actually, it turns out that growing cells accumulate largely

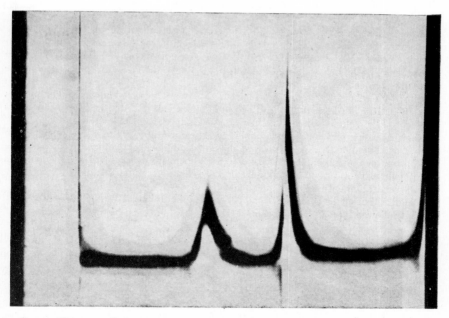

Fig. 2. Ultracentrifugation analysis of E. coli ribosomes. Centrifugation of a ribosome pellet in $10^{-4}\ M$ Mg. Note the 50-S particle (on the right) followed by a 30-S ribosome (Roberts et al., 1963).

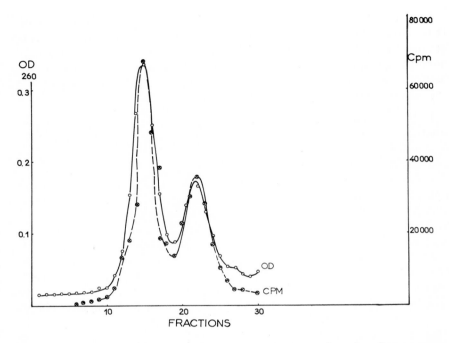

F<small>IG</small>. 3. Zone sedimentation of 50-S and 30-S ribosomes through a linear sucrose gradient. A preparation of ribosomes is obtained from *E. coli* cells previously labeled for 1 division time with C^{14}-uracil (0.2 μc/ml). Cells are broken open by alumina grinding in the presence of Tris (5×10^{-3} M) buffer (pH 7.2) containing Mg^{2+} ions (10^{-2} M). The ribosomes are collected by centrifugation of the extract at 100,000 g (2 hr). After one washing by resuspension in the Tris-Mg buffer, they are dispersed in a small volume of a Tris (5×10^{-3} M) Mg (10^{-4} M) (TM_4) buffer (pH 7.2) and dialyzed for a few hours against a large volume of the same low Mg^{2+}-containing buffer.

The suspension obtained is layered at the top of a 5–20% sucrose gradient made in TM_4. Centrifugation 8 hr at 23,000 rpm, in a "swinging bucket" rotor. After puncturing the bottom of the tubes, 29 fractions of 0.8 ml each are collected. OD measurements were made after a tenfold dilution. Radioactivity measured on 0.1 ml of each sample after precipitation with 5% TCA in the cold.

The direction of the centrifugation goes from right to left. Note the 50-S subunit on the left followed by a 30-S subunit on its right.

K^+ ions to such an extent that they realize an internal concentration close to 0.1M (Solomon, 1962). Under those conditions the *relative* proportion of 100-S particles is greatly reduced. This fact, plus the observation that the particles found associated with mRNA, in extracted polysomes, are of the 70-S type (Warner *et al.*, 1963) show that ribosomes function as a 70-S entity. Indeed, 30-S or 50-S ribosomes when used separately are inactive in protein synthesis.

How does Mg^{2+} influence the dissociation equilibrium of 70-S ribosomes? It is usually thought that it neutralizes the negatively charged phosphate groups, thus allowing the ribosomal RNA moieties of 50-S and 30-S sub-units to form an association, probably by the exchange of hydrogen bonds between complementary base pairs. There are observations in support to this assumption:

1. It has been found by Watson and his associates that, upon moderate treatment by formaldehyde, under conditions where the groups most likely to react are the free NH_2 groups of adenine, guanosine, or cytosine, 30-S and 50-S particles lose their ability to bind together (Watson, 1964).

2. Monier (1964) has recently observed that, at high Mg^{2+} concentrations, the 16-S RNA, which we will see is the main RNA constituent of the 30-S particles, can associate with the 23-S ribosomal-RNA, usually present in the 50-S particles, to form a new 30-S RNA fraction or even heavier aggregates.

That Mg^{2+} ions actually bind to the phosphate groups in ribosomes, can be established by titrating these groups in the presence of increasing Mg^{2+} ion concentrations. At saturation, the Mg^{2+}/P ratio is about $\frac{1}{2}$, as expected (Edelman *et al.*, 1961; Watson, 1964). K^+ ions have a competitive effects toward Mg^{2+}, binding when the concentration of this cation is low. When *free ribosomal-RNA* is mixed with increasing quantities of Mg^{2+}, almost identical binding curves are found, at least for Mg^{2+} concentrations which do not precipitate RNA. It is interesting to note (Watson, 1964) that there are about 5000 negatively charged groups in the RNA present in a

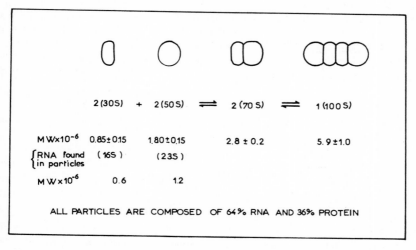

FIG. 4. Dissociation equilibria between ribosomal particles (Watson, 1965).

70-S particle, of which about only 450 are neutralized by ribosomal proteins. This is why the neutralizing effect of divalent cations is probably so important. *In vivo*, owing to the enormous concentration of ribosomes in the cell, the molarity of the phosphate groups of ribosomal RNA is $0.12M$, a level which is about two times too large to be neutralized by the internal Mg^{2+} concentration (which has been estimated to be close to $3 \times 10^{-2} M$) (Lubin and Ennis, 1964). This is probably why cells are also rich in polyamines that can neutralize the surplus of negatively charged phosphates. (Watson, 1964).

III. Shape and Molecular Weights

Figure 4 and Table II schematize the relative shapes of the ribosomes and summarize the best values obtained concerning their molecular weights (Roberts *et al.*, 1963). We see, clearly, that 50-S ribosomes are rather "round shaped," whereas 30-S and 70-S ribosomes are "elongated." Electron micrographs of 70-S particles clearly reveal the dimeric form of these particles, but their resolution does not permit us to see more details (Hall and Slayter, 1959).

The molecular weights indicated here have been calculated from sedimentation constants, diffusion constants, or viscosity measurements. The functional unit (70 S) has a molecular weight of 3,000,000. If we realize the time it has taken biophysicists to derive the complete three-dimensional structure for the oxygen-carrying molecule of myoglobin, which is 200 times smaller, it may probably take much longer to understand the molecular architecture of ribosomes (Watson, 1964) unless they appear to harbor a regular pattern composed of a small number of infraunits as some people, like Spirin, for instance, seem to believe (Spirin, 1964). It can at least be concluded from examining preparations of ribosomes stained with uranyl acetate that they are not organized like plant viruses, with an outside protein shell surrounding an RNA thread. But no real insight will be

TABLE II

DIMENSIONS OF *E. coli* RIBOSOMES[a]

Particle	Shape	Dimensions (Å)[b]	Mol. wt. $\times 10^{-6}$
30 S	Prolate	95 × 170	0.76
50 S	Oblate	170 × 140	2.0
70 S	Oblate	200 × 170	3.4

[a] From Roberts *et al.* (1963, p. 307).
[b] Dimensions calculated by electron microscopy examination of purified ribosome preparations.

possible until ribosomes can be crystallized. According to recent reports (Langridge, 1964), cysts of certain amebas have been shown to contain crystalline objects, of the size of the 70-S particles, and to exhibit the same conformational changes in solution as ribosomes. This might constitute a good starting point for crystallographic studies.

IV. Principal Components in Ribosomes

Purified ribosomes are practically pure ribonucleoproteins; they contain 40% protein and 60% RNA, and this proportion does not seem to vary much from species to species.

A. Proteins

Three types of protein components can be found in ribosomes: (1) the nascent protein, that is, the fraction of the soluble protein not yet released from these particles; (2) the structural proteins, that is, the bulk of the ribosomal proteins linked to RNA; and (3) some enzymatically active proteins.

1. The nascent proteins do not amount to more than 0.1% of the total soluble proteins of the cells. In *E. coli* they represent the equivalent of what is synthesized in 5 seconds of normal growth (McQuillen *et al.*, 1959).

2. Enzymes: When it was first observed that ribosomes contain enzymes, some hope began to develop that this enzymatic activity was associated with the functioning of these particles in protein synthesis. A few years ago, Elson (1958) described the presence of a very potent ribonuclease (RNase) attached to ribosomes. This discovery looked, at first glance, promising because the bound RNase could be regarded as the enzyme responsible for the destruction of mRNA, after its translation has been completed. This idea was tempting in as much as the bound RNase was found to be a *latent* enzyme, unable to attack the RNA of the ribosome itself unless the enzyme was activated by treatment with strong urea solutions. Furthermore, most of the RNase was found to be located exclusively on the 30 S. However recent reports from Neu and Heppel (1964) have led one to question the significance of these observations. These authors found that RNase is not "physiologically" attached to ribosomes; it is located somewhere between the wall and the membrane; but during cell extraction, it becomes *artificially* attached to the 30-S ribosomes with which it forms a stable complex. Furthermore, it has been suggested that RNase, in general, has no major function in the cell despite previous thoughts, since Gilbert and Watson (1964) recently obtained mutants of *E. coli*, which although completely free of RNase, can grow at a perfectly normal rate. As far as the proteases (Bolton and McCarthy, 1959), DNase (Elson, 1958), and poly A synthetase (August *et al.*, 1962), the presence of which had also been

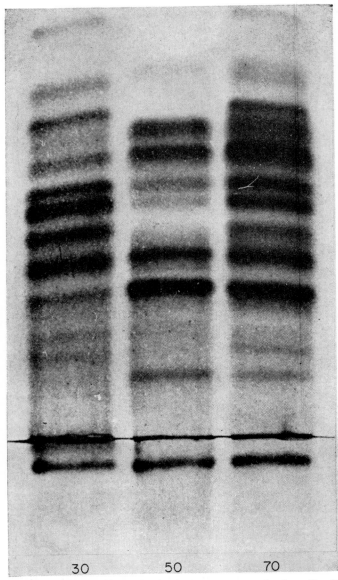

FIG. 5. Starch-gel electrophoretic pattern of ribosomal proteins from *E. coli* ribosomes. The acetic acid-soluble proteins from the three ribosomal preparations are submitted to electrophoresis at pH 5.6. The proteins are stained with Amido Black. One can see a striking difference in the protein composition of the 30-S and 50-S subunits. The bands characteristic of 70-S ribosomal proteins are represented by the sum of the bands observed, respectively, in the 50-S and 30-S preparations. No additional bands are encountered (Waller, 1964).

reported on ribosomes, are concerned, the question is equally open as to whether they represent true "ribosome-bound" components, or whether they become artificially stuck to the particles in the course of their isolation. It may be, after all, that ribosomes have no enzymatic activity at all per se, besides their role as catalysts for the binding of aminoacyl-sRNA to mRNA.

More interesting and intriguing is the problem of the nature of ribosomal proteins.

3. Ribosomal proteins: This study is quite recent, owing to the difficulty in analyzing these proteins, for they are very insoluble in an aqueous phase. Yet after dissolution in glacial acetic acid, a treatment which precipitates the RNA, they can be recovered by freeze drying and redissolved in strong urea solutions from which samples can be submitted to all sorts of analysis (Waller and Harris, 1961).

It turns out that only two main α-amino terminal residues can be detected by the use of the dinitrofluorobenzene technique: alanine and methionine. On the basis of their amino acid composition and of the amount of α-NH$_2$ terminal residues, Waller and Harris have calculated that the average molecular weight of ribosomal proteins is between 25,000 and 30,000 (Waller and Harris, 1961).

The peculiarity about these proteins is that, although they fall into two distinct classes depending upon their "end-terminal residues," not all chains within each of the two major classes are chemically identical. For instance, by disk electrophoresis the presence of at least 30 different bands can be shown in each 70-S ribosomal particle. Approximately ten are found in the small 30-S subunit, whereas the larger "50-S" most likely contains about 20 (Waller, 1964; Watson, 1964) (Fig. 5). Recent developments in the field of the so-called "suppressor mutations" have focused even more attention on the significance of these proteins (Gorini and Kataja, 1964).

B. Ribosomal RNA

Although four types of ribosomes can be found in the cell, their RNA moiety belongs to only two distinct classes (Kurland, 1960); one class corresponds to a polynucleotide sedimenting at 16 S and having a molecular weight of 550,000, whereas the other type of ribosomal RNA is twice as large. It sediments at 23 S and has a molecular weight of 1.15×10^6; 30-S particles contain only the 16-S type, whereas 50 S contain the 23-S type (Fig. 4).

The base composition of ribosomal RNA is remarkably constant. Not only do the 16-S and 23-S RNA have roughly the same average composition (Midgley, 1963; Roberts et al., 1963) (Table III) but, if one considers ribosomal RNA from bacterial species in which the composition of DNA differs considerably, one cannot see any concomitant variations in the RNA composition.

As an illustration of this fact, although the A + T/G + C ratios can vary between 0.35 (in *Sarcina*, or actinomycetes) and 2.7 (in clostridia) (Belozersky and Spirin, 1960), that is, by a factor of more than 7 the A + U/G + C ratio shows an amplitude of variation only between 1.03 and 1.4.

This finding has been one of the reasons to suspect that ribosomal RNA cannot be the real template for protein synthesis, because, were it the case, its average composition ought to vary somewhat in parallel to that of the homologous DNA.

The reason for this "monotony" in composition is probably that ribosomal RNA is made by a *small number of genes* in all species, and that those genes have undergone very few mutations in the course of the biological evolution.

TABLE III

NUCLEOTIDE COMPOSITION OF VARIOUS RNA'S[a,b]

Organism	DNA	sRNA	70 S	50 S	30 S
Escherichia coli	A 24	A 20.5	25.1	25.4	24.8
	T 24	U 16.5	20.4	19.6	21.5
	G 26	G 33.2	32.6	33.5	31.0
	C 26	C 29.8	21.9	21.5	22.7
Bacillus subtilis	A 29	A 20.2	25.9	26.2	26.5
	T 29	U 17.6	20.8	19.3	21.6
	G 21	G 32.9	31.0	32.0	29.6
	C 21	C 28.3	22.3	22.5	22.3
Proteus vulgaris	A 32	A 19.1	26.2	26.5	24.7
	T 32	U 18.3	20.7	20.8	20.4
	G 18	G 33.3	31.4	31.4	31.9
	C 18	C 29.3	21.7	21.3	23.0
Aerobacter aerogenes	A 22	A 19.7	25.5	25.6	25.3
	T 22	U 18.8	21.1	21.2	21.5
	G 28	G 32.3	31.5	31.2	30.8
	C 28	C 29.2	21.9	22.0	22.4
Pseudomonas aeruginosa	A 18	A 20.8	25.7	26.3	25.1
	T 18	U 17.1	21.0	21.3	20.5
	G 32	G 33.8	31.6	31.2	32.8
	C 32	C 28.3	21.7	21.2	21.6

[a] From Roberts *et al.* (1963, p. 306).

[b] Note that bacteria of different DNA composition show a total ribosomal RNA composition which is quite constant. There is a very slight difference only between the RNA's derived from 30-S and 50-S ribosomes.

That ribosomal RNA is, like mRNA, a direct "gene product" and does not accumulate by self-duplication is shown by the work of Yankofsky and Spiegelman (1962a, b, 1963), who have found that radioactively labeled ribosomal RNA can form artificial hybrids when heated in the presence of an excess of denatured DNA, this treatment being followed by a slow cooling of the mixture. Knowing the amount of RNA needed to saturate a given amount of DNA, Spiegelman has calculated that about 0.1% of the genome makes all the ribosomal RNA of the cell, and, furthermore, he has shown that the 16-S and 23-S subunits were complementary to different loci, a result indicating that, although they have the same average composition, their residues are not ordered according to the same sequence.

V. Physicochemical Properties

Ribosomal RNA exists as single-stranded molecules containing hairpin double-helical regions held together by hydrogen-bonded base pairs, as shown by Fresco et al. (1960).[3]

About 75% of the bases are involved in hydrogen bonding; the remainder most likely can participate in association with chains of mRNA (Asano and Watson, 1963; Hayes et al., 1963; Watson, 1964).

VI. Metabolic Stability

It is important to stress here that ribosomal RNA and ribosomes are *metabolically stable:* When they have incorporated a radioactive precursor in covalent linkage, they never exchange it with the surrounding medium. This conclusion derives mostly from the very careful experiments performed a few years ago by Koch and Levy (1955) and is also supported by the more recent work of Meselson (Davern and Meselson, 1960).

VII. Mechanism of Ribosome Synthesis

Although the genetic origin of ribosomal RNA has been clearly established (Yankofsky and Spiegelman, 1962a, b), still very little is known about the mechanism by which ribosomal RNA and ribosomal proteins are synthesized and about the way they become assembled to form a particle. Important questions remain to be answered.

[3] The optical properties (Doty et al., 1959), X-ray diffraction patterns (Spencer and Poole, 1965), mass per unit length (Timasheff et al., 1961), and acid base properties (Cox and Arnstein, 1963) all support the "hairpin loop" model. Very recently, fragments of ribosomal RNA from yeast have been crystallized (Spencer and Poole, 1965) and X-ray diffraction studies have confirmed the double helical nature of the secondary structure (Cox, 1965).

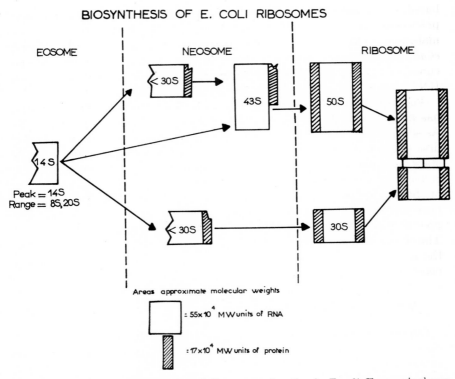

BIOSYNTHESIS OF E. COLI RIBOSOMES

FIG. 6. Schematic representation of ribosome maturation in *E. coli*. Eosome is shown as pure RNA (there are no indications that it contains some proteins). The 30-S neosome is thought to contain less than half of the protein of the 30-S ribosome. That a 30-S neosome which is a precursor of a 43-S neosome exists as a separate object is not a compulsory feature of this scheme. The 43-S neosome is shown with only one-quarter of the protein of the 50-S ribosome. It is not known what fraction of its protein enters directly or by way of the 30-S precursor to it (Roberts *et al.*, 1963).

1. We know that 16 S and 23 S are made under the control of certain genes on DNA, but are these RNA chains produced in one single step or does the cell first manufacture ribosomal RNA precursors which are gradually converted into the final product?

2. How are ribosomal proteins made? We know that they constitute a very special class of insoluble proteins (resembling the proteins from plant viruses). Does the synthesis of these proteins involve the participation of a mRNA distinct from ribosomal RNA, or is ribosomal RNA itself the primary template involved?

3. At what stage do RNA and protein combine to form a ribosome? Despite extensive analyses of these problems, most of them still remain partially unsolved. The experiments designated to answer them were

based on the use of short pulse labeling with radioactive RNA, or protein precursors, in order to monitor some eventual intermediates in ribosome maturation (Roberts et al., 1963; McCarthy and Aronson, 1961; Britten et al., 1962). Another approach has been to study the type of particles accumulated when protein synthesis is inhibited, under conditions where RNA synthesis continues (Kurland et al., 1962; Nakada, 1964).

The most elaborate theory to date to account for ribosome maturation has been proposed by Roberts and his colleagues (Roberts et al., 1963). As schematized in Fig. 6, three successive stages are postulated: (1) The first is the synthesis of a common RNA precursor called *eosome*. At this stage no protein is found attached to the RNA. (2) The second is the conversion of eosome to *neosome*. This probably occurs by the assembling of the small eosome into RNA of slightly bigger sizes (16 S for the 30-S neosomes; 23 S for the 43-S neosome). At this stage, proteins would be present and they would derive from a pool of pre-existing molecules. (3) The third stage is the completion of neosome to ribosomes. This is done by the addition of newly synthesized ribosomal proteins to the unmatured neosomal particles.

VIII. General Remarks

Concerning the construction of ribosomes, there are no clues about why ribosomes contain two dissociable subunits. The fact that each of these subunits, as we shall see in a moment, perform distinct biochemical functions is not a sufficient explanation, since *a priori* the multipotentiality of functions could be achieved just as well by a single nondissociable particle having different active sites. It has been advanced that the reason for the two dissociable moieties is that somehow they have to come apart during the process of translation, but no ones knows exactly how.

Despite these unsolved questions, very clear progress has been made during the past 3 years about our understanding of ribosome function, since it is was realized that the 30-S and 50-S subunits have distinct but complementary roles.

The 30 S is the site for mRNA attachment, as has been established by the experiments of Takanami and Okamoto (1963) who found that poly U firmly binds 30 S particles but not 50 S.

In contrast, the 50-S subunit contains the binding sites for charged or uncharged sRNA's. There are clearly several (probably two) binding sites; one is K^+-dependent and very freely reversible. As we saw in the preceding part, this is a site made jointly by the conjunction of mRNA and 50-S ribosomes. It is proved by the fact that, when poly U is mixed with a 70-S particle, only the phenylalanyl-sRNA becomes attached to the 50-S part of the ribosome. When poly A (which we know codes for lysine incorporation) is mixed with a 70-S, only the lysyl-sRNA becomes attached to the 50-S subunit (Spyrides and Lipmann, 1964). So, clearly, the specificity of the site is provided by mRNA. Very recently (Leder and Nirenberg, 1964; Nirenberg and Leder, 1964), using a simple trinucleotide GUU, Leder and Nirenberg showed that a 70-S ribosome specifically binds the valyl-sRNA. Quite remarkably, UGU and UUG did not permit binding. This remarkable experiment provides a way for determining not only the composition but the *sequence* of the coding units.

Apart from this K$^+$-dependent binding site and as can be seen in Fig. 2 (Part 1), one must consider the existence of another site holding the poly-peptide sRNA chains. This results from the work of Gilbert (1963), who observed that after polyphenylalanine synthesis in the presence of poly U, and a dissociation of the 70 S by lowering the Mg concentration, the poly-phenylalanyl-sRNA complex remains specifically bound to the 50-S sub-unit, although the mRNA (here poly U) has already been dissociated. If the Mg^{2+} concentration is lowered still further, by prolonged dialysis, the nascent protein chain can finally be dissociated. If the Mg^{2+} level is raised again, however, as shown by Schlessinger and Gros (1963), the liberated polypeptide can be *reassociated* to the 50-S ribosome presumably by virtue of the terminal sRNA to which the nascent polypeptide was esterified. Finally, it must be recalled that, apart from these observations suggesting the existence of, at least, two sRNA binding sites on 50-S particles, it had already been shown by Cannon and his co-workers (1963) that simple mixing of purified 50-S particles and (uncharged) sRNA, in the absence of mRNA, would lead to the fixation of *one* sRNA molecule per 50-S unit. There are good reasons to believe, as this reaction does not require energy but only the addition of Mg^{2+} ions ($10^{-2}M$), that it involves the same site as the one holding the sRNA-nascent-polypeptide complex.

PART 3. TRANSFER OF GENETIC INFORMATION

I. Introduction

Until now, we have surveyed the different steps involved in the incorporation of amino acids into a protein product, regardless of the *nature* of the protein formed and with the implicit assumption that all the proteins are made according to the same biochemical mechanism.

Although the aim of molecular biology is to emphasize the common structures in all living organisms, as well as the common pathways in the formation of those structures, it has the more ambitious goal of understanding *why*, despite their identical organization at the molecular level, cells look so different and are usually diversified into so many different specific functions.

This part of the chapter will be devoted to the mechanisms whereby DNA can control the specificity of proteins. This problem implies two general questions: (1) Under what form does DNA store the genetic information? (2) How does the cell translate the DNA code into the special language that the ordered polypeptide chains represent?

We shall not consider in detail the facets of the first question. We shall simply admit here that the code is composed of a succession of *nonoverlapping nucleotide triplets* (Crick, 1959) and that this linear succession of triplets defines a linear succession of amino acids within the protein. This principle of colinearity has received a decisive support from the work of Yanofsky (1963), who showed that, when two mutations occur on adjacent sites of a gene, they lead to adjacent alterations inside the polypeptide chain specified by this gene. More recently, Sarabhai and his colleagues (1964) have also observed that, when the gene which controls the synthesis of the head protein of the phage T4 exhibits certain mutations called "amber,"[4] the effect of which is to interrupt the reading of the relevant mRNA by the ribosomes, one can isolate from these different mutants polypeptide fragments whose lengths are proportional to the fraction of the specific gene which is delimited, at one side, by the proximal portion of the messenger, and at the other by the mutated codon itself.

As far as the composition and sequences of the coding triplets specifying each particular amino acid, we shall not go over this question in detail, although the experiments on the coding problem have been subject, as is known, to a considerable advance, thanks to the work of Nirenberg and Matthaei (1961), of Nirenberg and his colleagues (1963), and also of Ochoa and his associates (Ochoa, 1963; Speyer *et al.*, 1963). We shall rather focus at present on the second question: How is the genetic code translated?

It is *a priori* evident that a sequence of deoxynucleotides cannot dictate the positioning of specific amino acids without the involvement of a complicated machinery.

For more than 20 years, biologists had admitted that the decoding of the genetic information was ensured by two successive operations: (a) the *transcription* of DNA to a template (or messenger) RNA and (b) the *translation* of RNA to proteins.

It was not, however, until recently that the exact nature of the mRNA has been recognized. This is due to the fact that the process of peptide bond formation occurs at the surface of ribosomes and that ribosomes contain most of the cellular RNA (see Part 2). Therefore, nothing was more logical than to equate the ribosomal RNA with the specific template for protein synthesis. This concept could be expressed by the statement: Each gene makes a specific ribosome, which makes a specific protein.

[4] So defined because the viruses which harbor them can develop on certain bacterial hosts (such as the strain *E. coli* B) but not on some others (such as *E. coli* CR-63).

It may be appropriate, at this stage, to describe briefly the main observations which played the most decisive role in the revision of this classical concept and the development of the mRNA hypothesis.

1. Perhaps one of the most general reasons lies in the fact that the composition of DNA can vary considerably among several bacterial species, whereas the composition of ribosomal RNA remains practically constant (Belozersky and Spirin, 1960).

2. The mechanism which accounts for the synthesis of phage-specific proteins was also difficult to reconcile with the classical scheme: It was known that, soon after infection of bacteria by phages, the synthesis of ribosomal RNA is blocked (Cohen, 1948; Hershey, 1953; Nomura *et al.*, 1960), and yet that the infected system ceases synthesizing host proteins and starts immediately manufacturing the new phage "induced" proteins, involved in the replication process or in th construction of the phage particles. Would ribosomal RNA be the universal template one ought to expect upon injection of viral DNA the neoformation of specific ribosomal RNA. Ribosomal RNA being metabolically stable, a net increase in RNA ought to be observed following infection:

Not only was this not the case, but it was found by Volkin and Astrachan that, in the course of infection by T2 or T4 bacteriophages, there is formation of a *metabolically unstable* RNA, which harbors the same general composition as that of the infectious DNA (Volkin and Astrachan, 1956a, b, 1957). Obviously, the phage-infected system was the site of synthesis of a new mRNA resulting from the copying of the injected viral genome.

3. A third observation, which was not in consonance with the idea that stable ribosomes can *directly* program the synthesis of proteins, resulted from experiments (Naono and Gros, 1960; Bussard *et al.*, 1960; Gros and Naono, 1960) on the mode of action of a pyrimidine analog, the compound 5-fluorouracil. When 5-FU, which is known to replace uracil in the RNA of various cells, is added to populations of *E. coli* growing exponentially, there is formation of biologically and physically altered enzymes. The same situation is observed in experiments with thiouracil by Hammers and Hammers–Casterman (1959). The striking conclusion which can be drawn from these studies is that base analogs cause an appearance of altered enzymes at a rate which is *immediately* maximal. To interpret this result, one had to suppose that RNA templates are metabolically *unstable* and therefore cannot be equated with ribosomal RNA (Davern and Meselson, 1960).

4. Finally Pardee and colleagues (1959) did an experiment designated to answer questions related to the regulation of enzyme synthesis, but which turned out to be quite decisive in respect to the noninvolvement of

ribosomal RNA as a template for specific protein synthesis. They crossed an Hfr strain, Lactose$^+$, (that is, genetically capable of making the specific enzyme β-galactosidase) with a F$^-$ (genetically unable to make the enzyme, as a result of a mutation in the structural gene), and they studied the rate at which active β-galactosidase molecules appear in the female cytoplasm following the transfer of the galactosidase gene. One must recall that, in the course of such transfer experiments, only the DNA of the male penetrates the female to the exclusion of all other cell components. By measuring the rate at which the galactosidase gene is expressed in the zygote, the authors found it to be immediately maximum. Again, had the galactosidase genes manufactured a new specific ribosomal RNA, an autocatalytic rise in enzyme synthesis ought to be observed, for ribosomal RNA is metabolically stable.

Jacob and Monod (1961b) were thus led to postulate that the messenger carrying the information must be a short-lived intermediate, therefore distinct from ribosomal RNA. They made the complementary hypothesis that ribosomes do not contain, by themselves, the specific information for the synthesis of each particular protein, since they have to be programmed by exogenous messenger-RNA.

This new concept of information transfer has received a definitive support which comes from three independent lines of evidence:

1. A few years ago in the laboratory of J. D. Watson (Gros *et al.*, 1961a, b), we succeeded in identifying, among exponentially growing bacteria, a new fraction of a metabolically unstable RNA which has many characteristics similar to the fraction already observed by Volkin and Astrachan (1956a, b) in phage-infected system, thus showing that metabolically unstable RNA fractions are not restricted to infected cells but represent the general rule in all biological systems. We shall come back to this point later. There are good reasons to believe that at least part of this unstable RNA is nothing but the bacterial messenger, the existence of which was hypothesized by Jacob and Monod.

2. At about the same period, an enzyme was discovered in several laboratories which has been given the name of RNA polymerase (or replicase) and which is responsible for the enzymatic copying of DNA to RNA *in vitro* using ribonucleosidetriphosphates as substrates (Weiss, 1960; Hurwitz *et al.*, 1961; Chamberlain and Berg, 1962; Ochoa *et al.*, 1961; Stevens, 1961).

3. Perhaps the most convincing and dramatic proof for the mRNA concept is the discovery that ribosomes have no fixed specificity for orienting protein synthesis, but function like passive sites which can be programmed indifferently by all sorts of mRNA's.

Two sets of proofs have been put forward: One derives from *in vivo* experiments by Brenner *et al.* (1961) and the other from the *in vitro* experiments of Nirenberg (Nirenberg and Matthaei, 1961). Brenner *et al.* (1961) have clearly shown that, after infection by the phase T2, the newly synthesized specific mRNA attaches to pre-existing ribosomes, on which it programs the synthesis phage-specific proteins. Thus, the *same* ribosomes, which, before infection permits the synthesis of host-specific proteins, are converted, after infection, into phage protein-forming sites.

Perhaps even more dramatic is the demonstration by Nirenberg that, when *E. coli* ribosomes are used in a subcellular system containing all the suitable effectors, they can respond not only to the addition of *E. coli* RNA to synthesize proteins but also, quite remarkably, to the addition of RNA from widely different sources. Yeast RNA derived from ascites tumor cells, tobacco mosaic virus, or bacteriophages induce a very active synthesis of proteins on *E. coli* ribosomes. It has even been shown that addition of the RNA from the RNA phage called f2, leads to the *in vitro* production of a protein chemically *identical* to the protein of the virus (Nathans *et al.*,

TABLE I

SPECIFICITY OF AMINO ACID INCORPORATION STIMULATED BY POLYURIDYLIC ACID[a,b]

Experiment no.	C^{14}-Amino acids present	Additions	cpm/mg protein
1	Phenylalanine	Deproteinized at zero time	25
		None	68
		+ μg Polyuridylic acid	38,300
2	Glycine, alanine, serine, aspartic acid, glutamic acid	Deproteinized at zero time	17
		None	20
		+ 10 μg Polyuridylic acid	33
3	Leucine, isoleucine, threonine, methionine, arginine, histidine, lysine, tyrosine, tryptophan, proline, valine	Deproteinized at zero time	73
		None	276
		+ 10 μg Polyuridylic acid	899
4	S^{35}-Cysteine	Deproteinized at zero time	6
		None	95
		+ 10 μg Polyuridylic acid	113

[a] From Nirenberg and Matthaei (1961, p. 1588).

[b] The principle of these experiments is to study the incorporation of various C^{14}-labeled amino acids, added singly or in mixture, to extracts of *E. coli* previously incubated so as to become depleted in endogenous mRNA, but supplemented with poly U as an artificial messenger-template-RNA. The radioactivity incorporated in the protein fraction is determined. Note that phenylalanine is the amino acid, of the 18 tested, which is the most extensively incorporated into a peptide linkage.

1962). Finally, one must underline the remarkable finding that, if *artificial* messengers, such as synthetically made homo- or copolynucleotides are added to *E. coli* ribosomes, the system synthesizes homo- or heteropolypeptides, the composition of which is strictly determined by the composition of the polymers added. Table I recalls this discovery by Nirenberg and Matthaei (1961): In the absence of exogenous messenger, the system incorporates very little radioactivity whatever the source of radioactive amino acid may be. In contrast, when the artificial mRNA (poly U) is added, C^{14}-phenylalanine, and this amino acid only, is incorporated to a considerable extent. The experiment described on Table II demonstrates

TABLE II

POLYNUCLEOTIDE SPECIFICITY FOR PHENYLALANINE INCORPORATION[a,b]

Experiment no.	Additions	cpm/mg protein
1	None	44
	+ 10 μg Polyuridylic acid	39, 800
	+ 10 μg Polyadenylic acid	50
	+ 10 μg Polycytidylic acid	38
	+ 10 μg Polyinosinic acid	57
	+ 10 μg Polyadenylic uridylic acid (2:1 ratio)	53
	+ 10 μg Polyuridylic acid + 20 μg polyadenylic acid	60
	Deproteinized at zero time	17
2	None	75
	+ 10 μg UMP	81
	+ 10 μg UDP	77
	+ 10 μg UTP	72
	Deproteinized at zero time	6

[a] From Nirenberg and Matthaei (1961, p. 1588).
[b] Note that poly U was the only homopolymer tested to provide information for the synthesis of polyphenylalanine.

that poly U specifically codes for phenylalanine incorporation, since, from the four homopolymers tested—poly U, poly A, poly C, or poly I—only poly U has the property to induce *in vitro* the synthesis of polyphenylalanine. In fact, there is not always an absolute fidelity in the translation of artificial homopolymers. It is known today that, under certain conditions such as low temperatures of incubation (Szer, 1964), high Mg^{2+} concentration (Szer, 1964), low pH, presence of certain antibiotics (Davies *et al.*, 1964; Grunberg-Manago and Gros, 1964) having a special affinity for the ribosomes, certain homopolymers, which in the majority of cases code for the synthesis of a preponderant type of homopolypeptide, can direct, at least to a small extent, the incorporation of amino acids into other types of polypeptides. For instance, poly U *can* code for the incorporation of leucine and, more generally speaking, for the incorporation of amino acids the corresponding codon of which contains at least two uracil residues. This *lack of absolute fidelity* of translation by ribosomes (ambiguity) is thought to be at the basis of action of suppressor genes (Gorini and Kataja, 1964) which can restore defects caused by point mutations taking place in a large variety of independent cistrons (Yanofsky and Crawford, 1959).

This restriction being made, one can establish (under the conditions defined by Nirenberg in the use of his subcellular system) what are the major "code words" for all the naturally occurring amino acids. Table III

TABLE III

PRINCIPAL CODING UNITS FOR THE NATURALLY OCCURRING AMINO ACIDS[a]

Amino acid	Nirenberg *et al.* (1963)	Wahba *et al.* (1963)	Bretscher and Grunberg-Manago (1962), Michelson and Grunberg-Manago (1964)
Alanine	CCG, UCG, ACG	UCG, CAG, CCG	—
Arginine	CCG, AGA, UGC, CGA	UCG, GAA, GCC	—
Asparagine	UAC, ACA, AUA	UAA, UCA, CAA	U, A; A, C
Aspartic acid	CGA, GUA, GAA	CAG, UAG	CAA
Cysteine	UUG	UUG	UUG
Glutamic acid	CAG, GAA, AGU	AUG, AAG	AAC, A, G
Glutamine	AAC, AGA, AGU	UCA, CAA	CAA
Glycine	UGG, AGG, CGG	GGU, GGA, GGC	UGG
Histidine	CCA, ACU	UCA, CCA	CCA
Isoleucine	UUA, UAA	UUA, UAA, UCA	UUA
Leucine	GUU, CUU, UUU, UCC, UUA	GUU, CUU, AUU, CCU	CUU, AUU, UUU
Lysine	AAA, AAU	AAU, AAA	AAA
Methionine	UGA	UGA	—
Phenylalanine	UUU, CUU	UUU, UUC	UUU, UUC
Proline	CCC, CCU, CCA, CCG	CCU, CCC, CCA	CCU, CCA
Serine	CUU, CUG, ACG, UCC	CUU, UCC, CAG	UUC, CCU
Threonine	CAA, CAC	UCA, AAC, ACC	C, A
Tryptophan	UGG	UGG	U, G
Tyrosine	UUA	AUU, UAC	AAU
Valine	UUG, UGA	UUG	UUG

[a] This table is taken from Grunberg-Manago and Gros (1964).

recalls the composition of the different codons that have been assigned to the various amino acids. The mere fact that in a few cases more than one codon can define a single amino acid shows that the code is *degenerate*. In fact, of the order of 45 codons are known (Wahba *et al.*, 1963). Although this is beyond the scope of our discussion, it is worth pointing out that the code, so defined, appears to be universal (Von Ehrenstein and Lipmann, 1961; Weinstein and Schechter, 1962) in the sense that a given codon has the same meaning in cells from widely different origins.[5]

II. General Properties of Messenger RNA's

A. Size Heterogeneity

We have already stated in our introductory section that bacterial ribosomal RNA is made by a very small number of genes, at most 10 to 20 (Yankofsky and Spiegelman, 1962a, b). Therefore it is not so surprising that it falls between two major, physically well-delimited classes corresponding to the 16-S and 23-S components. If one realizes now that what we call mRNA includes the collection of all the RNA copies resulting from the transcription of a very large number of genes (perhaps a few thousands in an *E. coli* cell), we must then expect the messenger fraction to be highly poly-dispersed in size as the genetic determinants differ in lengths, depending upon the type of proteins they code for. [A slight restriction has to be made to this prediction, as we may expect some genes to function faster than some others as a result of a "derepression" state (cf. Part 4) and we may also expect their RNA products to be represented more often than others in the overall mRNA fraction.]

Before looking at the sedimentation profiles of mRNA, one has to make another remark in order to explain the principle of its identification. Although ribosomal RNA and sRNA represent 95% of the total RNA, and MRNA not more than 5% (Gros *et al.*, 1961a, b), this last RNA fraction results from the copying of perhaps more than 99% of the DNA, whereas the other RNA's are made up of a very small proportion of the genome. The reason why, despite this stoichiometric relationship, ribosomal RNA and sRNA predominate in the cell is because the mRNA fraction turns over very rapidly, whereas the other RNA's are stable. Therefore, if one gives a short pulse of a radioactive nucleic acid precursor to a population of

[5] Recently nucleotide sequences of RNA codons have been investigated by directing the binding of C^{14}-aminoacyl-sRNA to ribosomes, with trinucleotides of defined base sequence. The template activity of 45 trinucleotides has been described. Nucleotide *sequences* have been suggested for RNA codons corresponding to 10 amino acids. "Non-sense" codons have even been described that may serve as internal or terminal signals for the interruption of polypeptide synthesis (Leder and Nirenberg, 1964a, b; Nirenberg *et al.*, 1965).

bacteria in a steady state, we might expect that ribosomal RNA or sRNA will represent only a very small percentage of the total RNA labeled, the *bulk* being equivalent to mRNA.

Figure 1 shows a sedimentation profile of the RNA extracted from a culture of *E. coli* labeled for no more than 20 seconds. The RNA is layered on top of a sucrose gradient and the centrifugation proceeds for 10 hr. The UV-absorbing material, which harbors three well-defined peaks, monitors the stable RNA of the cell, sedimenting, respectively, at 23 S, 16 S, and

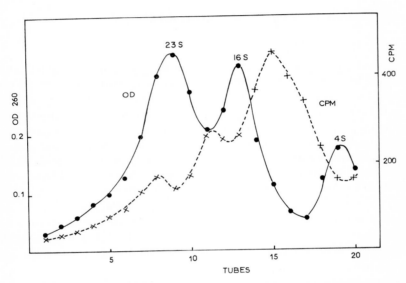

FIG. 1. Sedimentation profile of pulse-labeled RNA in *E. coli*. The RNA fraction from a population of *E. coli* submitted to a brief C^{14}-uracil exposure is layered at the top of a 5–20% sucrose gradient and centrifuged for 10 hr at 25,000 rpm. At the end of the run, samples are collected for OD and radioactivity measurements. From left to right, three peak fractions, sedimenting, respectively, at 23 S, 16 S, and 4 S can be observed. The rapidly labeled RNA moiety (dotted line) does not coincide with the UV profile. It includes a collection of molecules with widely different sedimentation constants.

4 S. The radioactivity reveals the distribution of the messenger fraction. It is obvious that this fraction includes RNA chains of various sizes, ranging from 6 S to more than 23 S.

This situation is not proper to *E. coli*; it can be observed with other organisms, the DNA of which harbor a completely different composition, such as with *Ps. aeruginosa* (Fig. 2) (Spiegelman, 1961). Finally, if one examines the mRNA made following infection of *E. coli* by phage T4, it appears, once more, that the radioactive material is quite polydispersed (Bautz, 1963) (Fig. 3).

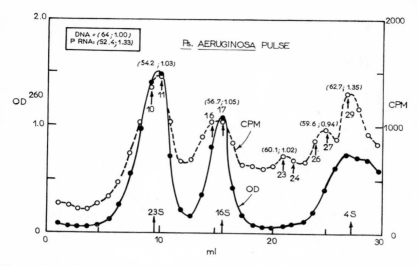

Fɪɢ. 2. Sedimentation profile of phenol-purified RNA from *Ps. aeruginosa* exposed to a 3-min. P^{32} pulse, 5 min after a "shift down." In this experiment the rapidly renewable RNA is labeled preferentially following a rapid transition from a rich to a poor medium, because after such a shift down, ribosomal- or sRNA fractions are not synthesized before a long lag period. Solid circles identify pre-existing RNA and open circles newly synthesized RNA. The first number in parentheses represents per cent GC and the second, the ratio of purines to pyrimidines. Arrows indicate the fractions taken for base-composition analysis. From Spiegelman (1961).

We have pointed out that one reason to expect such heterogeneity lies in the fact that the genes, which serve as templates, might themselves harbor different sizes, for it is known that not all the protein monomers are composed of the same number of amino acid residues. In fact, if one calculates, from the previous sedimentation patterns, the molecular weight of the chains of mRNA exhibiting the highest sedimentation coefficients, a value of 2 to 3 million is obtained. On the other hand, if one considers the average molecular weight of the most commonly known protein monomers, this average very seldom exceeds 30,000 or 40,000. A monomer of 40,000 would be coded by a mRNA of around 15 S. How can one explain the presence of mRNA fractions of much higher sedimentation velocities? Indeed, the possibility that protein monomers having a molecular weight of 200,000, or more may exist, is not completely excluded. One alternative to explain the presence of very high molecular-weight messengers is that genes very often form "clusters"; they are grouped into what Jacob and Monod have defined as *operons* (Jacob and Monod, 1961a; Jacob *et al.*, 1960a). An operon is a group of a few adjacent genes (from 2 to 10 in the majority of cases) which function *as a unit of phenotypic expression* and the regulation of which is coordinated by the existence

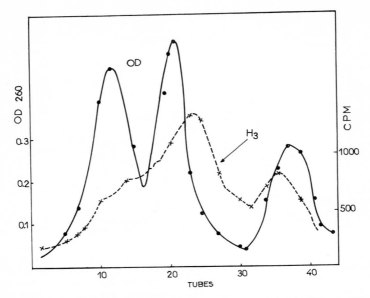

Fig. 3. Size distribution of T4-mRNA. Here 0.2 ml of RNA (OD = 43, specific activity = 1.7×10^5 cpm/ml) labeled with H^3-uracil from 4–8 min after infection is applied, on top of a gradient ranging from 5–20% sucrose in 10^{-2} M Tris (pH 7.2) plus 1×10^{-3} M Mg^{2+}. Centrifugation 5 hr at 38,000 rpm in the SW 39 rotor. Compare the profile obtained with that of Fig. 1 (Part III). (After Bautz, 1963).

of a genetic segment called an operator and located itself at the extremity of the unit. Once the existence of specific operons is admitted, it is very tempting to assume that the different genes constituting an operon are not copied *individually* but that the transcription of the operon is *integral* or *polycistronic*. Such an hypothesis would easily explain the existence of very long mRNA molecules (Fig. 4). Actually, the polycistronic transcription has received some direct support from experiments by Martin (1963), by Kiho and Rich (1964), and also by Attardi and his colleagues (1963) in which it has been found that the sizes of the mRNA's made by the operons controlling, respectively, the histidine biosynthetic enzymes, or the lactose degradative enzymes, have the same order of magnitude as the sizes of the operon themselves.

As far as the molecular characteristics of the mRNA's in systems represented by higher organisms, the question is slightly complicated from the fact that a large proportion of the rapidly labeled RNA is constituted by some sort of giant molecules, which appear to be precursors of the ribosomal RNA (Scherrer *et al.*, 1963; Penman *et al.*, 1963; Darnell *et al.*, 1963). Figure 5 shows a typical sedimentation pattern of the rapidly labeled RNA

ONE GENE   ONE MESSENGER   ONE OPERON   ONE MESSENGER

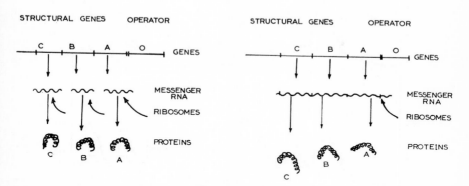

F<small>IG</small>. 4. The two alternative mechanisms of gene transcription (according to Martin, (1963).

fraction extracted from a neoplastic cell line (known as HeLa cells). As the duration of the pulse increases in time, one can follow the progression of the radioactive material from a region of the gradient corresponding to very heavy molecules (sedimenting at 45 S), down to the ribosomal RNA region. Although, at first glance, the radioactivity profile looks quite different from the one described earlier for bacterial systems, HeLa cells (and more generally cells from animal sources) contain a radioactively labeled mRNA which is more or less masked by the ribosomal RNA precursors mostly accumulated in the nucleus. If, instead of extracting the cell directly, one examines the rapidly labeled RNA present in cytoplasmic polysomes, one obtains a fraction sedimenting, as is illustrated in Fig. 6. Here we encounter a pattern similar to the one previously described for bacterial systems. The presence of mRNA chains inserted in multiribosomal complexes has now been shown in cells from different tissues (Hiatt, 1962; Noll et al., 1963).

B. Homology with DNA

As a second criterion for defining the messenger fraction, we have seen that the identity of base composition with DNA, or the homology of base sequence with this macromolecule, could be used. One could indeed predict that, the messenger fraction being composed by the sum of all the gene products, the nucleotide sequence of this fraction considered a whole should be complementary to one strand of DNA or identical to both, depending on how many DNA strands are copied.

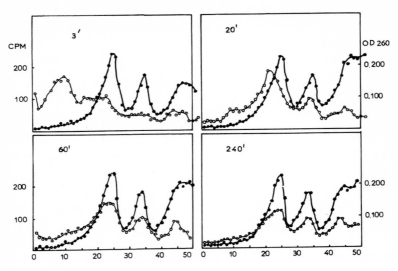

F<small>IG</small>. 5. Size distribution of rapidly labeled RNA in a population of HELA cells and its fate after actinomycin treatment. The 3' profile (upper left) shows the size distribution of the rapidly labeled RNA before actinomycin treatment. Note that the bulk of it sediments at 45 and 30 S. Following actinomycin treatment for 20, 60, and 240 min, there is a gradual conversion of the very heavy material into 16-S and 28-S ribosomal RNA. From Scherrer et al. (1963).

One could argue that complementariness toward DNA may not be the unique property of mRNA but would concern the other RNA's as well, since all the RNA species found in a cell result from the transcription of DNA. But it is easy to understand that, as ribosomal RNA or sRNA are made by no more than 0.1% of the genome, it is theoretically difficult to demonstrate their homology with a homospecific DNA unless a large excess of this nucleic acid be used. In contrast, since mRNA molecules are not *accumulated* under steady-state conditions, they will always find enough matching sites on DNA, under the conditions utilized for hybridizing RNA and DNA. So, in practice, the bulk of the RNA-forming complementary hybrids with DNA represent the collection of molecules composing the mRNA fraction.

Hall and Spiegelman (1961), by exploiting early observations of Marmur (Marmur and Lane, 1960) and of Doty and associates (1960), who had found it possible to hybridize complementary DNA strands previously separated by denaturation, or synthetic polyribonucleotides and polydeoxyribonucleotides (Schildkraut et al., 1961), discovered that rapidly labeled (messenger) RNA from normal or infected bacteria can form artificial hybrids with previously denatured DNA. Their first hybridization experiments were carried out in liquid phase: The pulse-labeled RNA from

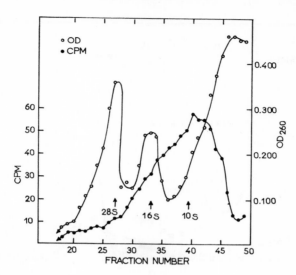

FIG. 6. Sedimentation analysis of RNA from polyribosomes. After incubation at 37°C for 45 min in PO_4-free medium, a culture of HELA cells is labeled for 40 min with 20 mc carrier-free P^{32}. A cytoplasmic extract is then prepared and layered onto three sucrose gradients (centrifugation 70 min at 24,000 rpm). Polyribosomes of fractions ranging from 180–400 S are collected, and centrifuged at 50,000 rpm for 90 min. The RNA is then extracted and analyzed on sucrose gradient. From Penman (1963).

Ps. aeruginosa was mixed, at 55°C, with melted DNA from the same strain. The ionic strength was raised and the mixture abandoned to slow cooling to 35°C. Finally, the reaction mixture was sedimented at equilibrium in a solution of $CsCl_2$. Figure 7 indicates that a certain percentage of the radioactivity of the RNA bands at the position corresponding to that of DNA. This is indicative of a real DNA-RNA *hybrid* and not of some aggregate complex, because an important fraction of the radioactive material located at this position resists a treatment by ribonuclease, otherwise sufficient to destroy most of the free RNA.

The phenomenon of artificial annealing exhibits a very strict specificity: If one mixes the *Pseudomonas* mRNA with *E. coli* DNA, there is no sign of hybrid formation (Figure 8). The techniques of hybridization have been considerably improved since then. We cannot analyze them in detail. Some are based on the possibility of immobilizing a preparation of denatured DNA inside a gel of purified agar. The mRNA to be studied is then adsorbed at 60°C onto the DNA-agar gel column thus obtained (Bolton and McCarthy, 1962). Several hours after mixing, the nonhybridized RNA portion is washed out by passing through a high-ionic-strength ($0.6M$ KCl) buffer, while the "DNA-like" fraction is eluted by a low-ionic-strength buffer. Other techniques take advantage of a separation of the

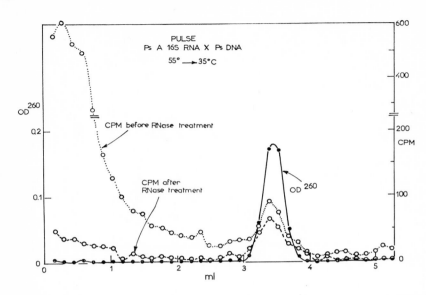

Fig. 7. Equilibrium density centrifugation of a DNA-RNA hybrid in CsCl. A mixture of H³-uridine-labeled mRNA from *Ps aeruginosa*. slow cooled with single-stranded DNA from the same species. Centrifugation 60 hr at 33,000 rpm. The closed circles identify the DNA band. The open circles give the effects on the cpm of treatment of the indicated fractions with RNase, prior to precipitation and counting. Note the presence of an RNase-resistant radioactive material at the peak position of DNA. From Spiegelman (1961).

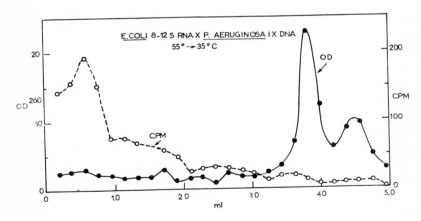

Fig. 8. Lack of complementariness between *E. coli* mRNA and *Ps. aeruginosa* DNA. Same type of experiment as in Fig. 7 (Part III) except that the mRNA derives from a strain of *E. coli*. In addition, double-stranded *E. coli* DNA was added as a marker and is represented by the second peak to the right. From Spiegelman, (1961).

DNA-RNA hybrid from the RNA core resulting from RNase action. This can be achieved on a G-100 Sephadex column (Scherrer, 1964). Finally, it has been discovery by Nygaard and Hall (1963) that heat-denatured DNA, as well as DNA-RNA hybrids, are retained by nitrocellulose filters, whereas native DNA or RNA are not. By the use of these hybridization techniques one is in position to answer a theoretically important question: Are the naturally occurring RNA's the copies of one or of two DNA strands? Preliminary evidence already suggested that mRNA derives from a unique DNA strand. This was deduced by Champe and Benzer from induced reversion experiments, using 5-fluorouracil with certain bacteriophage mutants (Champe and Benzer, 1962). Later, by the use of a DNA cellulose column, Bautz and Hall (1962) succeeded in isolating and purifying the messenger fraction made after infection of *E. coli* by the bacteriophage T4. Enough material could be obtained to carry out some chemical and physical studies on this specific messenger. Bautz (1963) first observed that it does not contain equivalent amounts of A and U nor of G and C, as one would expect from a symmetrical copying of DNA *in vivo*. Furthermore, by studying the sensibility of the purified messenger to RNase and its hyperchromicity, he came to the conclusion that it was single-stranded, having more or less the same conformation in solution as ribosomal RNA (though with slightly less secondary structure). More decisive proofs in favor of the unique copying of one single DNA strand have been brought forth by hybridization studies. It must be recalled that in most cases the two sister strands of DNA have the same average composition and therefore the same buoyant density, so it is impossible to separate them by $CsCl_2$ centrifugation. There exist, however, certain bacteriophage DNA's where this is not the case, for one strand contains much less guanine and cytosine than the other; it is therefore easy to fractionate the two complementary DNA chains of different buoyant densities resulting from previously melted DNA. When the mRNA produced after infection by these phages is purified and hybridized with each one of the two separated strands, it is found that only one strand, the *heavy* one, can form a hybrid. This experiment has been realized by Marmur with the DNA and mRNA from the phage SP8 infecting *B. subtilis* (Marmur *et al.*, 1963) and also by Tocchini-Valentini *et al.* (1963), who used the phage-α infecting *B. megaterium*. A similar conclusion in favor of the single strandedness of natural mRNA has also been obtained by taking advantage of the fact that there exists one particular phage, called $\phi \times 174$, the DNA of which is single stranded inside the finished particle but which replicates as a duplex. By hybridizing the corresponding mRNA with the DNA derived either from the particle or from the "replicative form," it is found that only the replicative form can hybridize the $\phi \times$ mRNA (Spiegelman, 1961).

Therefore, we reach the very important conclusion that, from the two complementary strands which compose a molecule of DNA, only one provides the genetic information. The other probably serves to replicate the "informative strand" according to the semiconservative model proposed by Watson and Crick (1953). These results do not exclude, however; that the two DNA chains can *alternatively* be copied on different regions.

When DNA is copied into RNA *in vitro* by the enzyme RNA polymerase, both strands are quite often transcribed (Hurwitz *et al.*, 1961). This is not always the case however: Hayashi and colleagues (Hayashi *et al.*, 1963; Bassel *et al.*, 1964) observed that when the replicative form of $\phi \times$ DNA, which exists as a circular molecule, is isolated as such, its transcription by the RNA polymerase is asymmetrical. In contrast, upon breakage of the molecule, both strands are transcribed. Circularity, or even physical integrity, is not, however, the only clue to explain the restriction in the transcription mechanisms: Geiduschek *et al.* (1964) recently observed that the purified RNA polymerase from *E. coli* can transcribe even partially broken T2-DNA molecules, in an asymmetrical fashion. Moreover, crude polymerase preparations from *B. megaterium* also transcribe only one strand (the heavy one) of phage-α DNA, even if this DNA is fragmented into quarters by repeated shearing.

In conclusion, the mechanism imposing a restriction on the choice of the informational strand by the RNA polymerase remains obscure. Nor does one have any hint of the DNA features which act as "punctuation signals" for the starting or finishing of the transcription.

C. Metabolic Instability

Many aspects of the pulse-labeling experiments previously described imply that bacterial mRNA is highly unstable. More precise experiments have been devised however to estimate the mRNA half-life and to calculate how many times it can function before being degraded.

The principle of these experiments is to use an inhibitor of RNA synthesis in order to terminate a short pulse of a radioactive RNA tracer. By doing so, the breakdown products resulting from the turnover of the mRNA cannot be reutilized for the synthesis of other RNA components (such as ribosomal or soluble RNA) and one can simply measure the rate of disappearance of the "acido-precipitable radioactivity" associated with the mRNA fraction. Furthermore, if the inhibitor used is selective enough not to interfere with the translation of RNA to protein, one can measure what quantity of protein continues to be synthesized before completion of the mRNA breakdown.

Figure 9 shows the results obtained when a short pulse of C^{14}-uracil in a culture of *B. subtilis* is followed by the addition of an inhibitor of RNA synthesis, such as actinomycin D (which specifically blocks the transcrip-

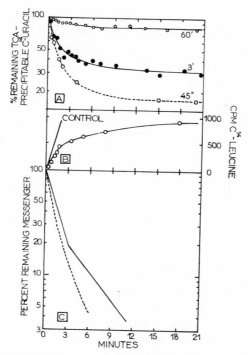

FIG. 9. Kinetics of mRNA decay in exponentially growing *B. subtilis*. (A) Loss of acid-precipitable uracil counts. C^{14}-Uracil added at −45 sec, − 3 min, and −60 min. Actinomycin D (10 γ/ml) added at time zero. After 10 min, most of the mRNA has decayed leaving in each case a plateau of acid-precipitable C^{14}-labeled stable RNA's (ribosomal and soluble). (B) Kinetic C^{14}-leucine incorporation in control and actinomycin-treated cells. (C) Loss of mRNA. Derivative of the experimental curve of (B). It shows the surviving messenger after actinomycin addition by assuming that the rate of leucine incorporation is proportional to the amount of mRNA in the cell. The dotted line derives from curve (A) (45⁶), from which the stable fraction has been subtracted. From Levinthal *et al.* (1963).

tion of DNA to RNA (Hurwitz and August, 1963; Levinthal *et al.*, 1962, 1963). The radioactivity which was incorporated into the mRNA decays according to first-order kinetics with a half-life of 1 min. In contrast, it is found that when ribosomal or soluble RNA are labeled, they do not lose radioactivity upon addition of actinomycin D. In the same experiment, one can measure the quantity of protein synthesized by the cells during the period of mRNA decay, using as an index the extent of incorporation of a radioactively labeled amino acid precursor. Calculation shows that, on the average, a molecule of bacterial messenger can be read at least 10 to 20 times before being destroyed. Similar results have been obtained by Soffer and Gros using dinitrophenol or proflavine as inhibitors of RNA synthesis in *E. coli* (Woese *et al.*, 1963; Soffer and Gros, 1964). So, even in bacteria, where the messenger appears so unstable, it functions like a catalytic template. In addition, one can say that the signal triggering the destruction of a coding unit is not its translation by the ribosome sRNA machinery. It can be shown however that, if the reading process is interrupted under specific conditions causing the cessation of polypeptide synthesis, such as the addition of chloramphenicol or the removal of oxygen (Levinthal *et al.*, 1963), then mRNA is destroyed at a much slower rate. This result is explainable on the assumption that, so long as a messenger chain is engaged in a complex with the ribosomes, it is not attacked by degradative enzymes. This could well illustrate the need for the endogenous nuclease to find the appropriate extremity of mRNA chains available. There is to some extent a competition between the attachment of nucleolytic enzymes and the attachment of ribosomes to mRNA. As far as the nature of the nucleolytic enzyme itself, it does not seem that the bacterial ribonuclease is involved. The most likely candidate is a "K"-dependent phosphodiesterase, discovered by Spahr and Schlesinger (1963), and recently purified 200-fold by Singer (Singer and Tolbert, 1964). This is an exonuclease that liberates 5'-nucleotide products.

It might be appropriate to comment at present on the relative stabilities of mRNA from other biological systems, particularly in animal cells. It is obvious that *here*, mRNA's are endowed with a much higher degree of stability. One of the best known examples is provided by the reticulocyte system responsible for the synthesis of hemoglobin. This system does not appear to be the site of RNA synthesis (Marks *et al.*, 1962), and one can barely detect any degradation of RNA. Yet one can demonstrate a relatively continuous synthesis of globin on the pentameric polysomes that have been discovered by Marks and his colleagues (Marks *et al.*, 1962) and by Rich (Rich *et al.*, 1963). This synthesis is not inhibited by actinomycin D. Other well-studied examples of protein synthesis on a stable mRNA template are provided by the synthesis of thyroglobulin in thyroid glands (Seed and Goldberg, 1963).

Here too, the stability of mRNA is suggested by the lack of sensibility of protein synthesis to actinomycin D. Yet these situations might constitute extreme cases, because the cells considered are highly differentiated. Certainly, nondifferentiated systems, such as the one represented by a population of HeLa cells, produce *unstable* mRNA fractions. This is clearly shown in HeLa cells by the fact that the specific polysomes disappear gradually after addition of actinomycin D. The best estimates that Penman, Scherrer, and Darnell (1963) give for the half-life period of mRNA in HeLa cells is 3 hr, a time considerably longer than that characteristic of mRNA in bacteria but perhaps not so long if we take into account the relative rates of protein synthesis in these two systems.

The very high rate of mRNA renewal in bacteria is perhaps best expressed by Levinthal's calculation showing that, when a gene is not repressed, it makes on the order of 3000 mRNA molecules at each generation. This means that the polymerase has to incorporate 1000 nucleotides per second into a polynucleotide product (Levinthal, *et al.*, 1963).

The instability of the bacterial messages is at the basis of the rapidity with which regulatory mechanisms can manifest themselves in these microorganisms, as we shall see in the next part.

PART 4. REGULATION OF PROTEIN SYNTHESIS

I. Introduction[6]

In the preceding lectures we have described the general features of the protein-forming machinery and considered it an autonomous complex of templates, enzymes, and effectors. We have already stated that the structure of DNA in a cell line is invariable and is perpetuated by the mechanism of semiconservative replication as first proposed by Watson and Crick (1953). Yet, the biochemical properties expressed by a cell can differ deeply, according to the nature of the medium in which the cell is placed. Manifestations of this phenomenon are observed not only in microorganisms that are endowed with the capacity for enzymatic adaptation but also in multicellular organisms when submitted to hormonal influences.

Therefore, it is not surprising that, for a long time, people have thought that the genetic control of protein structures and functions could be "bypassed" under certain conditions of environment, and that the "milieu" could change the properties of a cell without the participation of the genetic apparatus. It is well established today, thanks mostly to a considerable body of experimental evidences derived from chemical studies with microorganisms, that even external stimuli which might lead to profound disturbances in the enzymatic equipment of the cell do so by a series of complex reactions involving special products manufactured by the genes: the repressors.

II. General Manifestations of Regulation of Enzyme Synthesis

The most dramatic manifestations of regulation in bacteria are provided by the existence of two symmetrical phenomena known, respectively, as enzymatic *adaptation* (or better, induction) and enzyme *repression*. We shall briefly illustrate these by the use of simple examples.

Let us consider a population of *E. coli* growing exponentially in a mineral medium with succinate as the sole carbon source. If we sample aliquots at

[6] This section is largely inspired by two general articles by Jacob and Monod (1961a, 1964).

various periods of growth, in order to measure the β-galactosidase activity (this can be done very simply by shaking the suspension with a standard β-galactoside in which the galactoside moiety is coupled with a chromophoric nucleus, o-nitrophenol) (Lederberg, 1950; Cohn and Monod, 1951), we observe that the rate at which the substrate is split is very slow. Now, let us add to the culture a β-galactoside such as lactose, or better a β-galactoside analog such as the compound isopropylthiogalactoside (IPTG) which *cannot* serve as a substrate for the enzyme. We shall then observe that, 2 to 3 min following this addition, the β-galactosidase activity begins increasing rapidly in the population. If we measure the activity of *fully* induced organisms, it is now equivalent to *several thousand* times that of the noninduced culture. Knowing the turnover number of the enzyme and its molecular weight, we can estimate that the relative amount synthesized corresponds to around 6% of the total protein of the cell. This phenomenon of enzyme induction is today classical; many examples of it are known (Dubos, 1940; Monod, 1944, 1947; Spiegelman, 1946; Pollock, 1950; Stanier, 1951). What is especially remarkable in it is that a simple metabolite, such as IPTG in the example above, which shows no affinity for the enzyme induced, can trigger the expression of very specific genetic determinants, which, before its addition, were unable to direct the synthesis of the enzyme in question. We shall say that IPTG "induces" the functioning of a structural gene termed "z," the integrity of which confers to the cell the potentiality to make β-galactosidase.

The phenomenon of enzyme repression illustrates a perfectly symmetrical manifestation of the regulation exerted on protein synthesis. Here, we can take as an example the negative regulation occurring when an amino acid, "end product" of a biosynthetic sequence, shuts off the synthesis of the enzymes involved in its fabrication.

For instance, the synthesis of arginine requires not less than seven distinct enzymes for converting a common carbon precursor glutamate to the appropriate product. This is schematized in Eq. (8).

$$
\text{Glucose} \xrightarrow{} \alpha\text{-Ketoglutarate} \xrightarrow{} \text{Glutamate} \xrightarrow{1} N\text{-Acetylglutamate} \xrightarrow{2}
$$

$$
N\text{-Acetylglutamic semialdehyde} \xrightarrow{3} N\text{-Acetylornithine} \xrightarrow{4} \text{Ornithine} \xrightarrow{5}
$$

$$
\text{Citrulline} \xrightarrow{6} \text{Arginosuccinate} \xrightarrow{7} \text{Arginine} \tag{8}
$$

When a wild-type strain of *E. coli* is grown in a mineral medium, with glucose and NH_4 as sole carbon and nitrogen sources, arginine is indeed manufactured (by definition), and since growth can perpetuate exponentially, it means that the seven arginine enzymes in question keep being synthesized at a steady rate. This could be confirmed by suitable enzymatic determinations. Now, let us add arginine to the growth medium; the growth rate will remain unchanged, but if we measure the level of the seven enzymes already mentioned, it is easy to demonstrate that their synthesis is immediately inhibited, despite the fact, again, that the metabolite arginine exhibits no particular affinity for most of the enzymes involved.

This phenomenon called enzyme repression is quite ubiquitous in the metabolism of bacterial cells (Monod and Cohen-Bazire, 1953; Gorini and Maas, 1958; Maas, 1961; Vogel, 1957). It is known today that biosynthesis of most, if not all, of the enzymes systems involved in the formation of the essential metabolites are specifically repressed by the metabolites resulting from their activity.[7]

Although the phenomena of enzyme induction and enzyme repression appear, at first glance, to involve distinct mechanisms, they call, in fact, for a similar interpretation that has been proposed by Jacob and Monod (1961) and that we shall summarize as follows: The genome of a microorganism is made of two categories of genes: (1) those called *structural* genes which control the potentiality to make specific enzymes and the mutation of which can lead to the formation of an altered protein molecule. These genes determine the primary structure of the protein itself. (2) Those called regulator genes because they control the *functioning* of the structural genes.

Let us consider again the phenomenon of induction. We have seen that, before the addition of the compound IPTG, the structural gene z does not *make* β-galactosidase. We shall say that it is so because the strain of *E. coli* contains a regulator gene, called "i," which manufactures a cytoplasmic inhibitor or repressor, which prevents the functioning of z. With an inducer added, the repressor will be inactivated, and, as a result, the synthesis of β-galactosidase will start at maximal rate.

Using a similar way of reasoning for the arginine biosynthetic system, we can say that there exists another regulator gene which controls the functioning of all the structural genes involved in arginine formation. Yet, in this case, contrary to what happens in the preceding example, the product of the regulator gene is inactive; this is an *aporepressor*, for it becomes activated only *after* having reacted with arginine. We shall say that arginine is a *corepressor*.

The two symmetrical manifestations of the regulation of enzyme synthesis can be schematized as follows: By calling Rg a regulator gene in general, Rg$_d$ a regulator gene involved in the regulation of degradative

---

[7] The phenomenon of repression of biosynthetic sequences by metabolites must not be confused with the phenomenon of feedback or end-product inhibition in which the ultimate product of a biosynthetic pathway inhibits the *activity* of the first enzyme of this pathway.

enzymes, Rg_b a regulator gene for biosynthetic enzymes, we can propose Eqs. (9).

$$Rg_d \rightarrow \text{Repressor} + \text{Inducor} \rightarrow R_{\text{inactive}}$$

$$Rg_b \rightarrow \text{Aporepressor} + \text{Metabolite} \rightarrow \text{Repressor} \qquad (9)$$

These two reactions are based on the same mechanism: the interaction of the regulator gene product with a metabolite. Although such a scheme might appear a little obvious today, this has not been so for a long time. It is enough to say that a completely opposite explanation could *a priori* fit the experimental facts. It could be assumed for instance that the regulator gene involved in the functioning of a degradative enzyme, Rg_d, manufactures a cytoplasmic "preinducer" which, by reacting with the exogenous inducer, forms an activated complex which can trigger the activity of the structural gene. Still another alternative hypothesis could be proposed to account for enzyme induction without even invoking regulator genes, for instance, by assuming simply that the exogenous inducer *directly* activates the structural genes. In fact, this way of thinking was defended for many years before it became possible to test for the dominancy or the recessivity of the regulator genes.

Before discussing these experiments, we must make an additional remark concerning the inducible or repressible systems.

In most instances, induction or repression of enzyme systems leads to a quantitative coordination of the expression of the various genes involved in these systems (Jacob and Monod, 1961a). For example, the addition of IPTG triggers simultaneously the synthesis of at least three distinct protein products: the β-galactosidase controlled by the z gene; the thiogalactoside acetylase, controlled by the "a" gene; and the galactoside permease, probably controlled by a distinctive "y" determinant. Whatever the degree of induction might be, the relative rates at which these three proteins are synthesized remain the same. Similarly, we could show that repression by histidine (an amino acid manufactured by the cooperation of nine distinct enzymes), reduces simultaneously and to the same extent the synthesis of the nine enzymes involved in its formation (Ames and Garry, 1959).

This situation is very difficult to explain unless it is assumed that structural genes involved in the ultimate control of the same function very often form a *unit of expression* which can be called an *operon* (Jacob *et al.*, 1960a; Jacob and Monod, 1961a; Ames and Martin, 1964) as proposed by Jacob and Monod. The inhibitory interaction between repressors and the genes of an operon will be governed by a special genetic segment called *operator*. The operator will be localized at one extremity of the segment forming the operon, but will be distinct from the structural genes themselves.

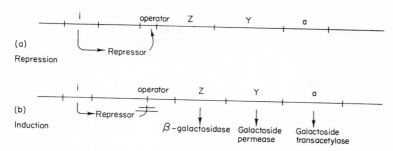

FIG. 1. Schematic representation of the regulatory apparatus of the lactose region in *E. coli*. i, regulator gene; z, y, and a, structural genes for β-galactosidase, galactoside permease, and galactoside acetylase, respectively; R, repressor; o, operator.

As an illustration, the genetic regulatory apparatus of the lactose enzyme family can be schematized as in Fig. 1.

III. Demonstration of the Existence of Regulator Genes

It is now appropriate to survey briefly the experimental evidence in favor of the existence of regulator genes, distinct from structural genes. We shall also discuss the nature of the repressor and of its interaction with the inducer.

At first, we shall define by *constitutive mutations* or, better, *constitutive regulator mutations* (as there are several classes of constitutive alleles) mutations which result in an uncontrolled synthesis of a particular enzyme, irrespective of the presence or absence of the effector to which the wild type is sensitive. Such mutants are known, not only among inducible, but also repressible, systems, as well as in the system of lysogenic bacteria (Jacob and Monod, 1961a; Kogat *et al.*, 1956; Buttin, 1961; Kalckar and Sundarajan, 1961). Two important properties of these mutants are the following:

1. The effect of the mutation (like that of induction) is pleiotropic. Example: in a lactose constitutive mutant, syntheses of galactosidase, permease, and acetylase take place at maximal rate, without induction.

2. The mutation is at the level of regulator genes, as it never appears to modify, to any extent, the molecular properties of the enzymes produced (Jacob and Monod, 1961a).

The definitive proof in favor of the existence of regulator genes had to wait for transfer experiments in which crosses between inducible and constitutive mutants of the lactose series could be studied specifically. In a series of classical experiments Pardee, Jacob, and Monod (Pardee *et al.*, 1959) analyzed the enzyme-forming capacity of a zygote resulting from a

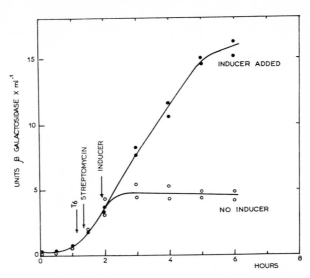

Fig. 2. Synthesis of β-galactosidase in a bacterial zygote ♂z⁺i⁺/ ♀ z⁻i⁻. The strains ♂
(SmˢT6ˢ) and ♀ (SmʳT6ʳ) are cultivated on synthetic medium with glycerol as a carbon
source. At $t = 0$, the cultures are mixed (1 ♂ per 5 ♀ ; around 2×10^8 bacteria/ml)
and shaken at 37°C. The experiment is performed on four identical but separated
samples. Phage T6 (10^4/ml) and streptomycin (1000 μg/ml) are added at the periods
indicated to prevent further conjugation and to eliminate the males. At regular intervals,
samples are taken (1) to determine the number of recombinants Z⁺Smʳ and (2) to measure
the β-galactosidase activity. At 115 min, two of the four suspensions receive some
methyl-β-D-thiogalactoside (10^{-3} M). Note the synthesis of β-galactosidase following T6
and streptomycin addition. As the synthesis is immediate upon conjugation and as the
number of z⁺i⁻ recombination events is very small, the synthesis can only be attributed
to the expression of the z gene in the zygote. From Jacob and Monod (1958).

cross between an inducible, lactose⁺ donor and a constitutive lactose⁻
recipient cell. None of the conjuguants per se was able to synthesize β-
galactosidase, since the male was not induced and the female was lactose
negative. In contrast, immediately after the transfer of the chromosome, a
very active synthesis of β-galactosidase was observed in the zygote. The
synthesis proceeded for some time and ceased, at which point it was
possible to trigger it again by the addition of IPTG (Fig. 2). These results
could easily be interpreted by assuming that in the cytoplasm of the donor
strain the z gene could not express its phenotype because of the presence
of repressor substances produced by a regulator gene (which we shall designate by the symbol i). In the female cytoplasm, it was assumed that no
repressor was present in such a way that the newly incoming z gene could
start to function. Yet, since the i gene derived from the donor strain was
also transferred into the female, it would be expected to produce increasing

TABLE I

PRODUCTION OF β-GALACTOSIDASE, GALACTOSIDE TRANSACETYLASE, AND GALACTOSIDE PERMEASE BY HAPLOID AND HETEROGENOTE REGULATOR CONSTITUTIVE MUTANTS[a,b]

Genotypes	Noninduced			Induced		
	β-Galactosidase	β-Galactoside permease	Transacetylase	β-Galactosidase	β-Galactoside permease	Transacetylase
1. $i^+z^+y^+$	<0.1	<1	<1	100	100	100
2. $i^-z^+y^+$	120	120	120	120	120	120
3. $i^-z^+y^+/Fi^+z^+y^-$	2	2	2	250	120	120
4. $i^+z^+y^+/Fi^-z^-y^+$	2	2	2	250	250	120
5. $i^-z^-y^+/Fi^-z^+y^+$	250	250	250	200	250	250
6. $\Delta izy/Fi^-z^+y^+$	200	200	200	200	200	200

[a] From Jacob and Monod (1961a, p. 193).

[b] The three activities are given in per cent of those obtained with fully induced haploid, wild type. Note that (1) as shown for types 3 and 4, the regulator constitutive allele is recessive to wild type; (2) the activities found in heterogenotes are two or three times greater than those found in haploids; this is probably due to the presence of several F factor per chromosome. i: regulator gene (i^+ inducible; i^- constitutive); z and y: structural genes for β-galactosidase and galactoside permease, respectively; F: sex factor of E. coli K12; Δizy: deletion of the lac region.

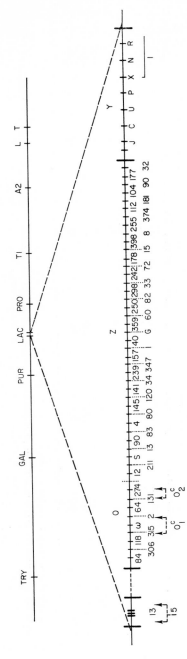

Fig. 3. Genetic map of the *lac* region of *E. coli*. The upper line represents the position of the *lac* region among linked characters in the bacterial chromosome. The lower line represents an enlargement of the *lac* region. For the significance of symbols, i, a, y, z, and o, see the legend of Fig. 1 (Part IV) (Jacob and Monod, 1961a).

levels of repressors. This would soon lead to an interruption of enzyme synthesis in the zygote, unless an exogenous inducer would counteract the repressor accumulated. This reasoning allowed one to consider *constitutive mutants* strains in which the regulator gene for β-galactosidase forms no repressor or an inactive one. In summary, the sign "+" could be ascribed to the regulator gene i present in inducible strains, the sign "−" to the same regulator gene in constitutive mutants.

By a series of experiments of the types summarized in Table I, it was easy to confirm that constitutive regulator mutants, are *recessive* to wild-type, in tests for heterozygosis.

Furthermore, by proper mapping, it was soon possible to locate the i gene outside the structural z cistron, some distance to its left (Jacob and Monod, 1961a) (Fig. 3). Similar results have also been obtained not only for other series of inducible systems but also for repressible systems; for example, mutations affecting a regulator gene R, located far from the cluster of the structural genes concerned with tryptophan biosynthesis, lead to the "derepressed" synthesis of the enzymes of this pathway (Cohen and Jacob, 1959). Similarly, two regulating genes R_1, R_2 have also been discovered and their properties extensively studied in the alkaline phosphate system, which is normally repressible by phosphate ions (Garen and Echols 1962). The i^- mutation is not the unique type of alteration of the regulator gene involved in the control of the lactose operon. Other classes of mutants have been discovered, the behavior of which helps clarify also the nature of this i gene and of its cytoplasmic product. Willson and associates (1964) described the existence, in certain inducible systems, of noninducible strains resulting from a mutation at the same site as the constitutive i^- mutants, and which are characterized from the fact that they behave like *dominants* in respect to wild-type (Table II). These mutants have been designated by the symbol "i^s." It is easy to explain their behavior in supposing that, instead of making an inactive repressor (constitutivity), they make a "superrepressor" unable to react with the exogenous inducer. The existence of the i^- and of the i^s mutations, their properties of behaving, respectively, like recessive and dominant alleles, the transfer experiments of Pardee and co-workers (1959) showing that the repressor is cytoplasmic, demonstrate in a conclusive way the existence of regulator genes whose function is to control the activity of structural genes by a diffusible product, the repressor. Additional evidence in favor of the existence of repressors, exerting a *negative* control on gene activity in inducible strains, derives from the studies of Horiuchi and Novick with the lactose system (Horiuchi and Novick, 1961) and of Gallant and Stapleton (1963, 1964) with the phosphatase system. Their work shows that in *E. coli* strains, induction or derepression of specific enzyme systems can be

TABLE II

PRODUCTION OF β-GALACTOSIDASE, GALACTOSIDE PERMEASE, AND GALACTOSIDE TRANSACETYLASE BY HAPLOID AND HETEROGENOTE CONSTITUTIVE OPERATOR MUTANTS[a,b]

Genotypes	Noninduced			Induced		
	Gz	Permease	Acetylase	Gz	Permease	Acetylase
1. $o^+z^+y^+$	0.1	1	1	100	100	100
2. $o^cz^+y^+$	25	25	25	100	100	100
3. $o^+z^-y^+/Fo^cz^+y^+$	75	75	75	250	300	300
4[c]. $o^+z^-y^+/Fo^cz^+y^-$	75	1	1	250	120	120
5. $o^+z^+y^-/Fo^cz^-y^+$	1	75	75	100	250	250
6. $i^so^+z^+y^+$	2	2	2	2	2	2
7. $i^so^+z^+y^+/Fi^+o^+z^+y^+$	2	2	2	2	2	2
8. $i^so^+z^+y^+/Fi^+o^cz^+y^+$	150	150	150	150	150	150

[a] From Jacob and Monod (1961a p. 198).

[b] The three activities are given in per cent of those obtained with fully induced, haploid wild type. i, regulator gene (i^+, inducible; i^-, constitutive; i^s, superrepressed); z and y, structural genes for β-galactosidase and galactoside permease, respectively; F, sex factor of E. coli K12.

[c] The y^- mutant used here does not produce acetylase.

achieved by a simple temperature shift, the repressor present or its forming system being thermosensitive.

Horiuchi and Novick have particularly analyzed a mutant of E. coli, called E103, which at low temperatures is like the wild type in being inducible, but at higher temperature resembles a constitutive mutant, for it manufactures β-galactosidase at a high rate irrespective of the presence or absence of an exogenous inducer. For instance, at 19°C, the differential rate is 0.5% that of the maximum rate, at 43°C, it is 40% of the maximum. The mutation involved in this phenomenon is located in the "lac region." The thermal lability of the control system can be strikingly illustrated by a very simple experiment: By heating at 45°C a suspension of E 103 in a buffer for 15 min, one observes subsequently a constitutive synthesis of β-galactosidase following transfer of the cells in a growth medium at 14°C. This constitutive synthesis eventually shuts off again, since new repressor molecules will accumulate that are stable at 14°C. As expected, the addition of IPTG allows a new departure of enzyme synthesis.

All these previous considerations lead us to discuss (1) the chemical nature of the repressor, (2) the type of interactions between repressors and inducers or corepressors, and (3) the identity of the constituent at the site of which repressors exert their inhibition, i.e., by definition, the nature of the operator.

IV. Nature of Repressor Substances

Despite several experimental trials there are still very few indications regarding the chemical nature of the repressor. A few years ago, Pardee and Prestidge (1959) observed that a transfer of the i^+ gene during conjugation in the presence of 5-methyltryptophan (an inhibitor of protein synthesis) still allowed the accumulation of the repressor for β-galactosidase, since, as tryptophan was added at a time corresponding to $\frac{1}{2}$ generation later, no constitutive synthesis of enzyme could be observed. A similar experiment has also been done by Novick and Horiuchi (Horiuchi and Novick, 1961) in transferring in a growth medium at 14°C, in the presence of 5-MT, a suspension of *E. coli* E103 previously heated at 43°C. Still, more recently, Sypherd and Strauss (1963) have also reported experiments compatible with the fact that the repressor for β-galactosidase continues to accumulate in the presence of chloramphenicol.

It is difficult to ascertain whether these experiments are conclusive regarding the chemical nature of repressors, for there is reason to believe that inhibition of protein synthesis by the antimetabolites in use is never complete, and that the presence of even a small number of repressor molecules is probably sufficient to turn off the cognate operon. At least, if the hypothesis that repressor is a protein, or contains a protein, is not excluded by these experiments, the possibility remains open that repressors contain a polynucleotide moiety.

From the simple consideration of the facts that the interaction between inducer and repressors is (1) highly specific, and (2) instantaneous and immediately reversible upon removal of the inducer, it has recently been proposed by Monod *et al.* (1963) that this interaction consists in the formation of a stereospecific, and reversible, complex of the type produced during the reaction of an allosteric protein and an effector. In other words, the repressor must be a protein, or must contain a protein moiety, endowed with a double specificity; it should possess a recognition site for the inducer and a recognition site for the operator.

Experiments by Novick (1964) illustrate the remarkable stereospecificity of the repressor-effector interaction, and contribute in re-enforcing the idea that the repressor has a proteinaceous structure. Using certain temperature constitutive regulator mutants, in which the repressor is thermolabile, Novick observed that the rate of thermoinactivation was *decreased* by the presence of β-galactosides known to act as inducers of normal wild types. This situation is operationally identical to the protection of an enzyme against thermoinactivation by its specific substrate. It must also be recalled that, a few years ago (Monod *et al.*, 1951), Monod and his colleagues had described the existence of a series of β-galactoside derivatives which *competitively* prevent the interaction of inducers with the repressor for β-galactosidase synthesis. This was the case, for example, with the compound TPG (thiophenylgalactoside), which, at a very low concentrations, inhibits competitively the induction by IPTG.

Another possible approach for elucidating the chemical nature of repressor products could consist of investigating if the synthesis of inactive repressors by constitutive mutants of the i genes (i⁻ types) is suppressible by mutations occurring outside the lactose region. Suppressor genes are known which can restore a large variety of metabolic defects resulting from point mutations (Yanofsky et al., 1961; Garen and Siddiqi, 1962) whose effect is to cause the appearance of modified coding units in the mRNA. These suppressor genes are present in certain strains of E. coli such as C600 or C63. It is believed (Gorini and Kataja, 1964) that they operate by changing the conformation of ribosomes in such a way that they become capable of recognizing modified coding units on mRNA. Were an i⁻-type mutation suppressible, this would be a good argument in favor of the mutated product being a protein. Unfortunately, all assays so far have been unsuccessful. However, according to Novick and colleagues (1963), the chances of detecting i⁻ suppressed mutants are slight, as even a low

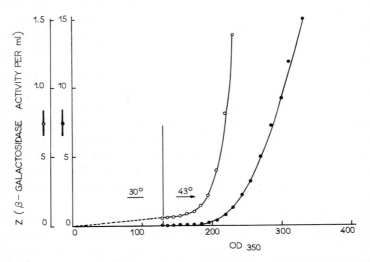

FIG. 4. Effect of transferring strain E. coli 694 R³¹ from growth at 30° to 43°C. Enzyme per ml (z) is plotted against B (bacterial mass measured by OD at 350 mμ). At 30 sec the enzyme followed the broken line. At the place indicated, the culture was transferred to 43°C. Results are given on two scales to display both early and late part of curves. Note the lag required before the differential rate of Gz synthesis becomes maximum at 43°C, suggesting that repressor molecules pre-existing at 30°C are still functional at 43°C but become diluted by the cell mass increase: a result due to the thermosensivity of the strain capacity to manufacture new repressors at this temperature. From Novick et al. (1963).

cellular level of repressors corresponding to 10% of the maximum level would not lead to much reduction in the rate of β-galactosidase synthesis. This conclusion results, in particular, from a series of interesting studies designed to relate the rate of Gz (β-galactosidase) synthesis and the repressor level, studies performed with a thermosensitive mutant in which the production of repressor is considerably reduced at temperatures above 43°C.

In such mutants undergoing a shift from 30°–43°C, it can be seen that considerable growth is required before the differential rate of Gz synthesis dz/db rises significantly, as if the repressor molecules had to be diluted by growth (Fig. 4). The relative repressor concentration R/R_0 is equal to B_0/B (where R_0 and B_0 are, respectively, the values of the repressor level and number of bacteria in the culture at the beginning of the temperature shift, and R and B represent the same parameters at subsequent time).

A plot of dz/db versus B_0/B is illustrated in Fig. 5. The dotted curve gives the values calculated in assuming the relationship $dz/db = K/K + B$,

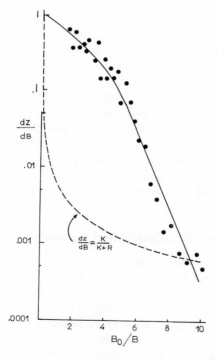

FIG. 5. Relation between rate of synthesis and repressor level. From the data shown in Fig. 4 (Part IV), the rate of synthesis of β-galactosidase (dZ/dB) was calculated and plotted on a semilog scale against corresponding values of B_0/B as described in the text. For comparison, also plotted is the theoretical curve $dZ/dB = K (K + R) = K/[K + R_0 (B_0/B)]$ fitted at $B_0/B = 1$ and $B_0/B = 0$ (Novick et al., 1963).

where K is the level of repressors at which one-half the operators are *free* of repressor. It is clear that this Michaelian type of expression cannot account for the experimental curve.

Three possible mechanisms could be in agreement with the observed kinetics:

1. The operator has many sites for interacting with the repressor, all of which have to be simultaneously free of repressor, to ensure the functioning of the specific operon.

2. The operator has only one site, but it needs to be free of repressor for some minimum time.

3. The repressor is metabolically unstable, in which case, if one assumes the mean life of the Gz repressor to be 0.2 generations, the results could be consistent with a Michaelian-type relationship.

This last assumption seems to be supported by independent observations by Gallant and Stapleton (1964), who used an alkaline phosphatase mutant, unable to produce repressor above 40°C.

Very recently, using a disk-electrophoretic method to compare the protein pattern of an *E. coli* strain, repressible by phosphate for the synthesis of alkaline phosphatase, and of a nonrepressible mutant, in which there is a defect at one genetic regulator site (R_2), Garen and Otsuji (1964) have observed a selective modification in one unique protein band, which most likely represents the product of the regulator gene R_2. Unfortunately, there are *two* genes concerned with the regulation of alkaline phosphatase synthesis, whose respective functions are still difficult to ascertain. It cannot therefore be excluded that at least one of their products is involved in some biochemical step for activating phosphate as a corepressor, the other gene manufacturing the true aporepressor itself. The fact that the R_2 *protein* is found outside the cell membrane also suggests that it is not the true aporepressor.

V. The Operon: a Polarized Unit of Expression

Whatever might be the nature of the repressor and its mechanism of action, its effect is not generally exerted on a single gene, but on a series of genes geographically clustered and involved in the same physiological function. The existence of these specific clusters endowed with a special function is ascertained by at least three independent lines of evidence.

1. As we have just mentioned, induction or repression modify the level of expression of a series of genes involved in the same function. Furthermore, the relative rates at which the enzymes controlled by these groups of genes are formed remain identical under a large variety of regulatory conditions. Thus, the genes related to the structure and activity of the enzymes in question form a unit of regulation and expression which has

been called an operon. An example of the quantitative coinduction of enzymes belonging to the same operon is given in Fig. 6, where the rate of Gz synthesis is plotted against the rate of acetylase synthesis for various levels of induction or in different constitutive strains. The relationship is expressed by a straight line (Jacob and Monod, 1961a).

2. There exist certain constitutive mutants (called operator constitutive mutants or Oc) in which the existence of a single mutation causes, like in the i⁻ types described before, the uncontrolled synthesis of all the enzymes

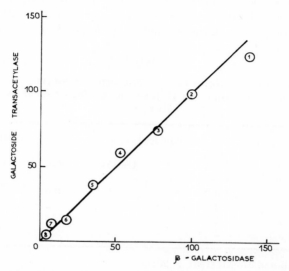

FIG. 6. Coinduction of β-galactosidase and galactoside transacetylase. The rates of synthesis of β-galactosidase and galactoside transacetylase are expressed in arbitrary units, the rates achieved by fully induced wild-type organisms being taken as 100. (1) uninduced constitutive mutant of the regulator (i⁻); (2) wild type induced by isopropyl-β-D-thiogalactoside (10⁻⁴ M); (3) wild type induced by methyl-β-D-thiogalactoside (10⁻⁴ M); (4) wild type induced by methyl-β-D-thiogalactoside (10⁻⁴ M) + phenyl-β-D-thiogalactoside (10⁻³ M); (5) wild type induced by melibiose (10⁻³ M); (6) wild type induced by lactose (10⁻³ M); (7) wild type induced by methyl-β-D-thiogalactoside (10⁻⁵ M); (8) wild type induced by phenylethyl-β-D-thiogalactoside (10†³ M). From Jacob and Monod (1961a).

of the operon (pleiotropic effect). But, contrary to the previous i⁻ constitutive alleles, these mutants are *dominant* to the wild type (Jacob and Monod, 1961a). Besides, the effect of the Oc mutation is exerted only in *cis* position, that is, on the genes covalently associated with the modified operator. We shall temporarily interpret those mutations as suggesting the existence of a specific gene, the operator, serving as receiver for the negative signal emitted by the regulator gene (under the form of a repressor).

The existence of constitutive mutants (Jacob and Monod, 1961a) which are dominant in respect to the wild type can be explained if one assumes that they contain an operator which has mutated toward a form (Oc) *insensitive* to the repressor action. This way, the entire operon remains out of control. These constitutive mutants, resulting from a change in the operator locus, will be called constitutive *operator* mutants, in contrast to constitutive *regulator* mutants which, we have seen, are recessive.

The main properties of the Oc mutants are summarized in Table III.

3. The discovery of polar mutants (Jacob and Monod, 1961a; Franklin and Luria, 1961; Englesberg, 1961; Ames and Hartman, 1963) has also confirmed that specific operons function as integral units. Polar mutants

TABLE III

PRODUCTION OF β-GALACTOSIDASE, GALACTOSIDE PERMEASE, AND GALACTOSIDE TRANSACETYLASE BY HAPLOID AND HETEROGENOTE, "SUPERREPRESSED" REGULATOR MUTANTS[a,b]

Genotypes	Noninduced			Induced		
	Gz	Y	Acetylase	Gz	Y	Acetylase
1. $i^+z^+y^+$	<0.1	<1	<1	100	100	100
2. $i^sz^+y^+$	2	2	2	2	2	2
3. $i^ss^+y^+/Fi^+z^+y^+$	2	2	2	2	2	2
4. $i^sz^+y^+/Fi^-z^+y^+$	2	2	2	2	2	2

[a] From Jacob and Monod (1961, p. 201).

[b] Activities expressed in percent of those observed with fully induced haploid wild type. The levels obtained with heterogenotes are always higher than those observed with haploid bacteria. This is presumably due to the presence of several F factors per chromosome. The high basal level observed in strains carrying an i^s mutation is due to the presence of constitutive mutants in the cultures. o, operator (o^+, wild-type; o^c, constitutive). For the other symbols, see Tables I and II.

result from a point mutation, the effect of which not only alters the structure (and activity) of the protein corresponding to the cistron bearing the mutation, but also leads to a reduction in the rate of synthesis of the enzymes directed by the genes, which are situated, in the same operon, further away than the mutation considered, with respect to the operator.

For example, many mutations are known in the z region which not only cause the production of an altered β-galactosidase, but can also considerably reduce the production of the galactoside permease and acetylase. Similarly, point mutations in the y region are known which can affect both the production of permease and acetylase, but not of β-galactosidase. In brief, there is a *polarity* in the effect caused by certain mutations of the lactose region, the direction of the effect being from z to y and from y to a. Very analogous situations have been observed within other operons, for instance, within the histidine region composed of nine adjacent genes.

In summary, the coordinate regulation of certain genes during induction or repression and the existence of Oc, or polar, mutants provide convergent evidence in favor of the existence of operons as polarized units of expression. The direct proof that each operon functions as a unit results from analyses of the mRNA produced during this functioning. These analyses strongly suggest that the messenger copy is "integral," that is, exhibits the same size as the operon itself (see page 49). For example following the induction of β-galactosidase, there is appearance of a new type of mRNA chain, which can be fractionated from the "bulk" mRNA, providing induction is preferential; that is, under conditions where the proteins of the lactose region constitute a very large proportion of the total proteins. Two such situations have been found. On the one hand, Gutman and Novick (1963) have isolated galactosidase hyperproducing strains, in which Gz represents around 25% of the newly synthesized proteins. They have succeeded in showing, by rapid labeling of such strains with a radioactive RNA precursor, the appearance of a new type of RNA fraction sedimenting at 30 S. Naono and associates (1965) have taken advantage of the observation that, during diauxic growth of *E. coli* in a medium containing a mixture of glucose and lactose, the bacteria preferentially synthesize the proteins of the lactose operon before a new wave of exponential growth is initiated on lactose, as the second carbon source. Sedimentation analyses (Fig. 7) of the RNA, pulse labeled at the onset of lactose adaptation, clearly reveal the differential synthesis of an RNA fraction, hybridizable with DNA's containing the homologous lactose genes and sedimenting at around 26 S.

Kiho and Rich (1964) have also come to the conclusion that the mRNA made by an induced lactose operon is a very long polynucleotide which represents the integral transcription product of the operon. First, they showed that, upon induction of *E. coli* spheroplasts, followed by rapid sedimentation of their extract on a sucrose gradient, the polysome to which galactosidase activity is attached sediments as a unit containing from 30–50 ribosomes. Second, polysomes derived from mutants having a deletion in the y region are shorter than wild-type polysomes. All these observations are consistent with the idea that the mRNA made by the lactose operon is a polynucleotide of molecular weight around 1.5×10^6. Considering that the z gene has enough information for making a monomer (which has a molecular weight of 65,000 or 130,000, depending upon whether the 130,000 polypeptide is considered a dimer) (Zabin, 1963), for the synthesis of which an mRNA of, at most, 1×10^6 would be required, it is likely that

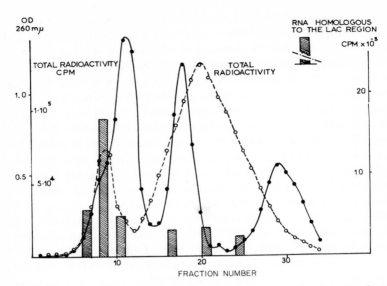

Fɪɢ. 7. Sedimentation profile of the rapidly labeled RNA during lactose adaptation, in diauxic growth. *E. coli* 200PS is cultivated in synthetic medium with glucose and lactose as carbon sources. When glucose is exhausted the cells begin to adapt to lactose following a 20-min lag. Before the second growth wave, a preferential synthesis of β-galactosidase and transacetylase can be observed. Such cells have been given a short pulse of H³-uridine. The total RNA was extracted and applied to a sucrose gradient (5–30%). After 10 hr of centrifugation at 25,000 rpm, samples are collected to determine (1) the optical density at 260 mμ and (2) the radioactivity. The radioactivity profile indicates the distribution of the rapidly labeled (messenger) RNA. It shows two major peaks at 14 S and at 26 S. Subfractions, delimited as indicated, were pooled and a test for complementariness toward the lactose genes was performed: This was realized by a stepwise hybridization, first on a DNA bearing a deletion of the *lac* region, and second, on a DNA rich in lactose genes (the purified Flac episome, was used for this purpose). The rectangular areas indicate the amount of RNA exhibiting a specific homology to the lactose genes. Note that most of the lactose-specific mRNA is located in the 26-S fraction of the rapidly labeled RNA (Naono *et al.*, 1965).

the lactose-specific mRNA forms a polysome on which the three protein monomers coded by the lactose operon are synthesized.

Similar conclusions supporting a polycistronic transcription of specific operons have been reached by Martin (1963), in the case of the histidine operon, and by Matsushiro (1964) in the case of the tryptophan operon.

Finally, the demonstration has recently been made by Beckwith (1964) that the expression of the operon in certain polar mutants of the lactose system is subject to restoration by mutations *external* to the operon itself. It has been shown that many of the Beckwith suppressor mutations had the ability to restore the translation of altered mRNA, such as those found in *rII* mutants of phage T4 or in alkaline phosphatase mutants.

servations suggest that between the segment "operator" and the beginning of the operon (proximal portion of z), there must exist a particular segment called the *promotor* ("p"), the deletion of which will inactivate the entire *lac* operon, unless this operon is connected—as a result of a large deletion—with another operon depending upon another promotor.

The simplest interpretation of these data at the present time is that the operator locus is not translated. It probably represents the point of attachment of the repressor to DNA. The repressor can block either the transcription of DNA to mRNA or the translation of mRNA to protein. If the transcription goes in the direction operator → acetylase, then the promotor can be regarded as the initiator of transcription and presumably the repressor blocks the transcription by becoming attached to the operator.

Were *transcription* to begin at the other pole and *translation* to proceed in the direction operator → acetylase, the repressor could conceivably block either the dissociation of mRNA from DNA (operator not transcribed) or the reading of the mRNA by the ribosomes (operator transcribed), in which last case the promotor would correspond to the segment where translation by ribosomes necessarily begins.

(a) **Operator not transcribed**

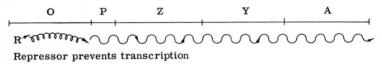

Repressor prevents transcription

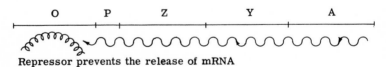

Repressor prevents the release of mRNA

(b) **Operator transcribed**

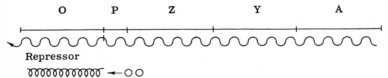

Repressor prevents the attachment of ribosomes

As we can see, in conclusion, alternative possibilities are offered for the site of repressors action in protein synthesis:

1. They could interfere directly at the genetic level, on the transcription of DNA to mRNA.

2. They could interact at the level of the functioning of the specific mRNA-ribosome complex, preventing the mRNA from being read, without interfering with its production.

3. They could, by inhibiting the reading of mRNA, prevent *indirectly* its dissociation from DNA [by retroaction, if the attachment of ribosomes to mRNA is necessary to disjoin the mRNA-DNA complex (Bremer and Konrad, 1964; Byrne *et al.*, 1964; Stent, 1964)].

Whatever the exact mechanism of repressor action might be, it has at least convincingly been shown, by a large body of experiments, that repression governs the *concentration* of the different types of mRNA in bacteria.

This point results mostly from studies designed to measure the level of specific mRNA's before, or after, induction of specific enzymes (Attardi *et al.*, 1963; Hayashi *et al.*, 1963).

1. Before induction, practically *no* mRNA fraction complementary to the homologous operon considered can be detected.

2. On the contrary, following the induction by a gratuitous inducer, a large proportion of the total mRNA fraction is found to be composed of molecules which are homologous to the relevant operon.

The accumulation of a specific mRNA following induction of a particular operon can also be demonstrated by the kinetic experiments of Kepes (1963a, b) and of Magasanik (Hartwell and Magasanik, 1963). These authors have observed that induced cells manufacture, in addition to active enzyme molecules, a certain *potential* to make more enzyme, after the inducer has been removed. This enzyme-forming potential decays with first-order kinetics upon removal of the inducer; its formation is blocked by 5-fluorouracil. In all likelihood, it is nothing but the specific mRNA accumulated by the induced organisms.

REFERENCES

Acs, G., Hartman, G., Boman, H. G., and Lipmann, F. (1959). *Federation Proc.* **18**, 178.

Adler, M., Weissmann, B., and Gutman, A. B. (1958). *J. Biol. Chem.* **230**, 717.

Ames, B. N., and Garry, B. (1959). *Proc. Natl. Acad. Sci. U.S.* **45**, 1453.

Ames, B. N., and Hartman, P. (1963). *Cold Spring Harbor Symp. Quant. Biol.* **28**, 349.

Ames, B. N., and Martin, R. G. (1964). *Ann. Rev. Biochem.* **33**, 235.

Amos, H., and Korn, M. (1958). *Biochim. Biophys. Acta* **29**, 444.

Apgar, J., Holley, R. N., and Merrill, S. H. (1962). *J. Biol. Chem.* **237**, 796.

Asano, K., and Watson, J. D. (1963). *Federation Proc.* **22**, 525.

Attardi, G., Naono, S., Rouvière, J., Jacob, F., and Gros, F. (1963). *Cold Spring Harbor Symp. Quant. Biol.* **28**, 363.

August, J. T., Ortiz, P. J., and Hurwitz, J. (1962). *J. Biol. Chem.* **237**, 3786.

Bassel, A., Hayashi, H., and Spiegelman, S. (1964). *Proc. Natl. Acad. Sci. U.S.* **52**, 796.

Bautz, E. K. F. (1963). *Cold Spring Harbor Symp. Quant. Biol.* **28**, 205.

Bautz, E. K. F., and Hall, B. D. (1962). *Proc. Natl. Acad. Sci. U.S.* **48**, 400.

Beckwith, J. (1964). "Structure and Function of the Genetic Material" (Erwin-Baur-Gedächtnisvorlesungen III). Akadamie Verlag, Berlin.

Hall, C. E., and Slayter, H. S. (1959). *J. Mol. Biol.* **1**, 329.

Hammers, R., and Hammers-Casterman, C. (1959). *Biochim. Biophys. Acta.* **33**, 269.

Hartwell, L. H., and Magasanik, B. (1963). *J. Mol. Biol.* **7**, 401.

Hayashi, M., Spiegelman, S., Franklin, N. C., and Luria, S. E. (1963). *Proc. Natl. Acad. Sci. U.S.* **49**, 729.

Hayes, D. H., Guérin, M. F., and Hayes, F. (1963). *Colloq. Intern. Centre Uatl. Rech. Sci.* **124**, 57.

Hecht, L. I., Stephenson, M. L., and Zamecnik, P. C. (1958a). *Proc. Natl. Acad. Sci. U.S.* **29**, 460.

Hecht, L. I., Zamecnik, P. C., Stephenson, M. L., and Scott, J. F. (1958b). *J. Biol. Chem.* **233**, 954.

Hecht, L. I., Stephenson, M. L., and Zamecnik, P. C. (1959). *Proc. Natl. Acad. Sci. U.S.* **45**, 505.

Herbert, E. (1958). *J. Biol. Chem.* **231**, 975.

Herbert, E. (1959). *Ann. N.Y. Acad. Sci.* **81**, 679.

Hershey, A. D. (1953). *J. Gen. Physiol.* **37**, 1.

Hershey, A. D., Burgie, E., and Ingraham, L. (1963). *Proc. Natl. Acad. Sci. U.S.* **49**, 748.

Hiatt, H. (1962). *J. Mol. Biol.* **5**, 217.

Hoagland, M. B. (1955). *Biochim. Biophys. Acta* **16**, 288.

Hoagland, M. B., and Comly, L. I. (1960). *Proc. Natl. Acad. Sci. U.S.* **46**, 1554.

Hoagland, M. B., Keller, E. B., and Zamecnik, P. C. (1956). *J. Biol. Chem.* **221**, 45.

Hoagland, M. B., Zamecnik, P. C., and Stephenson, M. L. (1957). *Biochim. Biophys. Acta.* **24**, 215.

Hoagland, M. B., Stephenson, M. L., Scott, J. F., Hecht, L. I., and Zamecnik, P. C. (1958). *J. Biol. Chem.* **231**, 241.

Holley, R. W., and Goldstein, J. (1959). *J. Biol. Chem.* **234**, 1765.

Holley, R. W., Apgar, J., Everett, G. A., Madison, J. T., Merrill, S. H., and Zamir, A. (1963). *Cold Spring Harbor Symp. Quant. Biol.* **28**, 117.

Holley, R. W., Apgar, J., Everett, G. A., Madison, J. T., Marquisee, M., Merrill, S. H., Penswick, J. R., and Zamir, A. (1965). *Science* **147**, 1462.

Horiuchi, T., and Novick, A. (1961). *Cold Spring Harbor Symp. Quant. Biol.* **26**, 247.

Horowitz, N. H., and Fling, M. (1953). *Genetics* **38**, 360.

Hunt, J. A., and Ingram, V. M. (1958). *Nature* **181**, 1062.

Hurwitz, J., and August, J. T. (1963). *Progr. Nucleic Acid Res.* **1**, 59.

Hurwitz, J., Furth, J. J., Anders, M., Ortiz, P. J., and August, J. T. (1961). *Cold Spring Harbor Symp. Quant. Biol.* **26**, 91.

Ingram, V. M. (1958). *Biochim. Biophys. Acta* **28**, 539.

Ingram, V. M., and Sjöquist, J. A. (1963). *Cold Spring Harbor Symp. Quant. Biol.* **28**, 133.

Jacob, F., and Monod, J. (1958). *Compt. Rend.* **246**, 3125.

Jacob, F., and Monod, J. (1961a). *Cold Spring Harbor Symp. Quant. Biol.* **26**, 193.

Jacob, F., and Monod, J. (1961b). *J. Mol. Biol.* **3**, 318.

Jacob, F., and Monod, J. (1964). *Bull. Soc. Chim. Biol.* **46**, 149.).

Jacob, F., and Wollman, E. L. (1957). *Compt. Rend.* **245**, 1840.

Jacob, F., and Wollman, E. L. (1958a). *Compt. Rend.* **247**, 154.

Jacob, F., and Wollman, E. L. (1958b). *Symp. Soc. Exptl. Biol.* **12**, 75.

Jacob, F., and Wollman, E. L., editors (1961). "Sexuality and the Genetics of Bacteria". Academic Press, New York.

Jacob, F., Perrin, D., Sanchez, C., and Monod, J. (1960a). *Compt. Rend.* **250**, 1727.

Jacob, F., Schaeffer, P., and Wollman, E. L. (1960b). *Symp. Soc. Gen. Microbiol.* **10**, 67.

Jacob, F., Brenner, S., and Cuzin, F. (1963). *Cold Spring Harbor Symp. Quant. Biol.* **28**, 329.

Kalckar, H., and Sundararajan, T. A. (1961). *Cold Spring Harbor Symp. Quant. Biol.* **6, 2** 227.

Kayser, D. (1964). Personal communication.

Kellenberger, E. (1960). *Symp. Soc. Gen. Microbiol.* **10,** 39.

Kepes, A. (1963a). *Cold Spring Harbor Symp. Quant. Biol.* **28,** 325.

Kepes, A. (1963b). *Biochim. Biophys. Acta* **76,** 293.

Kihara, H. K., Hu, A. S. L., and Halvorson, H. O. (1961). *Proc. Natl. Acad. Sci. U.S.* **47,** 489.

Kiho, Y., and Rich, A. (1964). *Proc. Natl. Acad. Sci. U.S.* **51,** 111.

Kleinschmidt, A., and Zakn, R. K. (1959). *Z. Naturforsch.* **146,** 770.

Koch, A. L., and Levy, H. R. (1955). *J. Biol. Chem.* **217,** 947.

Kogat, M., Pollock, M., and Tridgell, E. J. (1956). *Biochem. J.* **62,** 391.

Kurland, C. G. (1960). *J. Mol. Biol.* **2,** 83.

Kurland, C. G., Nomura, M., and Watson, J. D. (1962). *J. Mol. Biol.* **4,** 388.

Lagerkvist, V., and Berg, P. (1962). *J. Mol. Biol.* **5,** 139.

Lamborg, M. R., and Zamecnik, P. C. (1963). *Biochim. Biophys. Acta* **42,** 206.

Langridge, R. (1964). Reported at the Gordon Conference on Nucleic Acids, New Hampton.

Leder, P., and Nirenberg, M. W. (1964a). *Proc. Natl. Acad. Sci. U.S.* **52,** 420.

Leder, P., and Nirenberg, M. W. (1964b). *Proc. Natl. Acad. Sci. U. S.* **52,** 1521.

Lederberg, J. (1950). *J. Bacteriol.* **60,** 381.

Levinthal, C. (1959). *Rev. Mod. Phys.* **31,** 249.

Levinthal, C., Keynan, A., and Higa, A. (1962). *Proc. Natl. Acad. Sci. U.S.* **48,** 1631.

Levinthal, C., Fan, D. P., Higa, A., and Zimmerman, R. A. (1963). *Cold Spring Harbor Symp. Quant. Biol.* **28,** 183.

Lipmann, F. (1941). *Advan. Enzymol.* **1,** 99.

Lipmann, F. (1949). *Federation Proc.* **8,** 597.

Littlefield, J. W., and Dunn, D. B. (1958). *Biochem. J.* **70,** 642.

Littlefield, J. W., and Keller, E. B. (1957). *J. Biol. Chem.* **224,** 13.

Littlefield, J. W., Keller, E. B., Cross, J., and Zamecnik, P. C. (1955). *J. Biol. Chem.* **217,** 111.

Lubin, M., and Ennis, H. (1964). *Biochim. Biophys. Acta* (in press).

Luborsky, S. W., and Cantoni, G. L. (1962). *Biochim. Biophys. Acta* **61,** 481.

Maas, W. (1956). *Federation Proc.* **15,** 305.

Maas, W. (1961). *Cold Spring Harbor Symp. Quant. Biol.* **26,** 183.

Maas, W., and Davis, B. D. (1955). *Proc. Natl. Acad. Sci. U.S.* **38,** 785.

McCarthy, B. J., and Aronson, A. I. (1961). *Biophys. J.* **1,** 227.

McCully, K. S., and Cantoni, G. L. (1962). *J. Mol. Biol.* **5,** 80.

McQuillen, K., Roberts, R. B., and Britten, R. J. (1959). *Proc. Natl. Acad. Sci. U.S.* **45,** 1437.

Marks, P., Burka, E. R., and Schlessinger, D. (1962a). *Proc. Natl. Acad. Sci. U.S.* **47,** 2163.

Marks, P., Willson, C., Kruh, J., Hiatt, H., and Gros, F. (1962b). *Biochem. Biophys. Res. Commun.* **8,** 9.

Marmur, J. (1964). Personal communication.

Marmur, J., and Lane, D. (1960). *Proc. Natl. Acad. Sci. U.S.* **46,** 453.

Marmur, J., Greenspan, C. M., Palecek, E., Kahan, F. M., Levine, J., and Mandel, M. (1963). *Cold Harbor Symp. Quant. Biol.* **28,** 191.

Martin, R. G. (1963). *Cold Spring Harbor Symp. Quant. Biol.* **28,** 357.

Matsushiro, A. (1964). Personal communication.

Tissières, A., Schlessinger, D., and Gros, F. (1960). *Proc. Natl. Acad. Sci. U.S.* **46**, 1450.

Thomas, C. A. (1963). *In* "Molecular Genetics" (J. H. Taylor, ed.), Part 1, p. 113. Academic Press, New York.

Thomas, C. A., and Berns, K. I. (1961). *J. Mol. Biol.* **3**, 277.

Tocchini-Valentini, G. P., Stodolsky, M., Aurisichio, A., Sarnat, M., Guaziosi, F., Weiss, S. B., and Geiduschek, E. P. (1963). *Proc. Natl. Acad. Sci. U.S.* **50**, 935.

Ts'o, P. O. P., Bonner, J., and Vinograd, J. (1956). *J. Biophys. Biochem. Cytol.* **2**, 451.

Vinograd, J. (1964). Personal communication.

Vogel, H. (1957). *In* "The Chemical Basis of Heredity" (W. D. McElroy and B. Glass, eds.), Johns Hopkins Press, Baltimore, p. 276.

Volkin, E., and Astrachan, L. (1956a). *Virology* **2**, 149.

Volkin, E., and Astrachan, L. (1956b). *Virology* **2**, 433.

Volkin, E., and Astrachan, L. (1957). *In* "The Chemical Basis of Heredity" (W. D. McElroy and B. Glass, eds.), p. 686. Johns Hopkins Press, Baltimore.

Von Ehrenstein, G., and Lipmann, F. (1961). *Proc. Natl. Acad. Sci. U.S.* **47**, 18.

Wahba, A. J., Gardner, R. S., Basilio, C., Miller, R. S., Speyer, J. F., and Lengyel, P. (1963). *Proc. Natl. Acad. Sci. U.S.* **49**, 116.

Waller, J. P. (1964). *J. Mol. Biol.* **10**, 319.

Waller, J. P., and Harris, J. I. (1961). *Proc. Natl. Acad. Sci. U.S.* **47**, 18.

Warner, J. R., Knod, P., and Rich, A. (1963). *Proc. Natl. Acad. Sci. U.S.* **49**, 122.

Watson, J. D. (1964). *Bull. Soc. Chim. Biol.* **46**, 1399.

Watson, J. D., and Crick, F. H. C. (1953). *Nature* **171**, 737.

Weil, R., and Vinograd, J. (1963). *Proc. Natl. Acad. Sci. U.S.* **50**, 730.

Weinstein, I. B., and Schechter, A. N. (1962). *Proc. Natl. Acad. Sci., U.S.* **48**, 1686.

Weisblum, B., Benzer, S., and Holley, R. W. (1962). *Proc. Natl. Acad. Sci. U.S.* **48**, 1449.

Weiss, S. B. (1960). *Proc. Natl. Acad. Sci. U.S.* **46**, 1020.

Willson, C., Perrin, D., Cohn, M., Jacob, F., and Monod, J. (1964). *J. Mol. Biol.* **8**, 582.

Woese, C., Naono, S., Soffer, R., and Gros, F. (1963). *Biochem. Biophys. Res. Commun.* **11**, 435.

Yanofsky, C. (1963). *Cold Spring Harbor Symp. Quant. Biol.* **28**, 581.

Yanofsky, C., and Crawford, I. P. (1959). *Proc. Natl. Acad. Sci. U.S.* **45**, 1016.

Yanofsky, C., Helinski, D. R., and Maling, B. D. (1961). *Cold Spring Harbor Symp. Quant. Biol.* **26**, 11.

Yankofsky, S. A., and Spiegelman, S. (1962a). *Proc. Natl. Acad. Sci. U.S.* **48**, 1069.

Yankofsky, S. A., and Spiegelman, S. (1962b). *Proc. Natl. Acad. Sci. U.S.* **48**, 1465.

Yankofsky, S. A., and Spiegelman, S. (1963). *Proc. Natl. Acad. Sci. U.S.* **49**, 539.

Zabin, I. (1963). *Cold Spring Harbor Symp. Quant. Biol.* **28**, 431.

Zachau, H. G., Acs, G., and Lipmann, F. (1958). *Proc. Natl. Acad. Sci. U.S.* **44**, 885.

Zillig, W. D., Schachstschabel, D., and Krone, W. (1960). *Z. Physiol. Chem.* **318**, 100.

Zipser, D. (1963). *J. Mol. Biol.* **7**, 739.

Zipser, D., and Perrin, D. (1963). *Cold Spring Harbor Symp. Quant. Biol.* **28**, 533.

The Description of Molecules by the Method of Molecular Orbitals[1]

ALBERTE PULLMAN

Institut de Biologie Physico-Chimique,
Université de Paris,
Paris, France

I. Introduction

My purpose here is to provide you with a general idea of the principal methods now available for the description of the "fine structure" of molecules. These lectures will go beyond the usual limit of presenting only the simplest approximations of the methods, because application of quantum-mechanical procedures to biochemistry and biophysics, which at the beginning was, naturally, restricted to the utilization of the simplest approximations, has now passed this stage and, as related in this volume by B. Pullman, higher approximations are being steadily and progressively introduced into the field. This course is therefore intended to give biochemists and biophysicists the appropriate basis for the understanding of

[1] This work was sponsored by grant No. CY-3073 of the U. S. Public Health Service (National Cancer Institute). Part of the material for this paper was prepared during the stay of the author at the Theoretical Chemistry Institute, University of Wisconsin, Madison, Wisconsin, sponsored by grant No. GM-11315-01 awarded to the Institute by the National Institute of Health.

of all individual wave functions is an eigenfunction of the total Hamiltonian with a total energy equal to the simple sum of individual energies. But since electrons cannot be individualized, any such products in which two electrons are interchanged may do as well. Thus the most appropriate total wave function is a generalized sum of such products. In fact, only one combination is possible, since a general principle of quantum mechanics imposes on the wave function of an electronic system the state of being antisymmetrical with respect to the exchange of any two electrons.

Thus the final expression of the wave function of a system of noninteracting electrons, in terms of individual wave functions, is the sum

$$\sum_P (-1)^P P(a(1) \ b(2) \ c(3) \ d(4) \cdots) \tag{7}$$

over all possible permutations. This can also be written in a determinantal form[2] as

$$\begin{vmatrix} a(1) & b(1) & c(1) & \cdots \\ a(2) & b(2) & c(2) & \cdots \\ \cdot & \cdot & \cdot & \cdots \\ \cdot & \cdot & \cdot & \cdots \\ \cdot & \cdot & \cdot & \cdots \\ a(n) & b(n) & c(n) & \cdots \end{vmatrix} \tag{8}$$

Both expressions should, of course, be multiplied by the appropriate factor to ensure the normalization condition that must be imposed on all wave functions:

$$\int |\Psi|^2 \, d\tau = 1 \tag{9}$$

The determinantal form (8) is very practical for the following reason: It is known that a determinant is zero if two of its rows are identical. This leads to the following rule: *Two electrons in a system cannot have the same wave function.* Now, quantum mechanics tells us that the wave function of a single electron may be taken as a product of two factors: one depending on the position only, the *orbital* factor,

$$\varphi(x, y, z) \tag{10}$$

the second, called a *spin* function, which is allowed only two values, α or

---

[2] Such determinantal wave functions are often called Slater determinants, from the name of their promoter in polyelectronic systems (Slater, 1929).

β. Thus every function $a, b, c, d, \cdots$ is of one of two forms,

$$\varphi(\nu)\alpha(\nu) \tag{11}$$

or

$$\varphi(\nu)\beta(\nu) \tag{12}$$

The foregoing rule thus demands that, if two electrons have the same spin, they have different orbital functions, and conversely. We can make this sound like a familiar rule by saying: *An individual orbital may be occupied at most by two electrons with antiparallel spins.*

Let us not dwell further on this rule for the moment but proceed with our representation of noninteracting electrons. Since the total energy is a simple sum of individual energies, the ground state (state of lowest energy) is obtained by filling up the available individual orbitals in the order of increasing energy by pairs of electrons with antiparallel spins until housing of all the electrons is achieved. Excited states are obtained by taking one (or more) electron(s) from one (or more) of the occupied orbitals and putting it (them) into one (or more) empty orbital(s). You recognize here a familiar procedure, known as the *Aufbau principle*, which is widely used for the description of atoms; in fact, it is used also for molecules. But we have derived it in a case of noninteracting electrons, whereas real atomic and molecular systems do involve interaction.

The reason the foregoing rules are applied to real systems is that, precisely in order to keep the simple orbital representation, methods have been devised which rest on the following idea: *Suppose that a system of interacting electrons can still be represented by a determinantal wave function built on individual orbitals, but try to determine the individual orbitals so as to take interaction into account at the one-electron level.*

This is the basis of the method of molecular orbitals. We shall see that many branches have developed from this original stem, having essentially in common the description of each electron by an individual orbital. We shall for the moment pursue the original scheme as it emerges from the previous considerations.

However, before entering the practical carrying out of the program, let us point out what we called earlier the "built-in" limitations of our model: The exclusion principle that we have rediscovered above forbids more than two electrons to occupy the same orbital; it does not impose that one orbital *must* accommodate two electrons. The fact that we put two electrons in each orbital comes from the fact that the Aufbau principle is derived in a hypothetical system of noninteracting electrons: To obtain the lowest energy, the lowest individual orbitals must be occupied by the maximum number of electrons, that is, two. But in a real system, electrons avoid each other as much as possible, because of their Coulomb repulsion. A

Thus, the ground-state energy depends on all the orbitals φ_i. Carrying out its minimization with respect to a small variation $\delta\varphi_i$ (leaving the MO's orthogonal), we get the general Fock equations (one for each φ_i):

$$F\varphi_i = \epsilon_i\varphi_i \tag{21}$$

where F is the Hartree–Fock Hamiltonian defined in terms of the previous operators by

$$F = H + \sum_j (2J_j - K_j) \tag{22}$$

Equation (21) has the formal aspect of an ordinary Schrödinger equation, and indeed each ϵ_i plays the role of an individual energy corresponding to the orbital φ_i. However, the Hartree–Fock operator has the special feature that it depends on all the orbitals which are occupied in the system: Thus each φ is given by an equation which depends on all the φ's. The way out of this circle is to choose arbitrarily a starting set of φ's, calculate the $F(\nu)$'s, solve the series of equations for a new set of φ's, and go over the same series of operations again and again until the nth set of φ's reproduces the $(n-1)$th set to a good accuracy (hence the name "self-consistent" [SCF] of the procedure). The orbitals obtained in this fashion are in principle the best possible orbitals compatible with a determinantal Ψ.

One restriction must, however, be made on this last statement: A choice must be made of a starting set of φ's. Since it is impossible to guess *ab initio* the appropriate analytical form of a molecular orbital, we shall see that one must rely on a "reasonable" possibility, but the initial choice will then impose restrictions on the flexibility of the resulting orbitals. As a consequence, the final orbitals are the best possible orbitals *of the form chosen*. This will become clearer after the next section.

IV. The LCAO Approximation

As we said at the beginning, one-electron problems are rigorously soluble. It might thus be tempting to think that the simplest one-electron molecular problem (H_2^+) could give a clue to the shape of the individual molecular orbital, at least in a diatomic case. Unfortunately, even this possibility is excluded, since the analytical form of the H_2^+ solution is too complicated to be used as a trial function. Thus how do we choose the starting orbitals?

The solution stemmed from the following reasoning due to Lennard-Jones (1929): Suppose that we deal with a chemical bond formed between two monovalent atoms A and B by the pairing of their valence electrons, one on A, the other on B. In the molecule AB, the two electrons forming the bond must be assigned a molecular orbital φ, which will differ from the atomic orbitals that each electron occupied in the isolated atoms. Nevertheless, it is natural to assume that, when one electron in the molecule is close to nucleus A, its molecular orbital will resemble the atomic orbital it would occupy in A, and the same for B. This leads to the idea that the molecular orbital may be approximated by a linear combination:

$$\varphi = C_1 \chi_A + C_2 \chi_B \qquad (23)$$

The idea can of course be extended to a polyatomic molecule and generalized so that each molecular orbital in a molecule will be a linear combination of *all* the atomic orbitals occupied by the electrons in the constituent atoms (Mulliken, 1932, 1933):

$$\varphi = \sum_r C_r \chi_r \qquad (24)$$

Moreover, it can be carried out to the extreme by also including in this basis excited orbitals on each atom, orbitals with varying exponents, etc. (see, for instance, Mulliken, 1962, for a list of the possible extensions of the basis).

The form taken by the Fock equations when the molecular orbitals are assumed to have the LCAO form (24) has been shown by Roothaan (1951) to yield a system of homogeneous linear equations in the C_i's [replace $\varphi_i(\nu)$ in (21) by $\sum_q C_{iq}\chi_q(\nu)$, multiply each side on the left by $\chi_p^*(\nu)$, and integrate over ν]:

$$\sum_q C_{iq}\{F_{pq} - \epsilon S_{pq}\} = 0 \qquad (25)$$

where

$$S_{pq} = \int \chi_p^*(\nu)\chi_q(\nu)\, d\tau_\nu \qquad (26)$$

is the *overlap integral* and F_{pq} is the pq matrix element of the Fock operator,

$$F_{pq} = \int \chi_p^*(\nu) F \chi_q(\nu)\, d\tau_\nu \qquad (27)$$

F_{pq} may be decomposed into

$$F_{pq} = I_{pq} + G_{pq} \qquad (28)$$

with[3]

$$I_{pq} = \int \chi_p^*(\nu) H(\nu)\chi_q(\nu)\, d\tau_\nu \qquad (29)$$

[3] In some publications, the core integrals are called H_{pq}. Because of the numerous quantities which are labeled in this way, we prefer the notation of Parr and Mulliken (1950).

as applied to the particular case of ethylene. In simple language, it may be understood in the following fashion: The two p_z orbitals admit, as a nodal plane, the plane of the molecule, and the two lobes of the corresponding wave functions are antisymmetrical with respect to this plane. On the contrary, all the other atomic orbitals are symmetrical with respect to the plane of the molecule (Fig. 1). Thus any integral S_{pq} involving two orbitals p and q of these different kinds will cancel. Moreover, the Hartree–Fock Hamiltonian F is a totally symmetrical operator, which means that it does not affect the symmetry properties of the functions on which it operates. Thus any integral F_{pq} will behave as S_{pq}. In other words, there will be no matrix elements in our secular equations between p_z and other AO's. The secular determinant reduces to blocks separated by zeros, with a 2×2 block corresponding to the p_z-dependent MO's. As a consequence, the 16 resulting molecular orbitals fall into two categories: the so-called π molecular orbitals, linear combinations of the p_z atomic orbitals only, and the other 14 orbitals, called the σ orbitals, which can depend on all the 14 other atomic orbitals. In fact, in this last group, other reductions occur,

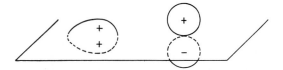

Fig. 1. Orbitals of two different symmetry types with respect to the molecular plane.

because of the high molecular symmetry of ethylene (Berthod, 1961). (A general treatment of the use of the molecular symmetry in the SCF-LCAO method was given by Roothaan, 1951.) Such reductions, however, depend on the particular arrangement of the atoms, whereas the σ–π separation results from the symmetry characteristics of the atomic orbitals.

An interesting feature of this σ–π MO separation is that it is a characteristic of all the previously defined conjugated molecules. In effect, one of the known experimental features of such compounds is the coplanarity of the atomic centers. Thus if coordinate axes similar to those used in ethylene are adopted for each atomic center, all the p_z atomic orbitals of the basis point in parallel directions, perpendicular to the molecular plane and, for the same reasons as before, no mixing occurs between the p_z's and other AO's. Thus in all conjugated molecules, the SCF molecular orbitals again will separate into the pure π orbitals:

$$\varphi_\pi = \sum_r c_r \chi_z(R) \qquad (37)$$

summed over all the atomic p_z orbitals of the contributing atoms and σ orbitals built on the other AO's of the basis, each family corresponding to a different secular equation. Of course, these two secular equations are inter-dependent in the sense that each element F_{pq} of both depends, as was seen earlier, on all the occupied molecular orbitals, σ and π. Thus, although their orbitals separate, the systems are not independent. However, another feature encourages us to classify them into two distinct categories: SCF computations that have been done with explicit inclusion of all the electrons for unsaturated compounds [ethylene, Berthod (1961); acetylene, Burnelle (1960); McLean (1960); see also McLean et al. (1960); formaldehyde, Goodfriend et al. (1960); N_2, Scheer (1955); carbon dioxide, Mulligan (1951)] show that, among the orbitals occupied in the ground state, the π orbitals are the highest in energy[4] (with the possible exception of lone-pair orbitals). Accordingly, the π electrons are the most *labile*, the most easily ionized or excited, in agreement with decades of well-known chemical and physicochemical evidence attributing special properties to doubly bonded systems. Thus, the theory of conjugated compounds has been de-veloped on the basis of a complete σ–π separation, which amounts to the following:

1. π Electrons are treated alone as a system in the resulting field of the nuclei and the σ electrons. In other words, one writes a Hamiltonian *for the π electrons*,

$$H_\pi = \sum_\nu H^{\text{core}}(\nu) + \sum_{\mu<\nu} (r_{\mu\nu})^{-1} \tag{38}$$

defining a *core*, which includes everything but the π electrons. Provided H is so defined, an SCF-LCAO-MO procedure can be applied to the π system alone, and the best π MO's can thus be computed using the equation

$$|\, F_{pq}^\pi - \epsilon S_{pq}\,| = 0 \tag{39}$$

where the matrix elements F_{pq}^π are defined from a Hartree–Fock operator appropriate for π electrons by equations formally identical to (19)–(22):

$$F^\pi = H^{\text{core}} + \sum_j (2J_j{}^\pi - K_j{}^\pi) \tag{40}$$

where j runs over π orbitals only.

The correspondent to Eq. (28) is

$$F_{pq}^\pi = I_{pq}^\pi + G_{pq}^\pi \tag{41}$$

---

[4] Recent results by Hoffmann (1963) may seem to throw some doubt on this con-clusion, but because of the approximations involved in Hoffmann's procedure, more calculations are necessary to settle this question (Moscowitz and Barnett, 1963).

C. Core Integrals

The core integrals I_{pq} entering the SCF equations for a π system are

$$\int \chi_p(\nu) H^{\text{core}}(\nu) \chi_q(\nu) \, d\tau_\nu \tag{51}$$

where χ_p and χ_q are the atomic p_z orbitals of atoms P and Q. Each time H^{core} operates on a given atomic orbital χ_q, one uses the partitioning (49), writing it in a convenient fashion:

$$H^{\text{core}} = T + V_Q + \sum_{A \neq Q} V_A + \sum_i V^0_{H_i} \tag{52}$$

The calculation of the core integrals may then be carried out using a procedure initiated by Goeppert-Mayer and Sklar (1938), which rests on the following remark: If χ_Q is an atomic eigenfunction in the sense that it satisfies the equation

$$(T + V_Q)\chi_Q = W_Q \chi_Q \tag{53}$$

where $-W_Q$ is the appropriate valence-state ionization potential of atom Q, every I_{pq} may be written

$$I_{pq} = S_{pq} W_Q + \sum_{A \neq Q} \int \chi_p(\nu) V_A(\nu) \chi_q(\nu) \, d\tau_\nu + \sum_i \chi_p(\nu) V^0_{H_i} \chi_q(\nu) \, d\tau_\nu \tag{54}$$

This has the practical advantage that all energy quantities in a hydrocarbon molecule may be referred to W_C and that, in the energy differences which occur in excitation energies, for instance, W_C disappears, so that its numerical value does not influence the result. This is, of course, not valid for heterocyclic molecules, where different W_Q values appear. It has, however, proved convenient to generalize the use of this kind of development. As to the evaluation of the terms in the summations of expression (54), there are two possibilities: One is the use of the explicit potentials of each atom of the core (except Q) as in Eq. (48). An explicit example of such a development can be found in a paper of Sender and Berthier (1958) on formaldehyde. The other possibility invokes the definition of *penetration* integrals, again due to Goeppert-Mayer and Sklar (1938). The procedure, often called the GMS expansion, uses the fact that $V_A(\nu)$ may be considered the potential of the *neutral* atom A *minus* the repulsion of its π electron. Thus

$$\int \chi_p(\nu) V_A(\nu) \chi_q(\nu) \, d\tau_\nu = -(A, pq) - [(aa, pq) - \tfrac{1}{2}(aq, pa)] \tag{55}$$

where the *penetration* integrals are defined as

$$A, pq = -\int \chi_p(\nu) V_{A^0}(\nu) \chi_q(\nu) \, d\tau_\nu \tag{56}$$

The symbol $V_A{}^0$ refers to the neutral atom A. The exchange term $\frac{1}{2}(aq, pa)$ was neglected in the original decomposition and is generally omitted in the calculations. With these conventions, the core integrals take the convenient form

$$I_{pq} = S_{pq}W_q - \sum_{A \neq Q} A, pq - \sum_i H_i, pq - \sum_{a \neq q} aa, pq \qquad (57)$$

Methods assuming spherically symmetrical neutral atoms for the evaluation of the penetration integrals can be found in the papers by Goeppert-Mayer and Sklar (1938); and by Sklar and Lyddane (1939), corrected by Parr and Crawford (1948). More general formulas have been given by Ruedenberg (1961). Partial tables are scattered in the literature (Parr and Mulliken, 1950; Barnett and Coulson, 1951; Berthier, 1953; Fischer, 1952; Scrocco and Salvetti, 1952; Lofthus, 1961; Guérillot et al., 1965). As to the hydrogen penetration integrals, the practice not to introduce them established itself from the outset. This is no doubt questionable in principle (Fischer, 1952) and by no means necessary. However, it has been shown that, in the I_{pp} core integrals for *carbon compounds*, the sum

$$\sum_{A \neq Q} A, pp + \sum_i H_i, pp \qquad (58)$$

is practically constant for each carbon, whether primary, secondary, or tertiary (Julg and Pullman, 1955). This may be considered justification for the approximation of I_{pp} values in hydrocarbons by an expression of the type

$$\alpha_p = \text{Constant} - \sum_{a \neq p}(aa, pp) \qquad (59)$$

where the penetration integrals are admittedly lumped into the constant. Such approximations are widely used in semiempirical methods (*vide infra*).

D. Electron-Repulsion Integrals

The practical calculation of the G_{pq} terms and even, as we have seen, of the core integrals requires the knowledge of the electron-repulsion integrals (pq, rs) previously defined. When Slater atomic orbitals are used for the LCAO basis (Slater, 1930), which is the most general case, standard formulas or tables can be used for the calculation of the two-center integrals —for instance, the tables by Kotani et al. (1955), Preuss (1956–1961), Sahni and Cooley (1959–1960), and the series of articles by Roothaan et al. referred to in Wahl et al. (1964).

Three- and four-center integrals have been one of the stumbling blocks of quantum-chemical calculations for many years because of technical difficulties hampering their evaluation. Automatic computation methods have been devised recently (Shavitt and Karplus, 1962) which seem to

which is of the greatest interest in connection with the problem of conjugated molecules is the following:

Let us define around each center r the quantity

$$n_i(C_{ir}^2 + \sum_{s \neq r} C_{ir}C_{is}S_{rs}) \tag{66}$$

so that the summation of (66) over all atoms r gives the orbital population (65). If, now, we sum expression (66) over all the occupied orbitals, we obtain what Mulliken called the "gross atomic population" or, in more familiar terms, the *electronic charge* (in e units) around atom r:

$$Q_r = \sum_i n_i(C_{ir}^2 + \sum_{s \neq r} C_{ir}C_{is}S_{rs}) \tag{67}$$

For definitions of the other structure indices and their discussion, we refer the reader to the reviews mentioned before.

F. The Problem of Excited States

Suppose for the moment that the SCF-LCAO-MO model is the best that can be carried out for the ground state of a molecule. What can we expect from it for the representation of excited states and the subsequent evaluation of excitation energies? There are two possibilities:

1. Carry out to an extreme the use of the Aufbau principle, that is, utilize the virtual orbitals (the unfilled molecular orbitals in the ground state) obtained in the resolution of the previous SCF equations, for the representation of excited states. For example, the first excited state is obtained by promoting one electron to the first empty orbital. Appropriate Slater determinants may be written for any of the "configurations" obtained in this fashion—the name *configuration* being taken to mean a given state of occupation of the molecular orbitals. For configurations involving singly occupied orbitals (*open-shell* configurations), a single Slater determinant is not a satisfactory wave function, since it is not an eigenvalue of both the total S_Z and S^2 spin operators. Rules for finding the appropriate combinations of Slater determinants were devised a long time ago for the atomic case.

The energies of the excited configurations can easily be calculated using the total Hamiltonian (3), and the corresponding excitation energies thus obtained. The first application of this kind of procedure to π-electron systems is the calculation of benzene, previously mentioned (Goeppert-Mayer and Sklar, 1938). General expressions for the first singlet and triplet excitation energies were given in Roothaan's first paper (1951). Detailed examples of the appropriate wave functions and energies for excited configurations of different multiplicities can be found in early papers by

Craig (1950). A recent, clear summary of the procedures involved can be found in Section 5 of Parr's book (1963).

2. The strong objection to the preceding model is its use for excited states of molecular orbitals which are determined to be the best ground-state orbitals. In principle, it would be more satisfactory to use orbitals determined as best for the state considered by minimizing the energy of each appropriate excited-state wave function. Although such an approach is now theoretically possible through different techniques which have recently been reviewed by Berthier (1964), the extent of the practical applications to excited states of π systems is still very limited, for different practical reasons.

3. The results obtained in (1) can be improved in principle by the technique of *configuration mixing*, first applied to conjugated systems by Craig (1950). In short, this amounts to writing all the possible configurations Γ_P built with all the molecular orbitals as in (1), and, for a molecular state of a given symmetry, to looking for a wave function which would be a linear combination of all the corresponding Γ_P:

$$\Psi = \sum_P C_P \Gamma_P \tag{68}$$

The C_P can be calculated by the standard variation method, minimizing the energy of Ψ calculated with the exact Hamiltonian. This lowers the energy of each symmetry species with respect to the single-configuration representation of (1).

The significance of configuration mixing is, however, twofold: On the one hand, applied to excited states built on ground-state orbitals, it may be conceived of as an attempt to make up for the fact that, the best orbitals not being used, the energy of each state is not adequately minimized: This is corrected, at least partially (since the basis is far from complete), by taking a linear combination of approximate configurations and reminimizing the energy. On the other hand, and at the same time, insofar as doubly occupied orbitals are involved, configuration mixing can be considered compensating in part for the fundamental correlation error mentioned at the end of Section II, by a partial redistribution of the electrons over the molecular orbitals (Löwdin, 1959; Pauncz, 1963).

G. The Inadequacy of the "Purely Theoretical" Scheme

By no means should this section title be taken as expressing a pessimistic feeling. From the preceding pages, it should be clear that a certain number of approximations have been included stepwise into the method of calculation: the correlation defect, the fixed σ core, the approximation chosen for the σ core itself, the limitation of the LCAO basis, and the choice of

amounts to a neglect of all two-electron integrals (pq, rs) in which $p \neq q$ or $r \neq s$. From a practical point of view, this annihilates the problem of the approximation of the three- and four-center integrals and also the problem of the exchange integrals, which are by far the most troublesome to evaluate. With this simplification, the SCF secular equation becomes

$$| F_{pq} - \epsilon \delta_{pq} | = 0 \tag{70}$$

(where $\delta_{pp} = 1$ and $\delta_{pq} = 0$ for $p \neq q$), where the unknown orbital energies ϵ occur in the diagonal terms only. Moreover, the π-electron repulsion terms G_{pq} in the expression

$$F_{pq} = I_{pq} + G_{pq} \tag{71}$$

are highly simplified, so as to become

$$q = p: \quad G_{pp} = \sum_i \{ C_{ip}^2 (pp, pp) + \sum_{r \neq p} 2 C_{ir}^2 (rr, pp) \} \tag{72}$$

$$q \neq p: \quad G_{pq} = - \sum_i C_{ip} C_{iq} (pp, qq) \tag{73}$$

In the original paper by Pariser and Parr (1953a), the ZDO hypothesis was adopted for calculating the electron-repulsion terms only, and it was shown, for ethylene and benzene, that the results of the nonsimplified calculations could be practically duplicated with the simplified scheme *provided that the core integrals were assigned estimated* (as opposed to calculated) *values.*

It has been pointed out by McWeeny (1954a, b, 1955a, b) that these apparently arbitrary features may be introduced in a rational fashion, provided that the basis of development of the molecular orbitals is assumed to be a set of *orthogonal* functions λ_r instead of the usual atomic orbitals χ_r. Thus, minimizing the total energy with respect to the coefficients of the development over the λ's,

$$\varphi_i = \bar{C}_{ir} \lambda_r \tag{74}$$

we get self-consistent equations by the same algebra as before, but the secular equation will be

$$| \bar{F}_{pq} - \epsilon \delta_{pq} | = 0 \tag{75}$$

where $\bar{F}_{pq}$ is defined over the λ orbitals as F_{pq} was defined over χ orbitals:

$$\bar{F}_{pq} = \int \lambda_p H \lambda_q \, d\tau \tag{76}$$

Equation (75) has the same simplified form as Eq. (70) obtained with the ZDO approximation. Let us look now at the $\bar{F}_{pq}$ elements: Their practical evaluation necessitates specification of the λ basis, since, like the corresponding F_{pq}'s, they may be written

$$\bar{F}_{pq} = \bar{I}_{pq} + \bar{G}_{pq} \tag{77}$$

with

$$\bar{G}_{pq} = \sum_{i} \sum_{rs} \bar{C}_{ir}\bar{C}_{is}[2(\bar{r}\bar{s}, \bar{p}\bar{q}) - (\bar{r}\bar{q}, \bar{p}\bar{s})] \tag{78}$$

The overbars indicate that all the symbols refer to the new basis.

As suggested by Löwdin (1950), a set of orthogonal λ's appropriate for molecular problems is best constructed by orthogonalization of the χ atomic orbitals through the matrix transformation

$$\lambda = \chi \mathbf{S}^{-1/2} \tag{79}$$

where $\mathbf{S}$ is the overlap matrix built with the overlap integrals S_{pq} on the χ's. Equation (77) may be more conveniently written as the development (Löwdin, 1947, 1950)

$$\lambda_p = \chi_p - \tfrac{1}{2}\sum_{r \neq p}\chi_r S_{rp} + \tfrac{3}{8}\sum_{\substack{r \neq s,t \\ s \neq t}}\chi_r S_{rs}S_{st}\cdots \tag{80}$$

With the Löwdin transformation (79) or (80), the integrals occurring in the Hartree–Fock matrix elements (77) and (78) may be expressed in terms of the usual atomic orbitals χ. When this is done, it turns out that, "broadly speaking, integrals of the form $(\bar{p}\bar{p}, \bar{q}\bar{q})$ do not differ greatly from their conventional counterparts (pp, qq)—but all other integrals of type $(\bar{p}\bar{q}, \bar{r}\bar{r})$ and $(\bar{p}\bar{q}, \bar{r}\bar{s})$ are almost completely transformed away" [quoted from McWeeny (1954b), where numerical values of $(\bar{p}\bar{q}, \bar{r}\bar{s})$ and (pq, rs) are tabulated for cyclobutadiene and benzene; similar tabulations can be found for ethylene on page 59 of Parr's book (1963), in Peradejordi (1964) for *trans*-butadiene, and in Pullman (1965), for formamide]. This means that in the expression [Eq. (78)] of the $\bar{G}_{pq}$ elements, only the terms bearing over Coulomb integrals will be nonnegligible. These $\bar{G}_{pq}$ elements are thus practically equivalent to the G_{pq} elements of Eqs. (72)–(73) obtained with the formal neglect of differential overlap.

It may be pointed out (Mulliken, 1953; McWeeny, 1955b, and many others since) that the identification of $(\bar{p}\bar{p}, \bar{r}\bar{r})$ to (pp, rr) and the annihilation of all exchange and hybrid integrals can be considered an approximation to the first order in the overlap integrals if the Mulliken formula for an overlap distribution is adopted. Indeed, writing

$$\lambda_p = \chi_p - \tfrac{1}{2}\sum_{r \neq p}\chi_r S_{rp} \tag{81}$$

one obtains

$$\bar{p}\bar{p} = pp - \sum_{q \neq p} pq S_{pq} \tag{82}$$

$$\bar{p}\bar{q} = pq - \tfrac{1}{2} S_{pq}(pp + qq) \tag{83}$$

If the Mulliken approximation is used and S^2 terms neglected, this yields

$$\bar{p}\bar{q} \equiv 0; \qquad \bar{p}\bar{p} \equiv pp \tag{84}$$

As to the core integrals, the interesting features of their transformation can be made clear also when the transformation (80) is limited to the terms of the first order in S. Then, if one neglects the smaller terms involving overlap between nonbonded atoms, the transformation formula is (Peradejordi, 1956)

$$\bar{I}_{pq} = I_{pq} - \tfrac{1}{2} S_{pq}(I_{pp} + I_{qq}) \tag{85}$$

The total expression of the complete matrix transformation can be found in Berthier et al. (1963). It is clear that (putting $I_{pq} = \beta_{pq}$):

(a) the $\bar{\beta}$ values are only slightly affected by the environment of the bond pq (since the neglected terms either are of second order in S or involve long-distance overlap).

(b) Their numerical values will be strongly reduced with respect to the β values bearing over atomic orbitals. In ethylene, for instance, the calculated β value is -8.76 eV (using Parr and Crawford's integrals); with the approximate formula (81), one obtains $\bar{\beta} = -2.8$ eV; with the exact transformation, the value is $\bar{\beta} = -3$ eV. For cyclobutadiene and benzene, McWeeny (1955b) calculated, for adjacent atoms, $\bar{\beta} = -2.86$ and -2.73 eV, respectively.

These values are precisely of the order of magnitude of the empirically chosen β values of the Pariser–Parr method with zero differential overlap. Moreover, when the complete matrix transformation is used, it is found that $\bar{\beta}$ values between nonneighbors are very small with respect to those for adjacent atoms, thus justifying their neglect by Pariser and Parr.

All in all, and to summarize, the results of the SCF-LCAO-MO procedure with or without configuration mixing may be obtained with fair accuracy by carrying out the calculations with the more economical equations (70)–(73) provided that:

1. The core integrals are reinterpreted as bearing over orthogonalized orbitals λ. (Although very little attention has been given until now to the α values, it is clear that they should be properly interpreted as α's, too. The correction is much smaller, however, than in the β case. See Ohno, 1964.)

2. The resulting molecular orbitals are interpreted as linear combinations of λ's. This means that the coefficients obtained are $\bar{C}_{ir}$'s and that, if we want to calculate atom populations, for instance (see Section V, E), it is in principle necessary to express the φ_i's in terms of the χ_r's by the appropriate Löwdin transformation so as to make explicit the C_{ir}'s. Neglecting the terms of the second order in S again, we easily see that

$$C_{ir} = \bar{C}_{ir} - \tfrac{1}{2}\sum_{q \neq r}\bar{C}_{iq}S_{qr} \tag{86}$$

In practice, the structure indices derived from the $\bar{C}_{ir}$'s are only slightly affected by the transformation and may generally be used as such (see, for instance, Suard, 1965).

The first part of the Pariser–Parr approximations is thus justified. But, up to this point, it provides us with a simplification of the numerical work without correcting for any of the inadequacies of the method listed at the end of Section V, G, in so far as it represents simply a more economical way to obtain the results of the complete calculations.

Some of the necessary corrections are brought about with the second important point of the Pariser–Parr approach, namely, the empirical reduction of the (pp, pp) and (pp, qq) integrals.

B. The Problem of the Two-Electron Integrals

In an attempt to explain the failure of the orbital methods to account for the quantitative features of the electronic spectra of molecules, Moffitt (1951) put the essential blame on the improper location of an atom and its ions on the energy scale, resulting in an incorrect estimate of the respective energies of the ionic and covalent structures, and thus of the total energy of the different configurations which are their mixtures. Pariser (1953) remarked that the occurrence of ionic structures in a molecule results, in the molecular orbital method, in the occurrence of the Coulomb repulsion integral (pp, pp) each time the same atom carries two electrons on the same orbital p. Moreover, each time this occurs, it implies that another atom is deficient in its π electron. It may then be considered that the couple C^+, C^- is involved.

To estimate (pp, pp), Pariser considers the dismutation reaction

$$2C \rightarrow C^+ + C^- \tag{87}$$

In the orbital representation, the energy of the C atom and of its plus and minus ions are, respectively,

$$E = E_{\text{core}} + I_p \tag{88}$$

$$E^+ = E_{\text{core}} \tag{89}$$

$$E^- = E_{\text{core}} + 2I_p + (pp, pp) \tag{90}$$

assuming, consistent with the procedures of Section III applied to atoms, that neither E_{core} nor the energy I_p of the π electron on the σ core is changed from C to C$^+$ or to C$^-$. Thus the energy involved in the dismutation reaction [Eq. (87)] is equal to (pp, pp). But, experimentally, the corresponding energy is equal to the ionization potential of atom C minus its electron affinity. Hence the Pariser relation

$$(pp, pp) = I - A \qquad (91)$$

Using the values of I and A for the appropriate valence-state of carbon yields[5]: $(pp, pp) \approx 11$ eV. If, however, a purely theoretical value of (pp, pp) is calculated, using Slater atomic orbitals with $Z = 3.18$, the result is 16.93 eV. It is thus not surprising that, if we use this last value throughout, a molecular calculation yields quite erroneous results.

It is clear from what we have already said of the correlation problem that the discrepancy between the calculated value of (pp, pp) and one evaluated by fitting experimental data is to be qualified at least partly (see Orloff and Sinanoğlu, 1965) as a correlation error: Roughly speaking, since electrons have a tendency to avoid each other, putting them on the same orbital allows too much closeness, thus too much importance to their Coulomb repulsion calculated as (pp, pp).

In fact, a detailed analysis of the correlation problem shows that not only should the one-center integrals be modified but also the two-center integrals and the core integrals (Kolos, 1957; Julg, 1958). However the delineation of the subdivisions of the correlation correction is still a matter of discussion (Arai and Lykos, 1963; Ellison and Huff, 1963), and it is possible that a clear-cut theoretical partition will call for new methods, such as a modified atoms-in-molecules method (for a review see Arai, 1960) or the use of *geminals* (Allen and Shull, 1961).

If, however, one decides to stay with the orbital representation previously described, the simplest way (for the time being) out of the correlation nightmare is to adopt the empirical correction advocated by Pariser and Parr, namely, the use of the empirical value of (pp, pp), instead of the

---

[5] A remark on this numerical value might be useful. Since valence-state ionization potentials and electron affinities are derived from atomic spectroscopic data by the standard procedures of Mulliken (1934) or of Moffitt (1954) extended by Companion and Ellison (1958), some fluctuations occur in their values according to the procedure adopted and to the more or less recent character of the data used. Thus in the original Pariser and Pariser–Parr papers, the one-center carbon integral was identified as $11.22 - 0.69 = 10.53$ eV. The value $11.54 - 0.46 = 11.08$ eV is recorded in Pariser (1956), although the value really used in the actual calculations of his article is 10.96 eV, for reasons explained on page 259. If the recent valence-state orbital-ionization potential and electron affinity of trigonal carbon calculated by Hinze and Jaffe (1962) are used, one finds $(pp, pp) = 11.16 - 0.03 = 11.13$ eV.

theoretical one, each time the integral appears in the calculation. As a logical consequence of this, the corresponding two-electron Coulomb repulsion integrals (pp, qq) should be consistently decreased from their theoretical value, at least when the distances between p and q are small. In general, for large distances, the theoretically calculated values may be adopted,[6] and a smooth interpolation curve may be used connecting the large-distance curve to the empirical (pp, pp) value adopted for zero separation. The best-known interpolation of this kind has been proposed by Pariser and Parr and amounts to fitting a second-order polynomial in R to the zero and to two large-distance values. Other methods of approximating the reduced values of the two-center integrals have been proposed by different authors: Pople (1953) used simply $(pp, qq) = R^{-1}$ for the interatomic distance R; Nishimoto and Mataga (1957) set $(pp, pp) = (a_{pp})^{-1}$ and $(qq, qq) = (a_{qq})^{-1}$, got a_{pp} and a_{qq} from the empirical values of the one-center integrals, and, defining $a_{pq} = \frac{1}{2}(a_{pp} + a_{qq})$, obtained (pp, qq) as $(a_{pq} + R)^{-1}$; Julg (1958, 1959) defines a "correlated" atomic orbital corresponding to the nuclear effective charge Z' which would yield the empirical value of (pp, pp), by Roothaan's formula

$$pp, pp = 5.324Z'$$

and uses this corrected orbital for the calculation of two-center integrals. For a recent, more elaborate discussion on his correlation factor, see Julg (1964). Another interpolation formula has been given recently by Fischer-Hjalmars (1964).

C. The Core Integrals

As we said, an analysis of the correlation phenomenon shows that the core integrals must be modified, too. Pariser and Parr decidedly choose the empirical way: Given the reduced Coulomb integrals, they determined β to fit spectral data on molecules. Fitting it to ethylene with configuration interaction yielded $\beta_{CC} = -2.92$ eV. For benzene, with limited configuration interaction (involving one jump between the degenerate orbitals), the value is -2.39 eV. Fitting an exponential curve to these two points, we get a plausible R dependence of β[7]:

$$\beta(R) = -2517.5 \exp (5.007R) \qquad \text{eV} \qquad (92)$$

The use of such integral values with limited configuration interaction has given a mass of satisfactory results with hydrocarbons (Pariser, 1956).

---

[6] For more economical calculations, these may be approximated by the uniformly charged sphere model of Parr (1952).

[7] Attention must be called to the errata on page 503 of Parr's book (1963).

Inserted in the SCF scheme, these values have allowed the calculation of resonance energies and ionization potentials, the evaluation of charge distribution in ions, etc. (Pople, 1953, 1957). For detailed references, see Parr's volume (1963). It must be pointed out in this connection that, as already mentioned, the core integrals α must be corrected, too, although they were not in the original Pariser–Parr procedure, since this was essentially devised for interpretation of spectral transitions in hydrocarbons. As soon as other properties are wanted, the α values have an influence, particularly as far as ionization potentials or dipole moments (Pople, 1953; Sidman, 1957; Pullman and Rossi, 1964) are concerned. In the α case, the correlation correction is difficult to ascertain (Julg, 1964), for it is not the only factor requiring a reduction of the α values. The practical procedure is to decrease adequately the valence-state ionization potentials (see Pullman and Rossi, 1964) entering the α expression and correlate the electronic integrals as described before.

Instead of choosing empirically the β values, some authors insist on *calculating* the core integrals in a rationalized Pariser–Parr scheme, using correlated values for the electronic repulsions and kinetic energy terms entering the expression of $\bar{\beta}$, as given by Eq. (85) (Berthier *et al.* 1963; Berthier, 1964; Suard, 1965), but the practice of such calculations on a large scale is so tedious and difficult that the simplification $\beta = kS$ of proportionality to the overlap integrals has been recently introduced in the calculations (Berthier, 1964; Berthier and Del Re, 1965).

Ground-state properties are generally well accounted for by stopping there. Excited-state properties may be refined by allowing for the residual configuration mixing. It must be remarked here that, with the Pariser–Parr approximations, the amount of configuration mixing is strongly reduced with respect to the nonempirical SCF calculations. This is to be expected, insofar as the empirization of the procedure makes up for the correlation error, at least in part.

VII. Hückel-Type Methods

As mentioned at the end of Section V, a completely different approach may be used for treating π-electron systems. Instead of trying to determine the *best* molecular orbitals of an LCAO form which minimize the energy corresponding to a determinantal wave function, one looks for *approximate* molecular orbitals (always of an LCAO form) in the following way: One considers that each π electron of the system moves in an "effective" field resulting from the field of the σ core, including the nuclei and the averaged repulsions of the other π electrons. If we define the corresponding individual "effective Hamiltonian" H_{eff}, the solving of an individual Schrödinger equation

$$H_{eff}\varphi = E\varphi \tag{93}$$

yields the individual energy E and orbital φ.

If one looks for a molecular orbital of an LCAO form, one is led to the well-known equations (details of their derivation can be found in Pullman and Pullman, 1963)

$$\sum_s C_s(H_{rs} - ES_{rs}) = 0 \tag{94}$$

with the definitions

$$H_{rs} = \int \chi_r H \chi_s \, d\tau \tag{95}$$

$$S_{rs} = \int \chi_r \chi_s \, d\tau \tag{96}$$

where H is the individual effective Hamiltonian. Again, the individual energies are solutions of the equation

$$|H_{rs} - ES_{rs}| = 0 \tag{97}$$

Formally, these equations are similar to the SCF-LCAO-MO equations previously obtained. It may conceivably be that, with luck—or insight— a good definition of H_{eff} may yield satisfactory solutions, without the tedious iteration procedure of the SCF method. In practice, two calculation procedures have evolved from these equations, the Hückel approximation and the Wheland–Mulliken approximation. Neither of them specifies the analytical form of H, but instead treats some of the matrix elements H_{rs} as *adjustable* parameters. Their main difference resides in the neglect (Hückel) or nonneglect (Wheland–Mulliken) of overlap. Their common feature is what Ruedenberg (1961) has called the *tight-binding approximation*, namely, the neglect in Eq. (97) of all matrix elements which involve nonbonded atoms. The classical discussion of the two approximations and their interconnections has been given elsewhere (Pullman and Pullman, 1952, 1963; Streitwieser, 1961). Here however, we would like to stress an interesting aspect of these interconnections in the light of the previous discussion (Section VI, A) of the overlap question.

When the molecular orbitals φ are defined in terms of atomic orbitals χ_r by

$$\varphi_i = \sum_r C_{ir}\chi_r \tag{98}$$

the equations to solve are (94) and (97), where all quantities are defined in terms of the χ's. If we transform the LCAO basis by a Löwdin transformation, as in Section VI, A, we may consider the φ's defined over the orthogonal λ's as

$$\varphi_i = \sum_r \bar{C}_{ir}\lambda_r \tag{99}$$

and the corresponding equations will reduce to

$$\sum_s \bar{C}_s(\bar{H}_{rs} - E) = 0 \tag{100}$$

$$|\bar{H}_{rs} - E| = 0 \tag{101}$$

where the unknown E occurs in the diagonal elements only.

Thus, calculations without overlap (Hückel-type) can be a way to reproduce with less labor the results of the calculations with overlap (Wheland–Mulliken type), provided that the quantities H_{rs} are interpreted as bearing over the orthogonalized basis λ. Using the general labeling β_{rs} for H_{rs} terms and α_r for H_{rr} terms, one can define the $\bar{\beta}$'s and $\bar{\alpha}$'s in terms of the β's and α's. It is interesting to remark that, with the same approximations as in Section VI, the expression obtained,

$$\bar{\beta}_{rs} = \beta_{rs} - \tfrac{1}{2}S_{rs}(\alpha_r + \alpha_s) \tag{102}$$

is identical to the definition of the resonance integral long ago proposed by Mulliken (1949). With the supplementary (and not necessary) tight-binding assumption, the equations bearing over quantities with the over-bars correspond to the Hückel approximation in its most general form. This shows that any attempt to *calculate* Hückel parameters is a rather complicated project, since it is the unbarred quantities which are defined over atomic orbitals. Thus, the unbarred quantities would have to be evaluated first along the lines outlined recently (Pullman, 1965) and then transformed into barred quantities. Because of the numerous "forced-in" approximations inherent to such an evaluation, it is perhaps wiser to determine the $\bar{\alpha}$'s and $\bar{\beta}$'s by empirical fit, as in the Pariser–Parr approach to the SCF method. This is, in fact, what has always been done, and the many successful interpretations of numerous properties of conjugated systems speak largely in favor of this approach.

Once a set of approximate (as opposed to best SCF) φ's are determined, they may be used in different fashions. In all cases, one starts by using the Aufbau principle, as explained before. Then occurs the branching of the method. In the simplest version (*"naïve" MO method* initiated by Hückel) the total Hamiltonian is *admitted* to be a simple sum of the individual

effective Hamiltonians, and thus the total energy is a simple sum of individual energies. That this is a rough approximation was shown long ago
by Coulson, pointing out the fact that, if interaction is admittedly included
in each individual Hamiltonian, a simple summing up will include it twice
in the total energy. However, it must be recalled that, since all energy
quantities are expressed in terms of a certain β unit, the use of a different
empirically determined unit for individual and total energies may adequately correct for this defect.

Now, the approximate φ's may be used in a different way. One can build
with them all the possible *configurations*, as defined in Section V, write the
appropriate corresponding Slater determinants, and recalculate the corresponding energies with the *exact* Hamiltonian defined in Section I. This
is the Goeppert-Mayer and Sklar *ASMO method*, which involves the same
basic integrals over atomic orbitals as the SCF method (the difference
residing in the different values of the coefficients C_{ir} of the χ's in the φ's).
Thus, from what we saw in Sections V and VI, the ASMO calculations
must be carried out with the use of the corrected Coulomb and core integrals. Finally, the residual configuration mixing may be allowed for (ASMO-
CI method).

To sum up, a schematic branching diagram of the molecular orbital
method is given in Fig. 3.

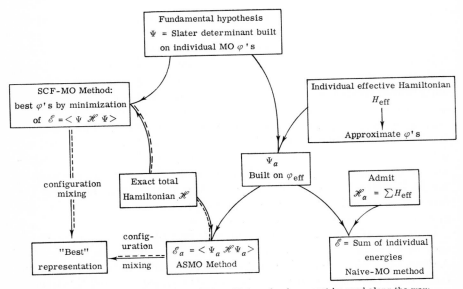

===== Implies that the Pariser-Parr fitting of integral values must be used along the way;
the symbol < > stands for integration over all space.

FIG. 3. The branching of the MO method for π electrons.

REFERENCES

Allen, L. C., and Karo, A. M. (1960). *Rev. Mod. Phys.* **32**, 275.

Allen, L. C., and Shull, H. (1961). *J. Chem. Phys.* **35**, 1644.

Arai, T. (1960). *Rev. Mod. Phys.* **32**, 370.

Arai, T., and Lykos, P. G. (1963). *J. Chem. Phys.* **38**, 1447.

Barnett, M. P., and Coulson, C. A. (1951). *Phil. Trans. Roy. Soc. London* **A243**, 221.

Berthier, G. (1953). *J. Chim. Phys.* **50**, 194.

Berthier, G. (1964). *In* "Molecular Orbitals in Chemistry, Physics, and Biology"
    (P. O. Löwdin and B. Pullman, eds.), p. 57. Academic Press, New York.

Berthier, G., and Del Re, G. (1965). *J. Chem. Soc.* In press.

Berthier, G., Baudet, J., and Suard, M. (1963). *Tetrahedron, Suppl.* **2**, 1.

Berthod, H. (1961). *Ann. Chim. (Paris)* **6**, 18.

Burnelle, L. (1960). *J. Chem. Phys.* **32**, 1872.

Clementi, E. (1965). *IBM J. Res. Develop.* **9**, No. 1.

Companion, F., and Ellison, F. O. (1958). *J. Chem. Phys.* **28**, 1.

Craig, D. P. (1950). *Proc. Roy. Soc. (London)* **A200**, 474.

Ellison, F. O., and Huff, N. T. (1963). *J. Chem. Phys.* **38**, 2444.

Fischer, I. (1952). *Arkiv Fysik* **5**, 377.

Fischer-Hjalmars, I. (1964). *In* "Molecular Orbitals in Chemistry, Physics, and Biology"
    (P. O. Löwdin and B. Pullman, eds.), p. 361. Academic Press, New York.

Goeppert-Mayer, M., and Sklar, A. L. (1938). *J. Chem. Phys.* **6**, 645.

Goodfriend, P. L., Birss, F. W., and Duncan, A. B. F. (1960). *Rev. Mod. Phys.* **32**, 307.

Guérillot, C. R., Lisillour, R., and Botrel, A. (1965). *Theoret. Chim. Acta* **3**, 111.

Hartree, D. R. (1955). "The Calculation of Atomic Structures." Wiley, New York.

Hinze, J., and Jaffe, H. H. (1962). *J. Am. Chem. Soc.* **84**, 540.

Hoffmann, R. (1963). *J. Chem. Phys.* **39**, 1397.

Hückel, E. (1931). *Z. Physik* **70**, 204.

Julg, A. (1958). *J. Chim. Phys.* **55**, 413.

Julg, A. (1959). *J. Chim. Phys.* **56**, 18.

Julg, A. (1964). *Theoret. Chim. Acta* **2**, 134.

Julg, A., and Pullman, B. (1955). *J. Chim. Phys.* **52**, 481.

Karplus, M., and Shavitt, I. (1963). *J. Chem. Phys.* **38**, 1256.

Kolos, W. (1957). *Acta Physiol. Polon.* **16**, 257, 267, 299; *J. Chem. Phys.* **27**, 591, 592.

Koopmans, T. A. (1933). *Physica* **1**, 104.

Kotani, M., Amemya, A., Ishiguro, E., and Kimura, T. (1955). "Table of Molecular
    Integrals." Maruzen, Tokyo.

Lennard-Jones, J. E. (1929). *Trans. Faraday Soc.* **25**, 668.

Lofthus, A. (1961). *Mol. Phys.* **4**, 409.

Löwdin, P. O. (1947). *Arkiv Mat. Astron. Fysik* **35A**, 9.

Löwdin, P. O. (1950). *J. Chem. Phys.* **18**, 365.

Löwdin, P. O. (1959). *Advan. Chem. Phys.* **2**, 207.

Lykos, P. G., and Parr, R. G. (1956). *J. Chem. Phys.* **24**, 1166.

McLean, A. D. (1960). *J. Chem. Phys.* **32**, 1595.

McLean, A. D., Ransil, B. J., and Mulliken, R. S. (1960). *J. Chem. Phys.* **32**, 1873.

McWeeny, R. (1954a). *Proc. Roy. Soc. (London)* **A223**, 306.

McWeeny, R. (1954b). Quart. Prog. Rept., Solid State and Molecular Theory Group.
    M. I. T., Cambridge, Massachusetts. January 15.

McWeeny, R. (1955a). Tech. Rept. No. 7. Solid State and Molecular Theory Group.
    M. I. T., Cambridge, Massachusetts. May 1.

McWeeny, R. (1955b). *Proc. Roy. Soc. (London)* **A227**, 288.

Moffitt, W. (1951). *Proc. Roy. Soc. (London)* **A210**, 224, 245.

Moffitt, W. (1954). *Ann. Rept. Progr. Phys.* **17**, 173.
Moscowitz, J. W., and Barnett, M. P. (1963). *J. Chem. Phys.* **39**, 1557.
Mulligan, J. F. (1951). *J. Chem. Phys.* **19**, 347.
Mulliken, R. S. (1932). *Phys. Rev.* **40**, 55; **41**, 49, 751.
Mulliken, R. S. (1933). *J. Chem. Phys.* **1**, 492.
Mulliken, R. S. (1934). *J. Chem. Phys.* **2**, 782.
Mulliken, R. S. (1949). *J. Chim. Phys.* **46**, 497.
Mulliken, R. S. (1953). *Symp. Mol. Phys., Nikko, Japan, 1953*, 17.
Mulliken, R. S. (1955). *J. Chem. Phys.* **23**, 1833.
Mulliken, R. S. (1962). *J. Chem. Phys.* **36**, 3428.
Mulliken, R. S., and Parr, R. G. (1951). *J. Chem. Phys.* **19**, 1271.
Nesbet, R. K. (1964). *J. Chem. Phys.* **41**, 100.
Nishimoto, K., and Mataga, N. (1957). *Z. Physik. Chem. (Frankfurt)* **13**, 140.
Ohno, K. (1964). *Theoret. Chim. Acta* **2**, 219.
Orloff, M. K., and Sinanoğlu, O. (1965). *J. Chem. Phys.* in press.
Pariser, R. (1953). *J. Chem. Phys.* **21**, 568.
Pariser, R. (1956). *J. Chem. Phys.* **24**, 250.
Pariser, R., and Parr, R. G. (1953a). *J. Chem. Phys.* **21**, 466.
Pariser, R., and Parr, R. G. (1953b). *J. Chem. Phys.* **21**, 767.
Parks, J. M., and Parr, R. G. (1958). *J. Chem. Phys.* **28**, 335.
Parr, R. G. (1952). *J. Chem. Phys.* **20**, 1499.
Parr, R. G. (1963). "The Quantum Theory of Molecular Electronic Structure." Benjamin, New York.
Parr, R. G., and Crawford, B. L. (1948). *J. Chem. Phys.* **16**, 1049.
Parr, R. G., and Mulliken, R. S. (1950). *J. Chem. Phys.* **18**, 1338.
Pauncz, R. (1963). *Tetrahedron, Suppl.* **2**, 43.
Peradejordi, F. (1956). *Compt. Rend.* **243**, 276.
Peradejordi, F. (1964). Thèse, Université de Paris, Paris.
Pople, J. (1953). *Trans. Faraday Soc.* **49**, 1375.
Pople, J. (1957). *J. Phys. Chem.* **61**, 6.
Preuss, H. (1956–1961). "Integraltafeln zur Quantenchemie," 4 vols. Springer, Berlin.
Pullman, A. (1954). *J. Chim. Phys.* **51**, 188.
Pullman, A. (1965). *In* "Modern Quantum Chemistry Conference." Academic Press, New York. In press.
Pullman, A., and Rossi, M. (1964). *Biochim. Biophys. Acta* **88**, 211.
Pullman, B., and Pullman, A. (1952). Les Théories électroniques de la chimie organique." Masson, Paris.
Pullman, B., and Pullman, A. (1963). "Quantum Biochemistry." Wiley (Interscience), New York.
Roothaan, C. C. J. (1951). *Rev. Mod. Phys.* **23**, 69.
Ruedenberg, K. (1961). *J. Chem. Phys.* **34**, 1892ff.
Sahni, R. C., and Cooley, J. W. (1959–1960). Tables of Molecular Integrals. NASA (*Natl. Aeron. Space Admin.*) D-146-I and II.
Scheer, C. W. (1955). *J. Chem. Phys.* **23**, 569.
Scrocco, E., and Salvetti, O. (1952). *Ric. Sci.* **22**, 1766.
Sender, M., and Berthier, G. (1958). *J. Chim. Phys.* **55**, 384.
Shavitt, I., and Karplus, M. (1962). *J. Chem. Phys.* **36**, 550.
Sidman, J. W. (1957). *J. Chem. Phys.* **17**, 429.
Sklar, A. L. (1939). *J. Chem. Phys.* **7**, 984.
Sklar, A. L., and Lyddane, R. H. (1939). *J. Chem. Phys.* **7**, 374.

Slater, J. C. (1929). *Phys. Rev.* **34,** 1293.

Slater, J. C. (1930). *Phys. Rev.* **36,** 57.

Slater, J. C. (1960). "Quantum Theory of Atomic Structure," 2 vols. McGraw-Hill, New York.

Streitwieser, A. (1961). "Molecular Orbital Theory for Organic Chemists." Wiley, New York.

Suard, M. (1965). *J. Chim. Phys.* **62,** 79, 89.

Van Vleck, J. H. (1934). *J. Chem. Phys.* **2,** 22.

Wahl, A. C. (1964). *J. Chem. Phys.* **41,** 2600.

Wahl, A. C., Cade, P. E., and Roothaan, C. C. J. (1964). *J. Chem. Phys.* **41,** 2578

Aspects of the Electronic Structure of the Nucleic Acids and Their Constituents[1]

BERNARD PULLMAN

Institut de Biologie Physico-Chimique,
Université de Paris,
Paris, France

I. A Preliminary Remark

This written account of my lectures at the International Summer Institute of Molecular Biophysics held in Squaw Valley, California, in August, 1964, differs in a few respects from the course that I actually gave at that institute. The principal reason for this is that a number of questions which I discussed at that course have already been described in my recent book, with Madame Pullman, on "Quantum Biochemistry" [Wiley (Interscience), New York, 1963].[2] The present discussion contains therefore essentially that part of my course which is related to new developments of the subjects discussed in "Quantum Biochemistry," or to new topics which arose or were subjected to a quantum-mechanical investigation since the publication of this book.

[1] This work was sponsored by Convention 61-FR-134 of the Délégation Générale à la Recherche Scientifique et Technique (Comité Cancer et Leucémie) and Grant CY-3073 of the U.S. Public Health Service (National Cancer Institute). It was prepared in part while the author was a visiting professor at the Institute of Theoretical Chemistry at the University of Wisconsin, Madison, Wisconsin (grant GM-11315-01 awarded to that Institute by the National Institute of Health).

[2] References to this book will be listed in this text in the form "Quantum Biochemistry," along with the appropriate page number.

Moreover, some of these new topics have also been summarized in review papers published recently from our laboratory. In such cases, it seemed useless to reproduce them here. References to these reviews are given in the last section of this paper.

II. Introduction

A. Advantages of the Quantum-Mechanical Approach to Biophysics

The application of quantum-mechanical methods to the study of the electronic structure of biomolecules or the investigation of biophysical and biochemical problems has two particular advantages.

The first advantage is the general, universal character of the method—its unlimited applicability. Thus, the usual experimental methods of physics and chemistry are generally intended for study of essentially one

TABLE I

Principal Applications of the Electronic Indices

(sometimes more, but never too many) specific molecular property, say, its dipole moment or its reactivity toward a given reagent. Each such method can therefore give only a partial view of the molecular reality. The situation is quite different in the quantum-mechanical studies: In these procedures a single calculation, the solution of the wave equation, leads to a multiplicity of results which, *in principle* (i.e., if we were really able to solve rigorously the extensive equation), yields complete information about all the structural properties of the atomic or molecular system under investigation. In fact, even if, as is the case *in practice*, we can only solve approximately somewhat reduced equations, the amount of information, although of course approximate and partial, still generally covers a wide variety of aspects of the problem studied. Thus, for example, an LCAO molecular orbital calculation carried out for a molecule yields as direct results the energies of the molecular orbitals and their forms (i.e., the coefficients of the atomic orbitals in the molecular ones). The precision of these results depends, of course, on the degree of refinement of the calculations. But whatever this degree, these two fundamental quantities, the energies and the coefficients, may then be used to define a set of energy and structure indices which can be applied, in turn, for the understanding (elucidation, interpretation, or prediction, as is the case) of a great variety of the chemical, physical, and, as we hope to show, biochemical and biophysical characteristics of the system. Table I exemplifies this situation for a restricted number of such indices and properties. (For a deeper discussion see "Quantum Biochemistry" pp. 115–181). It may reasonably be supposed that, because of the complexity of biophysical systems and problems, such a multivalent approach may be particularly useful in these sciences.

The second advantage of the quantum-mechanical approach to biophysics and biochemistry resides in the possibility that it offers to *antecede* experimentation in a number of fields in which this experimentation seems to be particularly difficult to carry out. Thus, calculations frequently allow us to determine the values (more or less exact values, of course, according to the degree of refinement of the calculations) of a series of physicochemical characteristics of molecular systems which seem to be at present beyond the possibilities of experimental determination or which are at least very difficult to measure presently. We shall find in this paper abundant evidence of such situations. When this happens, the calculations frequently enable us to discover, to predict, new correlations between structure and behavior, sometimes completely new aspects of biophysical problems. This particular advantage must, of course, be considered, in addition to the more common merit of the quantum-mechanical approach which consists of interpreting the observed experimental facts in terms of the *appropriate, fundamental, physical entities* which correspond to these facts and in thus correcting the vague or pictorial concepts frequently used by people not familiar with the rigorous concepts. In both cases—the more appropriate interpretation of known facts or the prediction of new relations—the approach may be useful in orienting experimental research in more profitable directions.

Because of some thoughtless remarks which are sometimes made about the significance of quantum mechanics in biological sciences, we shall come back to these questions again at the end of our paper, after having seen in the forthcoming pages a series of examples illustrating the previously mentioned advantages of the quantum-mechanical approach to biophysics and biochemistry.

B. Types of Procedure

The quantum-mechanical calculations which have been carried out up to now for the nucleic acids and their constituents (and in fact quite generally for biomolecules) are of three types:

1. Semiempirical LCAO molecular orbital calculations, frequently referred to as Hückel-type calculations ("Quantum Biochemistry," pp. 64–115). These types of calculations, which are by far the easiest and quickest to perform and which therefore were performed first and are still the most abundant, are particularly well suited for the *comparative* study of the electronic structure of molecules, in other words for the classification on a relative scale of compounds or molecular regions or their constituent atoms with respect to the electronic properties under investigation. It may be useful to stress that this type of calculations utilized for a long time only for π-electrons has recently been extended to σ systems (e.g., Del Re *et al.*, 1963; Yonezawa *et al.*, 1964; Berthod and Pullman, A., 1965a, b). The approximation applied so far for the study of bioligical σ systems is essentially that of Del Re (1958, 1964) and may in fact be considered the counterpart for σ bonds of the Hückel method as used for π electrons. It has been adapted for the study of the σ skeleton of conjugated systems (Berthod and Pullman, A., 1965a, b).

2. Self-consistent field molecular orbital calculations, in various approximations: semiempirical (Parr and Pariser) approximations, rationalized (Berthier) approximation, with or without configuration interaction, etc. These methods yield, in principle, as discussed by A. Pullman in this volume (see also Fernandez-Alonso, 1964), more reliable *absolute* values for a number of indices of electronic structure and should therefore

be suitable for a direct comparison of theoretical and experimental results. In practice, although the whole scheme of these procedures is more satisfactory than that of the semiempirical methods, they nevertheless suffer in calculations concerning heteromolecules (and practically all biomolecules are heteromolecules) from many of the drawbacks of the semiempirical methods. Generally, they do introduce in one way or another some semiempirical parameters into their scheme, in particular in connection with the different integrals related to heteroatoms. As a consequence of this situation, the absolute values of the quantities which they evaluate may be appreciably in error. These procedures, if carried out homogeneously for a large number of molecules, may, of course, always be used in the same way as the Hückel method, namely, for the comparison of the *relative* values of the quantities studied.

3. Calculations expressly calibrated for the exact evaluation of the absolute values of a specific molecular property. Because of the previously mentioned difficulties in obtaining simultaneously through a general calculation the exact (or at least very satisfactory) absolute values of a large number of molecular characteristics, such calibrations are sometimes necessary. They may be carried out both in the Hückel and in the self-consistent scheme. The calibration with respect to the specific property studied is carried out on a series of standard, generally simple, fundamental molecules and checked, if possible, on more complex molecules for which this specific property is known experimentally. The parameters determined in this way are then used for the prediction of the absolute value of this particular property in the complex molecules in which it is unknown. Although highly semiempirical, this procedure obviously may be very useful.

III. Nucleic Acids and Their Constituents

A. The Calculations

The nucleic acids are extremely huge, aperiodical polymers, and it is, of course, evident *a priori* that there is no possibility, at present, to calculate the electronic structure of a real molecule of a nucleic acid. The calculations have therefore been mostly restricted to the evaluation of the electronic characteristics of the essential components of these macromolecules, namely, the purine and pyrimidine bases and the purine-pyrimidine complementary pairs, although some simplified calculations have been carried out just the same on some electronic properties of the whole macromolecule (e.g., semiconductivity). In this review, we shall concentrate our attention essentially on the calculations concerned with

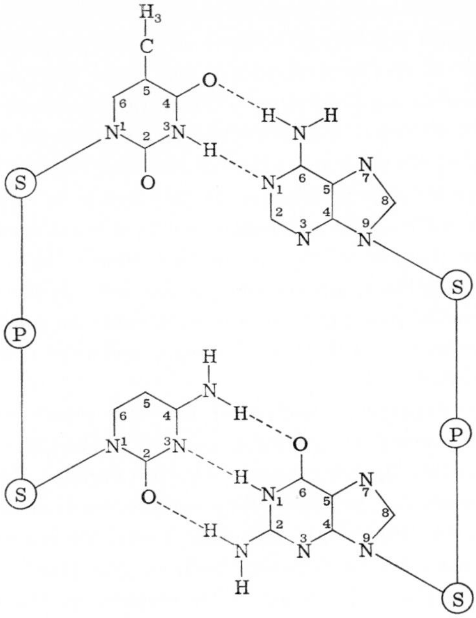

FIG. 1. "Miniature" nucleic acid.

the complementary base pairs and with the separated bases. In fact, our discussion will be centered mostly around a miniature nucleic acid formed by the two complementary base pairs, adenine-thymine and guanine-cytosine, bound together by the sugar-phosphate linkages, as illustrated in Fig. 1. In this work the interactions through the hydrogen bonds between the purine and pyrimidine of each pair are taken into account, but not the interactions between the two stacked pairs. This approximation thus corresponds obviously to the viewpoint that a certain number, at least, of the electronic properties of the base pairs are, in the nucleic acids, relatively independent of the influence of the adjacent base pairs. This, of course, is a hypothesis which has to be verified by comparison between the theoretical results obtained with this assumption and the experimental data. It is evident that it has more chance to break down in certain problems (e.g., spectroscopic ones) than in others (e.g., chemical reactivities of the bases). Anyway, it is a reasonable hypothesis to start with, if only in order to be able to determine to what extent it is verified and the fields in which it needs to be elaborated. It does not exclude, of course, any concept of the general stabilization of the nucleic acids through interactions due to the macromolecular configuration. In fact, as we hope to show here: (1) the hypothesis is *satisfactory* for a large number of the properties of the nucleic acids: (2) conclusions may be drawn from the calculated properties of the base pairs about at least some aspects of their mutual interaction.

The most numerous calculations available concern, of course, the free bases. They were carried out originally in our laboratory (Pullman, A., and Pullman, B., 1958, 1959) in the Hückel molecular orbital approximation with appropriate parameters chosen for the heteroatoms. They involved also a series of related compounds, base analogs, or metabolites. Parts of these calculations have been repeated since by other authors using generally slightly different sets of parameters (e.g., Fernandez-Alonso and Domingo, 1960: Fernandez-Alonso, 1961, 1964: Ladik and Hoffman, 1964: Ladik, 1964: Nagata *et al.*, 1963; DeVoe and Tinoco, 1962). Although the absolute values of the various indices calculated are, of course, different in these different calculations, their relative values insofar as can be judged from the published data, are in practice quite parallel, so that the general picture of the electronic structure of the bases is very similar. Ladik and Hoffman (1964), who obtained a charge distribution slightly different from ours, themselves acknowledge that our parameters are better than theirs in this respect.

The fundamental purine and pyrimidine bases have also been studied by the self-consistent field molecular orbital method, in different approximations: the semiempirical Parr–Pariser approximation (Veillard and Pullman, 1963), the Parr–Pariser approximation with configurational interaction (Nesbet, 1964), and the rationalized approximation of Berthier (Berthier *et al.*, 1965). Veillard and Pullman (1963) and Berthier *et al.* (1965) have carried out a detailed comparison of the results obtained by the Hückel and the self-consistent field methods. This comparison has demonstrated that the two procedures lead to practically the same results, in particular, as far as the relative values of the different electronic indices are concerned. It is only in a few isolated cases, which do not concern, moreover, the bases present in the nucleic acids, that some disagreement appears between the results of the two procedures for one or two electronic indices.

Very recently, the calculations have been extended to the σ skeletons of the purine and pyrimidine bases (Berthod and Pullman, 1963, 1964, 1965a: Bradley *et al.*, 1964) and the results combined with those for the π systems in the study of physicochemical properties depending explicitly on the contribution of both types of electrons.

The electronic structure of the complementary base pairs, adenine-thymine and guanine-cytosine was evaluated initially (Pullman, B., and Pullman, A., 1959) by the Hückel approximation, with an appropriate representation introduced to account for the effect of the hydrogen bonds.

In fact, the influence of the hydrogen bonds has by now been introduced in three different ways:

1. By considering simply the mutual polarization of the hydrogen-bonded bases, without any electronic exchange between them (Pullman, A., unpublished). This effect is obtained technically by suitably perturbing the Coulomb integrals of the N and O atoms of the bases linked by the hydrogen bonds. Thus the Coulomb integrals of the H-donor heteroatoms are uniformly diminished by 0.2 β and the Coulomb integrals of the H-acceptor heteroatoms uniformly increased by the same amount (β being the usual carbon–carbon resonance integral of the molecular orbital method), so as to take into account the decrease of electronegativity of the proton donor and the increase of electronegativity of the proton acceptor.

2. By alloting, moreover, a small exchange integral (0.2 β) along the hydrogen bonds (Pullman, B., and Pullman, A., 1959, 1961).

3. By explicitly taking into account in the calculations the $2p_z$ orbital of the hydrogen atom of the hydrogen bond, an empty orbital which may, however, serve as a bridge for the transmission of the electronic delocalization between the π-electron systems of the two linked bases (Pullman, A., 1963). The advantage of this third approximation is double. In the first place, the results definitely demonstrate that a certain amount of electronic delocalization occurs across the hydrogen bond established between the π-electronic systems. The second advantage is a technical one and results from the way in which this effect was introduced: The parameters appropriate for its description in the Hückel approximation have been deduced from self-consistent field calculations on the electronic structure of proteins in which the contribution of the $2p$ orbitals of the hydrogens involved in the hydrogen bonds has been taken into account (Suard, 1962). They are therefore particularly reliable. The essential parameters are the resonance integrals β_{XH} and $\beta_{H\cdots Y}$, which are found to

TABLE II

ENERGY CHARACTERISTICS OF THE BASE PAIRS (IN β UNITS)

Energy characteristic	A-T pair		G-C pair	
	Appr. b	Appr. c	Appr. b	Appr. c
Highest filled molecular orbital	0.43	0.45	0.29	0.30
Lowest empty molecular orbital	−0.88	−0.87	−0.78	−0.78
Resonance energy	6.11	6.17	6.42	6.52
Resonance stabilization through H-bonding	0.16	0.23	0.30	0.40

be worth 0.2 β, and the Coulomb integral of the H atom. When this last integral is written in the usual form $\alpha_H = \alpha_C + \delta_H\beta$, the value of δ_H is found to be of the order of -1.8.

Although the results obtained in this last approximation are the most satisfactory, their comparison with the results obtained in the two simpler approximations shows that the explicit involvement of the empty $2p$ orbital of the H atom has, in fact, only a small influence on the electronic indices. This can be seen in Table II, which presents the values of some important energy indices of the base pairs obtained in the last two approximations mentioned earlier, and in Fig. 2, which presents an analogous

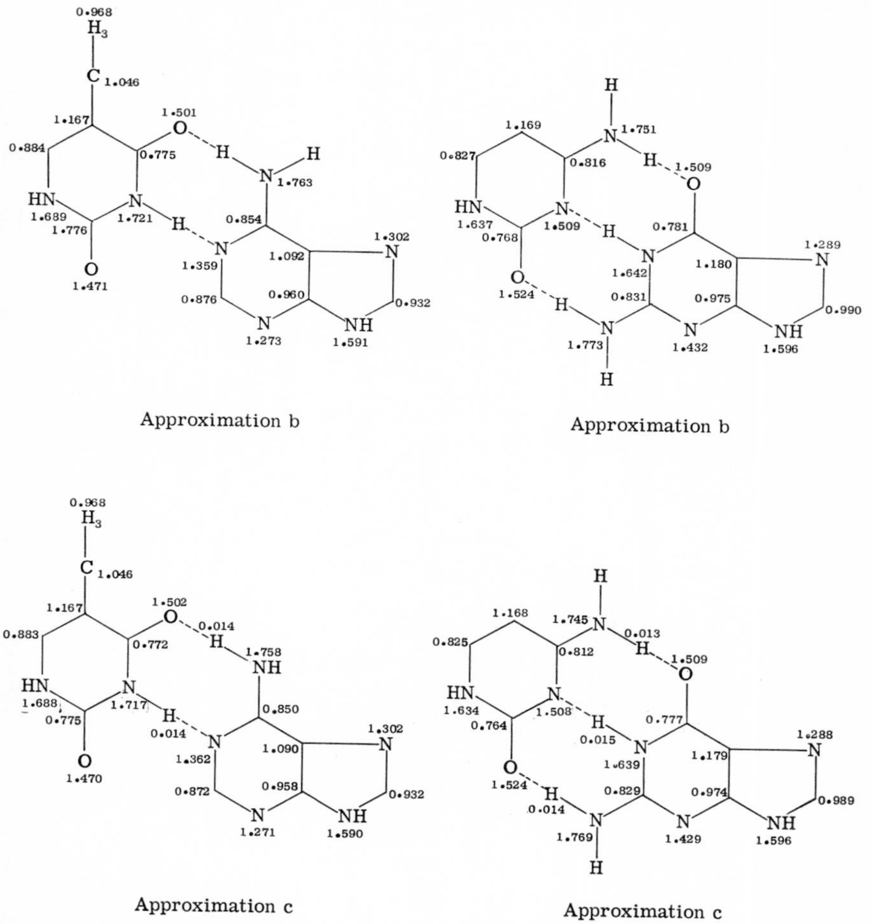

Approximation b

Approximation b

Approximation c

Approximation c

FIG. 2. Comparison of electronic charges.

comparison of the distribution of the electronic charges. In conformity with the generally accepted viewpoint, all these calculations correspond to the presence of two hydrogen bonds in the A-T pair and to three such bonds in the G-C pair.

One of the aspects of the results contained in Table II and Fig. 2, which is apparent when they are compared to similar results concerning the isolated bases ("Quantum Biochemistry," pp. 210, 217, 224), is that the electronic interactions across the hydrogen bonds are relatively small in the sense that they produce only very minor perturbations in the electronic structure of the bases, with the exception perhaps of the atoms directly involved in the hydrogen bonding. As a result of this situation, the bases

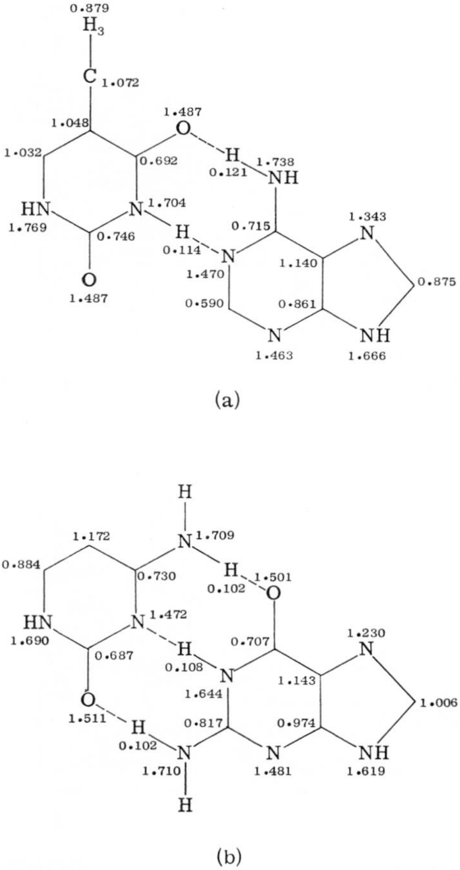

(a)

(b)

FIG. 3. Electronic charges (rationalized self-consistent field calculations). (a) Adenine-thymine pair; (b) guanine-cytosine pair.

conserve in the complementary pairs a large degree of autonomy. We are thus faced with the possibility of a dual viewpoint in which some electronic characteristics will be associated sometimes with the bases and sometimes with the pairs. As will be seen shortly, this situation does not represent any real difficulty in the analysis of the aspects of the electronic structure of the nucleic acids.

In connection with the point just raised, it may be mentioned that Ladik and Hoffman (1964) have also carried out calculations on base pairs introducing explicitly the empty $2p$ orbital on the H atoms of the hydrogen bonds. Owing, however, to a very unfortunate choice of the Coulomb integral for the H atom, they have obtained completely un-realistic results in which, for example, the hydrogen bonding of two bases introduces stabilization increments of the order of a few tens of kilocalories per mole. They have recently acknowledged this mistake and adopted for δ_H the value proposed by A. Pullman (Ladik, 1964).

Finally, the electronic characteristics of the complementary base-pairs have also been evaluated recently in the rationalized self-consistent field method (Berthier *et al.*, 1965). The most striking aspect of the results obtained in this achievement is the nearly complete parallel between these refined results and the semiempirical results of the Hückel procedure. This parallel is particularly striking when the relative values of the different electronic indices inside the base pairs are considered. In fact, it frequently extends even to the absolute values of the indices, when those of the Hückel method are evaluated with suitable semiempirical quantities attributed to the parameters of the method. We shall have a number of occasions in the following pages to indicate this parallel for specific electronic properties. Suffice here to reproduce (Fig. 3) the distribution of the π-electronic charges in the base pairs as obtained in this rationalized self-consistent field calculation.

This situation confirms the over-all validity of the previous results.

B. General Results

As stated earlier, the utilization of the previously mentioned techniques of quantum chemistry enables the determination of the values of the essential energetic and electronic indices characteristic of the base pairs, of the bases, or of their constituent atoms or groups of atoms. Although the exact values of these indices depend, of course, on the particular method utilized, the comparison of the different results clearly shows that *they all lead to substantially the same conclusions as far as the general aspects of the electronic structures are concerned.* In particular, the calculations naturally make possible the determination of the sites at which the different indices have their most significant values. This is frequently one of the most

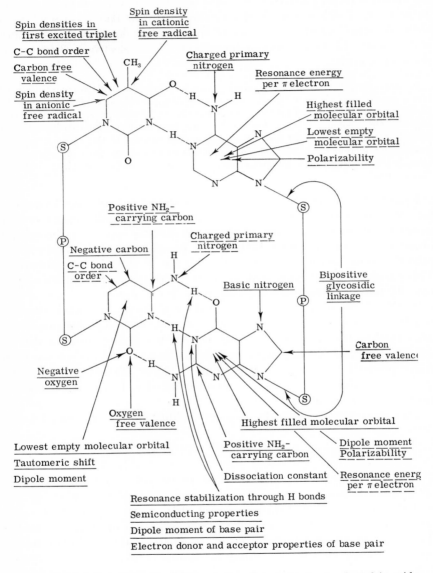

FIG. 4. Outstanding electronic indices of the nitrogenous bases of nucleic acids.

important aspects of the results, because this determination enables us to fix the essential sites at which will be located or with which will be connected the corresponding physicochemical properties of the nucleic acids. Now, all the methods utilized so far for quantum-mechanical calculations on the nucleic bases or base pairs definitely lead to practically the same conclusions in this respect. These conclusions are summarized in Fig. 4, which represents, therefore, the quintessence of the quantum-mechanical calculations for the "miniature" nucleic acid defined previously.

The precise meaning of the different qualifications indicated in Fig. 4 is the following: When a qualification is underlined by a heavy line, this signifies that this qualification has its most outstanding value at the particular site at which it is indicated (and which, as pointed out in the previous discussion, may be either a base pair, or a base, or a fraction of a base, i.e., an atom or a bond); when the qualification is underlined by a broken line, this means that this is its next most important location.

Thus, for example, the qualification "resonance energy per π electron" underlined with a heavy line points towards the adenine ring. This means that, among the four bases of the nucleic acids and so far as they preserve to a large extent their individuality in these acids, adenine is the one which has the greatest resonance energy per π electron. The same qualification, underlined with a broken line, is associated with guanine, which signifies that after adenine it is guanine which has the greatest resonance energy per π electron. The immediate conclusion from this situation is that the theory obviously *predicts* that the resonance stabilization of the bases, as measured by this index, should be greater for the purines than for the pyrimidines and that it should be the greatest for adenine. The reader acquainted with the concept of resonance energy may immediately guess the significance of this theoretical prediction for the understanding of a number of properties of the bases or even of the nucleic acid, or for possible predictions in this field.

As another example of the meaning and possible utilization of Fig. 4, let us consider the qualification "resonance stabilization through H bonds," which, heavily underlined, points to the H bonds of the guanine-cytosine pair and therefore means that the stabilization through hydrogen bonding is *predicted* to be greater for the G-C pair than for the A-T pair.

The two preceding examples concern electronic indices related to the bases or the base pairs. We may also consider examples of qualifications referring to the properties of more localized sites. Thus the qualification "basic nitrogen," heavily underlined, is associated with N_7 of the guanine ring. This means that, among all the nitrogen atoms present in the purine and pyrimidine bases of the nucleic acids, N_7 of guanine is predicted to be the most basic one. Again, one can easily imagine how useful such a prediction may be for the understanding of the properties of the nucleic acids that depend on basicity. Similarly, the qualification "C–C bond order," heavily underlined, is associated with the C_5–C_6 bond of thymine, a situation meaning that, among all the carbon-carbon bonds present in the bases of the nucleic acids, this is the one which should have the highest bond order, etc.

We stress again that Fig. 4 is the result of purely theoretical investigations. Its real significance and usefulness depend, of course, on how far the results that it sums up will help in elucidating the physicochemical and biochemical and biophysical properties of the nucleic acids; elucidation meaning, of course, both the explanation of known properties and, if possible, the prediction of new ones. The remaining part of this course will be devoted essentially to this task, as was the corresponding chapter in "Quantum Biochemistry." Because of its dimensions, we shall not be able to deal here with the totality of properties related to all the electronic indices indicated in Fig. 4. We shall concentrate our attention on some of them, chosen from those which are of particular actuality today and which were debated in the lectures given at Squaw Valley. During this discussion, we shall, of course, not limit ourselves to the qualitative aspect of things as indicated in Fig. 4 but shall also consider them more quantitatively, which means we shall examine the numerical values of the electronic indices concerned.

C. Some Properties of the Base Pairs

Let us consider first some properties connected with the base pairs. One such simple property is their resonance stabilization.

1. Resonance Stabilization

Purines and pyrimidines are highly conjugated heteroaromatic systems. Their stabilization resulting from the electronic delocalization may be measured by their resonance energies. Moreover, hydrogen-bond interactions between the complementary bases are associated with a supplementary resonance stabilization. The resonance energies are, however, relatively difficult to determine experimentally and, in fact, are completely unknown for the biological purines and pyrimidines. On the contrary, they are relatively easy to determine by theoretical methods, with a fair degree of exactitude. Extensive calculations have therefore been carried out for this molecular property ("Quantum Biochemistry," pp. 209–215), and this application of the quantum-mechanical methods thus represents an example of a case in which the theoretical calculations are *ahead* of experimental determinations.

As already discussed in "Quantum Biochemistry," the relative order of resonance stabilization of the purines and pyrimidines has a number of physicochemical and biophysical consequences, among which one of the most important concerns its significance for the radioresistance of these compounds ("Quantum Biochemistry," pp. 267–283). A more recent fundamental application of this same characteristic is in the field of mutagenesis (Pullman, B., and Pullman, A., 1962b; Pullman, A., and Pullman, B., 1963: Pullman, A., 1964a, b). At this place we wish, however, to stress only one aspect of the results concerned with the purine-pyrimidine pairs. Thus, the calculations indicate that, from the point of view of stabilization through electronic delocalization, the guanine-cytosine pair should be more stable than the adenine-thymine pair (Table II). The conclusion is valid both for the relative total stability of the two pairs and for the increment of stabilization resulting from the hydrogen bonding (which may be obtained by subtracting the resonance energies of the free bases from the resonance energy of the corresponding base pairs; the differential stabilization of the two pairs from that point of view is approximately equal to 0.15 $\beta \approx$ 2.5 kcal/mole). This general result would be conserved even if the G-C pair was considered to have only two hydrogen bonds, a situation indicating that the H bonds of the G-C pair are intrinsically stronger than those of the A-T pair. This last suggestion may be considered possibly confirmed by the observations that small amounts of 1-methyl-adenine are found in undenatured DNA methylated at low levels at which 1-methylcytosine is not detectable (Lawley and Brookes, 1963), or that the amino groups of the adenine moieties in undenatured DNA are more available for reaction with nitrous acid than are those of cytosine moieties (Litman, 1961).

At the time, in fact still not so long ago, when it was believed that the stability of the helical configuration of the nucleic acids is due essentially to hydrogen bonding, the greater resonance energy of the G-C pair than that of the A-T pair could be considered possibly responsible for the higher *denaturation* or *melting* temperature of the nucleic acids rich in guanine-cytosine over those rich in adenine-thymine. (Marmur and Doty, 1959: Doty et al., 1959). Today, when it is generally acknowledged that the stability of the double-stranded nucleic acids is due to other factors, linked essentially to the vertical interactions between the stacked bases (*vide infra*), this differential contribution of hydrogen bonding seems to be of a limited significance in this respect, a situation which does not diminish, of course, the fundamental importance of hydrogen bonding in ensuring the specificity of base complementariness.

On the other hand, hydrogen bonding may play a more important role in determining the structure of the mixed crystals formed between the different biological purines and pyrimidines. The problem was raised by the curious discovery of Hoogsteen (1959, 1963a, b), showing that the spatial arrangement of crystals containing a hydrogen-bonded complex of 1-methyl-thymine and 9-methyladenine[3] was different from the Watson–Crick pairing admitted for these two bases in DNA. As shown in Fig. 5, which represents the arrangement of the bases in Hoogsteen's crystal, the amino group of methyladenine is still connected to the oxygen attached to C_4 of methylthymine, but the nitrogen N_3 of methylthymine is bonded to N_7 rather than to N_1 of methyladenine. The thymine is "on the other side" of the amino group of adenine. A similar structure has been established more recently (Mathews and Rich, 1964) for the hydrogen-bonded complex of 2-ethyladenine and 1-methyluracil. These results indicate that the preferential arrangement of the A-T pair observed in the double helix need

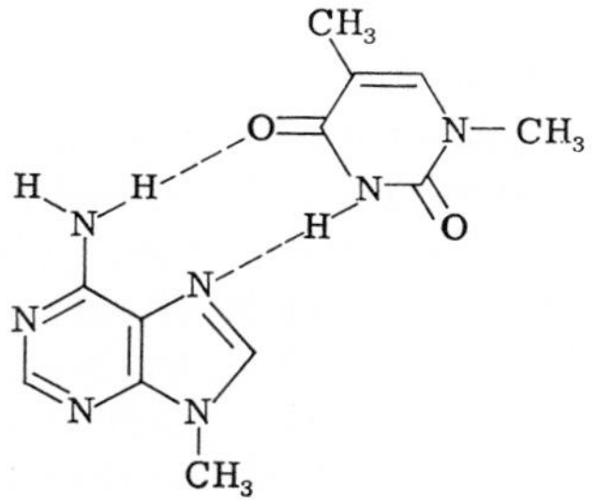

FIG. 5. Hydrogen bonds in a crystal of 1-methylthymine and 9-methyladenine.

not represent the most stable arrangement of the "isolated" pairs and that supplementary stabilizing factors, other than the hydrogen bonds, obviously operate in the helix, the most important of which is probably the proper fitting of the bases into the dimensions of the helix with a minimum of distortion introduced.

On the other hand, it is interesting to report that crystalline complexes formed between guanine and cytosine derivatives—9-ethylguanine + 1-methylcytosine (O'Brien, 1963), 9-ethylguanine + 1-methyl-5-bromo-cytosine (Sobell et al., 1963), and deoxyguanosine + 5-bromodeoxycytidine (Haschemeyer and Sobell, 1964)—exhibit the existence of the same hydrogen-bonded configuration as the one postulated in the Watson–Crick pairing (with three hydrogen bonds, as indicated by Pauling and Corey, 1956).

Although the special environment of the crystals may, of course, play an important role in producing these different configurations, the quantum-

[3] Methyl derivatives of the bases were chosen, with alkyl groups fixed at the glycosidic nitrogens, so as to prevent the involvement of these nitrogens in hydrogen bonding and to reproduce, therefore, the situation existing from that point of view in the nucleic acids.

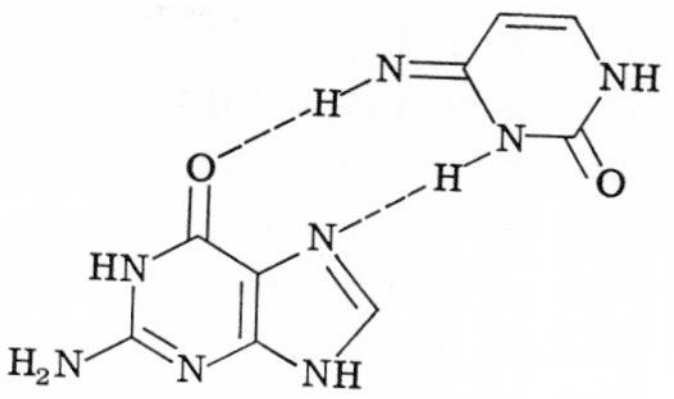

FIG. 6. Alternative pairing of the guanine-cytosine pair.

(a)   (b)

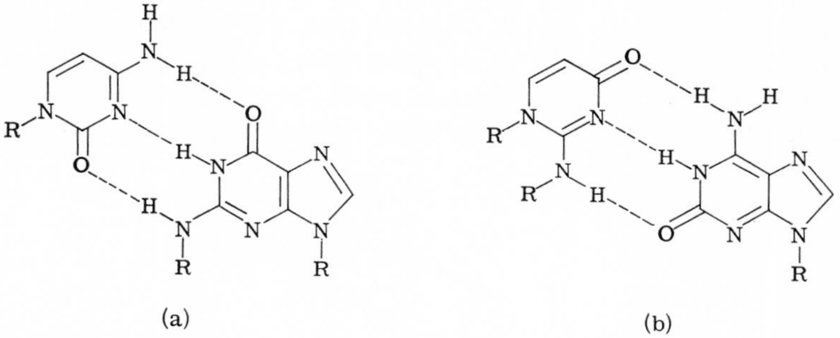

FIG. 7. Complementary pairs (a) Guanine-cytosine; (b) isoguanine-isocytosine.

mechanical calculations account, in fact, to some extent for the observed situation. Thus, the theoretical evaluation of the resonance energy of the Hoogsteen's adenine-thymine pair leads to a value practically identical with that calculated for the Watson–Crick pair. The two configurations thus appear from that point of view as essentially equivalent, and it must therefore be relatively easy for the environmental effects to stabilize preferentially one or the other of these configurations. The situation is quite different for the guanine-cytosine pair. As illustrated in Fig. 6, the possibility of an alternative coupling in this pair, analogous to the one just discussed for the A-T pair (i.e., which would involve in guanine N_7 instead of N_1) would necessitate the existence of cytosine in the imine form. Now, calculations indicate that the imine form of cytosine is about 2.3 kcal/mole less stable than its amine form and, moreover, that the resonance stabilization of the alternative pair would be much smaller (≈ 0.07 $\beta \approx 1.1$ kcal/mole) than the stabilization estimated for the Watson–Crick pairing. It has been explicitly *predicted*, therefore, on this basis ("Quantum Biochemistry," p. 215) that "it seems improbable that this alternative pairing may occur, even in a crystal." So far, this prediction seems to be verified.

The same type of considerations may perhaps represent at least a partial answer to the query raised by Rich (1962) as to why nature does not use the isoguanine-isocytosine pair, either in place of or in addition to the guanine-cytosine pair. Thus, as can be seen from Fig. 7, an isoG-isoC pair may be formed which would contain the same number and type of hydrogen bonds as the G-C pair and would, in fact, have nearly the same geometrical configuration, particularly in length and width. Now, the calculations indicate (Pullman, A., and Pullman, B., 1964) that these iso forms of the bases have smaller resonance energies than the usual forms and that the iso G-isoC pair has a resonance energy of about 0.1 β ($\approx$1.6 kcal/mole), smaller than the G-C pair. In view of the obvious general importance of molecular stability for the evolutionary selection of biomolecules (Pullman, B., and Pullman, A., 1962a; Pullman, A., and Pullman, B., 1964), it seems plausible that this difference in resonance stabilization played a role in favor of the choice of the G-C pair.

Before closing this section, two more recent discoveries are worth quoting. One, due to Haschemeyer and Sobell (1963), demonstrating in the

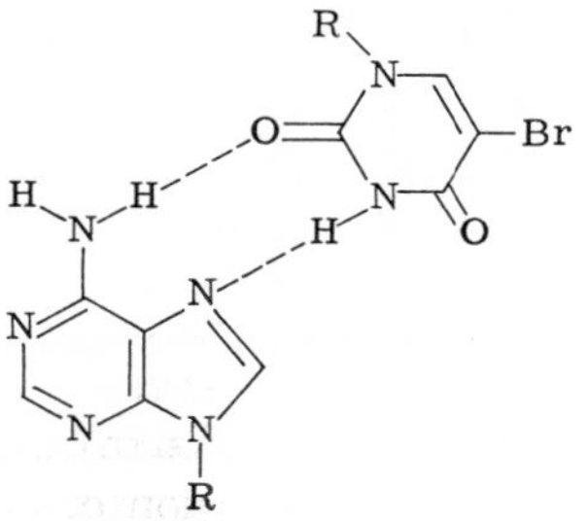

FIG. 8. Adenosine + 5-bromouridine coupling.

case of the crystal structure of the intermolecular complex of adenosine + 5-bromouridine, the existence of a third type of base pairing, different from both the Watson–Crick and Hoogsteen ones. This is illustrated in Fig. 8, which shows that the pyrimidine ring has been "turned over" with respect to the previous arrangements: In this adenosine + 5 bromouridine complex it is the oxygen O_2 of bromouracil that is hydrogen bonded to the amino group of adenine, instead of the oxygen O_4 as in the models of Watson–Crick and Hoogsteen. Although here again this result may reflect the effect of the crystal-packing forces, it may nevertheless also be due essentially to molecular structural factors, because the two oxygens of uracil have very similar electronic characteristics (e.g., they carry nearly identical π charge ("Quantum Biochemistry," p. 832), and it may consequently be possible for even small but different perturbations, such as those due to a methyl and a bromine substitution, to affect differentially the two oxygens and to orient differently their H-bonding tendencies. The problem needs, of course, a more quantitative investigation, and self-consistent field molecular orbital calculations are presently being carried out in our laboratory on the general problem of the structure of halogenou-racils, interesting from many viewpoints (see, e.g., Szybalski, 1962).

The second discovery concerns the crystal structure of isocytosine (McConnell *et al.*, 1964) which indicates the cocrystallization of the two tautomers (I) and (II) in a hydrogen bonded 1:1 complex. The coexistence

(I)   (II)

of two such tautomers is not surprising either, because of the very small energy difference in this type of tautomerization: $0.06 \ \beta \approx 1$ kcal/mole.

Finally, it may be useful to mention an extremely interesting result obtained recently in Duchesne's laboratory (Checcucci *et al.*, 1965) which has shown that the radioresistance of the crystalline G–C complex is appreciably greater than what might have been expected on the basis of the radioresistance of the isolated bases. This result is a further con-firmation of our general correlation between radioresistance of organic solids and their stabilization through π-electron delocalization as measured by their resonance energy. In the case of the G–C crystals, the very ap-preciable increase in radioresistance may, moreover, be due to the fact that the base pairs themselves are linked together by complementary H bonds, thus forming very huge graphite-type layers of delocalized π elec-trons (O'Brien, 1963).

2. Dipole Moments

As already mentioned, hydrogen bonds between the base pairs are no longer considered the major source of the stability of the double-stranded structure of the nucleic acids, although they obviously play the essential role of determining the base-pairing specificity. The main source of the stability is now believed to reside in the nonspecific interactions between the stacked base pairs, frequently referred to as "hydrophobic" interac-tions (Herskovits *et al.*, 1961; Helmkamp and Ts'o, 1961; Mahler and Mehrotra, 1962; Hamaguchi and Geiduschek, 1962; Falk *et al.*, 1963; Levine *et al.*, 1963; Zimm, 1960; Zimm and Kallenbach, 1962; Marmur *et al.*, 1963). Following a recent evaluation of Crothers and Zimm (1964), the stacking free energy in certain types of synthetic polynucleotides is about 7 kcal/mole of base pairs as against 1 kcal/mole for a hydrogen bond.

Truly, the term hydrophobic bonding is vague and comprises contributions due to electrostatic (dipole-dipole), induction (dipole-induced dipole), and dispersion (London–van der Waals) forces and a charge transfer component. The contributions of the electrostatic induced- and dispersion-type attractions to the helix stability have been evaluated in a representative calculation by DeVoe and Tinoco (1962) and some of their aspects reinvestigated by Sinanoğlu and collaborators (Sinanoğlu et al., 1964; Sinanoğlu and Abdulnar, 1964). DeVoe and Tinoco show that the electrostatic-, induction-, and dispersion-type interactions between the bases make a relatively large contribution to the energy of the helix. In accord with these authors, the main interactions between the coplanar bases in a base pair come from their permanent dipole moments. These dipole interactions are also large for adjacent stacked base pairs, but in this case the main attraction comes, according to these authors, from the dispersion forces. The total electrostatic induction and dispersion free energy has been calculated for the ten different possible arrangements of the stacked complementary pairs. Its value varies between -1.6 and -19.8 kcal per 2 moles of base, following the base composition and sequence. The helix stability is calculated to be proportional to the guanine $+$ cytosine content.

The calculations of the electrostatic energies require the knowledge of the magnitude and orientation of the permanent dipole moment of each base in a polynucleotide at neutral pH. Because of the insolubility of most purine and pyrimidine bases in nonpolar solvents, the experimental values are scarce and known only, among the compounds of interest to us, for 9-methylpurine (4.3 D), 9-methyladenine (3.0 D), and 1,3-dimethyluracil (3.9 D) (DeVoe and Tinoco, 1962). The theoretical evaluation of the moments of the nucleic bases has therefore been the subject of an intensive quantum-mechanical investigation. The moments have been calculated by DeVoe and Tinoco (1962) using Gibb's method for the calculation of the moments due to the σ electrons and a Hückel-type procedure for the moments due to the π electrons. They have been evaluated by Berthod and A. Pullman (1963) and by Bradley et al. (1964) using the Del Re's method for the calculation of the σ moments and the self-consistent field results of Veillard and B. Pullman (1963) for the calculation of the π moments. Berthod and A. Pullman (1963) have also tried in this approximation a semiempirical procedure for the calculation of the σ moments by additivity of bond moments (Orgel et al., 1951).

The method of Del Re (1964) as used in the preceding publications was however, calibrated by its author for the calculation of saturated molecules and needed obviously, on account of its parametrical nature, to be appropriately modified for conjugated compounds so as to take into account the changes brought about by variations in hybridization. The main parameters in Del Re's method are Coulomb integrals of the Hückel type which were initially chosen according to the relative gross electronegativity values of the atoms involved. Berthod and A. Pullman (1964, 1965a) refined this procedure for the problem of the skeleton of conjugated systems by using instead the concept of orbital electronegativity and the values of these quantities as evaluated by Hinze and Jaffé (1962) for the determination of the Coulomb parameters for each valence orbital. The description of the σ bonds by this modified procedure has been combined with a calculation of the π-electron system in the Hückel approximation with the accuracy of the parameters carefully refined for the reproduction of the dipole moments of a large series of fundamental, simple heterocyclics. The procedure was then applied to the values of the dipole moments of the nucleic bases (Berthod and Pullman, A., 1965a).

Although all these different methods yield theoretical dipole moments of the same order of magnitude, the best agreement with the known experimental values is obtained by the last procedure. In fact, as can be seen in Table III, which contains the results of this procedure (and in the last column also, for the sake of comparison, the results of DeVoe and Tinoco), the theoretical values are extremely satisfactory in the three cases for which experimental values are available. This encourages confidence in the predicted values of the moments for guanine (6.8 D), cytosine (7.2 D), and thymine (3.6 D). The order of magnitude of the predicted moments is in agreement with the DeVoe and Tinoco values with however,

TABLE III

DIPOLE MOMENTS OF THE NUCLEIC ACID BASES (IN DEBYE UNITS)[a,b]

Compound	μ_π	$\theta_\pi{}^\circ$	μ_σ	$\theta_\sigma{}^\circ$	μ total	$\theta^{\circ c}$	μ_{exp}	$\mu_{total}{}^d$	$\theta^{\circ d}$
9-Methylpurine	3.5	53	0.7	50	4.3	53	4.3	3.6	56
9-Methyladenine	2.7	74	0.4	83	3.1	75	3.0	2.8	88
1,3-Dimethyluracil	3.3	27	0.9	73	3.9	36	3.9	3.7	35
1-Methylthymine	2.8	29	0.9	73	3.5	39	—	3.5	33
9-Methylguanine	5.7	−33	1.2	−46	6.9	−36	—	6.9	−36
1-Methylcytosine	5.3	96	1.9	99	7.1	97	—	8.0	108

[a] Berthod and Pullman, A. (1965a).

[b] The values presented here correct some errors which slipped into the original reference.

[c] θ° is the angle of the moment with the axis N_1–C_4 of the pyrimidines (N_1 in the pyrimidine is the N atom involved in the glycosidic linkage) and N_3–C_6 of the purines.

[d] From DeVoe and Tinoco (1962).

a discrepancy of 1 D in the case of cytosine. Finally, Berthod and A. Pullman have also evaluated more recently the dipole moments of the nucleic acid base pairs guanine-cytosine and adenine-thymine. This has been done in two approximations. In the first one (Berthod and Pullman, A., 1965) the moments of the base pairs were obtained simply by vector composition of the individual moments of the components. It is, however, known that hydrogen bonding often results in an appreciable modification of the dipole moment of the complex, with respect to the sum of the component dipoles (see, e.g., Pimentel and McClellan, 1960; Gomel and Lumbroso, 1962). An extra term should therefore be added to the simple composition of the individual moments in order to take into account the dipole created by hydrogen bonding along the hydrogen bond itself. This has been done in the second approximation (Berthod and Pullman, A., 1964). The appropriate new parameters and the perturbations of the parameters corresponding to the isolated bases have been calibrated semiempirically with respect to two hydrogen-bonded complexes, whose experimental dipole moments were known. The results obtained for the nucleic acid base pairs in the two approximations are shown in Table IV. The important points which emerge from these results are:

1. The relatively very small resultant dipole moment of the A-T pair in contrast to the relatively great dipole moment of the G-C pair. This situation is due not only to the smallness of the dipole moments of adenine and thymine with respect to those of guanine and cytosine but also to the

TABLE IV

THEORETICAL DIPOLE MOMENT OF THE BASE PAIRS (IN DEBYES)[a,b]

Base pair	μ_σ	μ_π	μ_{total}	$\theta°$[c]
Adenine	0.50	2.70	3.17	—
Thymine	0.91	2.89	3.56	—
A-T pair				
Vectoral additivity	0.68	1.08	0.59	−50°
Explicit introduction of the H bond	0.68	1.30	0.91	−44°
Guanine	1.19	5.68	6.82	—
Cytosine	1.86	5.30	7.16	—
G-C pair				
Vectoral additivity	1.85	5.44	7.06	−98°
Explicit introduction of the H bond	2.42	5.90	8.13	−102°

[a] From Berthod and Pullman, A. (1964).

[b] The values presented here correct some errors which slipped into the original reference.

[c] $\theta°$ is the angle of the moment with the N_3–C_6 axis of the purine.

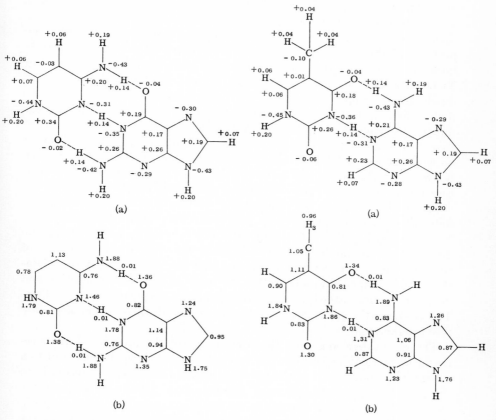

Fig. 9. Electronic charges in the base pairs. (a) σ net charges; (b) π charges.

fact that the component dipoles in the A-T pair are practically opposed in direction, whereas the component dipoles in the G-C pair point at approximately 120° from each other.

2. The general, far from negligible increase in the dipole moments of both pairs upon the explicit introduction of the contribution that is due to the H bonds.[4]

Figure 9 represents the distribution of the electronic charges, σ and π, corresponding to the Berthod–Pullman (A.) (1964, 1965) approximations for the calculation of the dipole moments. These diagrams are reproduced

[4] It may be useful to remark that the self-consistent field calculations of the charge distribution in the base pairs, the results of which are indicated in Fig. 3 lead to the values of the π components of the dipole moments in close agreement with those of Fig. 9. Thus the SCF calculation of Fig. 3 indicate a π dipole moment of 5.6 D for the G-C pair and of 0.7 D for the A-T pair.

here not only for the sake of an illustration of a particularly plausible σ and π charge distribution in the purine-pyrimidine pairs but, also, because their knowledge may be of more fundamental importance for the very problem of the evaluation (or rather, re-evaluation) of the electrostatic interaction forces in the nucleic acids. The evaluation due to deVoe and Tinoco consists, as previously stated, of the calculation of the dipole-dipole, dipole-induced dipole, and the London-dispersion components, the first and the last of these components being, as indicated, of the greatest importance. However, it is well known (e.g., Hirschfelder, 1957; this volume) that the usual "ideal" dipole concept only applies when the distance between the centers of the two molecules is much greater than the distance between the charge centers in both molecules. This is definitely not the case for the paired or stacked bases in the nucleic acids. Now, when the distance conditions are not fulfilled, the real electrostatic forces are quite different from what is inferred on the basis of the "ideal" dipole forces; in fact the energy of interaction may be orders of magnitude larger than the dipole-dipole interaction energy calculated from the dipole moments of the components. In such a case it is recommended to forego any consideration of dipole moments and, rather, to think of each of the positive and negative charges in the system as interacting in a simple coulombic fashion. The electrostatic energy will then be the sum of all these monopole-monopole interactions.

The reconsideration, from this view point, of the problem of the electrostatic interactions between the bases of the nucleic acids may lead to a substantial modification of the previous results. This can be inferred from the representative calculations of Bradley et al. (1964) on the in-plane electrostatic interaction energies in the complementary base pairs of DNA. When these energies are evaluated by the dipole-dipole approximation, the values found are −2.0 kcal for the guanine-cytosine pair and 0.9 kcal for the adenine-thymine pair. Because of the low value of the dispersion forces in this case (DeVoe and Tinoco, 1962), these are the essential forces, besides hydrogen bonding, for the in-plane interaction and, in this approximation, they correspond to a moderate attraction in the G-C pair and to a small repulsion in the A-T pair. Now, when the interactions are evaluated in the monopole-monopole approximation, with the hundreds of terms summed up, they lead to values bearing no apparent relationship to the previous ones: interaction energies of −16.8 kcal for the G-C pair and of −5.3 kcal for the A-T pair.

Both results correspond in this second approximation to much stronger attractive interactions, with the faithful reproduction of a stronger interaction in the G-C than in the A-T pair. It must, of course, be realized that the same computed charge densities are used in both monopole and dipole calculations. The results thus clearly show that the dipole approximation is not appropriate in the DNA system. It is therefore essential that the contribution of the electrostatic interactions to the stacking energy of DNA be re-evaluated in the monopole approximation. The charges reproduced in Fig. 9 may be used for this purpose, and, in fact, calculations of this type are presently being carried out in our laboratory.

It may also be remarked that, at relatively small distances, the energy of interaction through dispersion forces is much less than would be expected from the inverse six-power law (e.g., Hirschfelder *et al.*, 1954). This aspect of the stacking interactions in the nucleic acids therefore also needs to be re-evaluated.

3. Electron Donor-Acceptor Properties

It has been mentioned in the preceding section that charge-transfer forces may also be operative between the superposed base pairs and may thus contribute to the over-all stability of the ordered structure of the nucleic acids. Such a type of interaction is, in fact, to be expected on general grounds for parallel-oriented conjugated aromatics with an intermolecular separation of the order of magnitude of that present in the nucleic acids.

a. *Charge-Transfer Complexation.* Generally speaking, charge-transfer complexes are molecular or supramolecular entities formed from two (sometimes more) ordinarily stable molecular components through a more or less complete transfer of an electron from one of the components (the electron donor) to the other (the electron acceptor). The quantum theory of the phenomenon, which is the only satisfactory one, was developed in the 1950's by Mulliken (1952, 1956, 1964). Following this author's proposition (general reviews: McGlynn, 1958, 1960: Briegleb, 1961), the interaction of an electron donor (D) with an electron acceptor (A) may be described by saying that, when D and A combine to form a complex, the wave function for their association may be written approximately as

$$\Psi_N = a\Psi_{(DA)} + b\Psi_{(D^+A^-)} \qquad (a > b)$$

for the ground state, and

$$\Psi_E = b^*\Psi_{(DA)} - a^*\Psi_{(D^+A^-)} \qquad (a^* > b^*)$$

for the first excited state.

In these expressions, $\Psi_{(DA)}$ denotes the so-called *no-bond* wave function; it means the wave function corresponding to a structure in which the binding of the two components is effected by the "classical" intermolecular forces (the electrostatic, dispersion, H-bonding, etc., forces discussed previously), whereas $\Psi_{(D^+A^-)}$ denotes the so-called *dative-bond* wave function, corresponding to a structure of the complex in which one electron has been transferred from D to A and in which, besides the forces listed above, there may also be a weak chemical binding between the odd electrons now situated on the two components of the complex. It can be seen that the charge transfer is generally more pronounced in the excited state of the complex than in its ground state. The transition from the ground to the excited state is frequently associated with the appearance of a new absorption band, situated generally toward long wavelengths and which is the essentially and practically the only unambiguous indication of the formation of a charge-transfer complex.

The consideration of the energy quantities involved in the formation of the ground state and the transition to the excited state may be obtained by solving the appropriate secular determinant. The essential result concerned with the binding energy of the complex is that the resonance or stabilization energy E_R, owing to the charge-transfer complex formation, is given by

$$E_R = E_N - E_0 = (H_{01} - E_0 S)^2 / (E_1 - E_0) \tag{1}$$

where E_N is the energy of the ground state, E_0 the energy of the no-bond state, E_1 the energy of the dative state, H_{01} the resonance integral between the no-bond and the dative state, and S the overlap integral between the two states.

It can be shown that the difference $E_1 - E_0$ can be expressed as

$$E_1 - E_0 = I_D - E_A - (e^2/r_{DA}) + C_{DA} \tag{2}$$

where I_D is the ionization potential of the electron donor, E_A the electron affinity of the electron acceptor, r_{AB} the distance between the charged molecules in the complex, and C_{AB} the difference in the electrostatic and dispersion energies between the no-bond and dative states.

The substitution of $E_1 - E_0$ into Eq. (1) yields

$$E_R = E_N - E_0 = \frac{(H_{01} - E_0 S)^2}{I_D - E_A - (e^2/r_{DA}) + C_{DA}} \tag{3}$$

By assuming that, in a series of similar complexes formed between related molecules, H_{01} is proportional to S and that S and $[(e^2/r_{AB}) + C_{AB}]$ are approximately constant, one obtains the approximate formula

$$E_R = C_1 / (I_D - E_A - C_2) \tag{4}$$

which indicates that the stabilization of the complex should in such circumstances increase when I_D becomes smaller and E_A larger.

Although the assumptions on the constancy of the different quantities mentioned earlier are certainly not completely satisfied, it is nevertheless generally observed that, when the formation of charge-transfer complexes involves different electron donors but the same electron acceptor, a linear correlation exists between the ionization potential of the donor and the stability of the complex (or the position of the new charge-transfer band). In cases (in fact, quite numerous) in which the demonstration of the existence of a charge-transfer complex is difficult (e.g., when no charge-transfer band is seen), the existence of a correlation between the ionization potential of the electron donor and the degree of intermolecular association may be considered an indication (although not a proof) of the possible involvement of charge-transfer forces in the association. Sometimes, but less frequently, when the charge-transfer complexes involve different electron acceptors but the same donor, a similar linear relation exists between the stability of the complex (or the position of the new band) and the electron affinity of the acceptors.

Thus, the ionization potentials and the electron affinities of biomolecules, which measure, respectively, their electron donor and acceptor abilities, are fundamental quantities for the study of properties related to certain types of their intra- on intermolecular interactions. *In view, of the complete absence of experimental informations about the values of these quantities in biomolecules, the contribution of the theory, even if suggesting only approximate values, is obviously of particular importance.* We shall see in the next section numerous examples of the applicability of these data to a series of problems involving the interaction of purines, pyrimidines, and nucleic acids with different types of aromatic ring systems. In this section we shall limit the discussion to a few general remarks on the electron donor-acceptor properties of the base pairs of the nucleic acids.

The simplest evaluation of these properties may be obtained through the use of the Hückel approximation, it being understood that such an evaluation is particularly suitable for the determination of the *relative* electron donor-acceptor properties of the bases. The appropriate indices are the energies of the highest filled molecular orbital for the electron-donor capacity and the energy of the lowest empty molecular orbital for the electron-acceptor ability. The reliability of these quantities for conclusions in this field is substantiated by correlations obtained between the theoretical and experimental sets of data in series of fundamental molecules in which both are known (see, e.g., "Quantum Biochemistry," pp. 128–135).

The energy coefficients calculated for the highest filled and lowest empty molecular orbitals of the adenine-thymine and guanine-cytosine pairs have been indicated in Table II. We remind the reader that the electron donor property of a molecule is the greater (its ionization potential the smaller) the smaller the value of the energy coefficient of its highest filled molecular orbital and that the electron-acceptor property of a molecule or its electron affinity are greater the smaller the absolute value of the energy coefficient of its lowest empty molecular orbital. The fundamental result which springs from the data of Table II is that, inasmuch as the base pairs can really be considered to represent unique conjugated systems extending over their whole molecular surface, *the guanine-cytosine pair should be at the same time a better electron donor and a better electron acceptor than the adenine-thymine pair.* This state of affairs can easily be understood when the "origins" of the highest filled or lowest empty orbitals of the pairs are traced to those of the isolated bases from which they essentially derive: Table V ("Quantum Biochemistry," p. 219; Pullman, B., and Pullman, A., 1959).

This result means that *insofar as charge-transfer forces between stacked base pairs may contribute to the helix stability, one may expect the nucleic acids rich in guanine-cytosine to exhibit greater stability than those rich in adenine-thymine.* These forces operate, therefore, in the same direction as the electrostatic and dispersion forces, a situation which makes urgent the evaluation of their relative importance.

b. *Intercalation of Aminoacridines.* There is no direct experimental verification of the theoretical predictions concerning the relative electron donor-acceptor properties of the guanine-cytosine and adenine-thymine pairs. Some indirect verifications seem, however, to have been produced very recently. They are connected with studies on the heterogeneity of the interaction of DNA with acriflavine or proflavine by optical (Tubbs *et al.*, 1964) and thermodynamic (Chambron *et al.*, 1964) methods. Before presenting the results, it may be useful to recall briefly the general problem of the nature of the interactions between aminoacridines and DNA.

It seems established today that the aminoacridines are able to interact with the nucleic acids, in particular with DNA, either through aggregation with the negatively charged sites at the phosphate groups of the polymeric chain (Bradley and Felsenfeld, 1959; Bradley and Wolf, 1959; Stone and Bradley, 1961; Neville and Bradley, 1961) or through intercalation in a

TABLE V

The "Origins" of the Molecular Orbitals in the Base Pairs[a]

MO	Adenine	Adenine-thymine pair	Thymine	Guanine	Guanine-cytosine pair	Cytosine
Lowest empty orbitals	−0.87	−0.95 −0.87	−0.96	−1.05	−1.07 −0.78	−0.80
Highest filled orbitals	0.49	0.43 0.53	0.51	0.31	0.31 0.61	0.60

[a] For probable absolute values (in eV) of the ionization potentials and electron affinities of the bases and base pairs see Section III, C, 3, c.

"sandwichlike" fashion between two successive complementary pairs of the purine-pyrimidine bases, forcing them 6.8 Å apart instead of the usual 3.4 Å by extension and some untwisting of the phosphate-deoxyribose backbone. Owing essentially to the work of Lerman (1961, 1963, 1964; Luzzati *et al.*, 1961), the intercalation mechanism has recently received support from other laboratories (Weill and Calvin, 1963; Boettcher, 1963; Isenberg *et al.*, 1964). Its particular interest resides in the fact that it has been related (Brenner *et al.*, 1961) to the mutagenic activity of the amino-acridines in bacteriophages (Orgel and Brenner, 1961). Now, from the biological point of view, acridine-induced mutations form a somewhat exclusive class (e.g., Hayes, 1964): these compounds are postulated to act as mutagens by causing the insertion or the deletion of a base pair. In fact, it can be shown that if, during replication, the acridine-mutagen happens to slide between the bases on one chain of DNA but not on the other, it may easily lead to the addition (when the sliding in occurs on the *template* strand) or subtraction (when the sliding in occurs on the *new* strand) of a base pair upon subsequent replication of the double-stranded helix formed in such a perturbed way (e.g., Hayes, 1964, p. 295).

The aspects of the problem which are of particular interest to us in these pages concern their relation to the previously described results about the electronic properties of the base pairs and especially the theoretical predictions of their relative electron donor-acceptor abilities. As mentioned above, two types of recent studies on the heterogeneity of the acridine-DNA interactions seem to support the theoretical conjunctures. In the first place, the linear decrease of the quantum yield of fluorescence of acriflavine bound to DNA with the increase of the guanine-cytosine content of the nucleic acids may be interpreted as resulting from the parallel increase of a charge transfer interaction between the dye and the bases (Tubbs *et al.*, 1964). Such a charge transfer mechanism has been used successfully to explain a number of cases of quenching of fluorescence. In our example, acriflavine would act as the electron acceptor and the G-C pair as the electron donor.

In the second place, both the spectroscopic method of Tubbs *et al.* (1964) and the thermodynamic method of Chambron *et al.* (1964) lead to the conclusion that the dyes have a different affinity for different sites of intercalation and that most probably they intercalate preferentially between two A-T pairs rather than between two G-C pairs, the intercalation between an A-T and a G-C pair being of intermediate frequency. Tubbs *et al.* (1964) seem to be somewhat embarrassed to interpret these findings, particularly in view of the results mentioned above concerning the preferential quenching of fluorescence by G-C pairs, and seem inclined to attribute it to the possible role of other types of binding (e.g., hydrogen bonding) between the heteroatoms of the purines or pyrimidines on the one hand and those of the acridines on the other. Although such different modes of binding may, of course, play a role in the stabilization of the complex (*vide infra*), there is at present no indication which would suggest that such interactions should preferentially involve the A-T pair of DNA. In fact, it appears to us that there is available a much simpler explanation for the preferential intercalation of the aminoacridines between adjacent A-T pairs. Thus, as shown in this and in preceding sections, the results on both the charge-transfer interactions and on the electrostatic and dispersion interactions between stacked base pairs point to the general conclusion that there is a stronger interaction between neighbor G-C pairs than between neighbor A-T pairs. The intercalation which involves the rupture of this interaction should therefore involve a smaller activation energy when it occurs between adjacent A-T pairs than when it occurs between adjacent G-C pairs.

Another aspect of the problem concerns the properties of the aminoacridines which may possibly be related to their ability to intercalate and to mutate. In the first place it must immediately be remarked that there is no constant relationship between these two abilities: Thus some aminoacridines intercalate into DNA but are not mutagenic (Lerman, 1964). Mutagenicity is therefore obviously a more complex phenomenon than intercalation. With regard to a curious result of Webb and Kubitschek (1963), aminoacridines may even be antimutagenic, although this concerns a bacterial system. On the other hand, although the relative order of the mutagenic activity of the aminoacridines is known (e.g., it is the greatest for 5- and 2-aminoacridines and the lowest for 1-aminoacridine), no quantitative information is available about the relative ability of these compounds to intercalate into DNA. The principal electronic features that can be related to their mutagenic activity or can be particularly significant for the interactions of these molecules with the nucleic acids are summed up in Table VI (Pullman, B., 1962, 1964a, b).

Although a correlation appears to exist between the mutagenic activity of the molecules listed in this table and the electronic charge of their ring nitrogen or their basicity, it is, in fact, of very limited significance. Thus, the methylation of proflavine at positions 3 and 7 (to give acridine yellow) or at the amino groups (to give acridine orange), (see structure III),

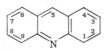

Numbering of atoms
in acridine

(III)

TABLE VI

ELECTRONIC CHARACTERISTICS OF AMINOACRIDINES

Compound	Energy coefficient of the:		Electrical charge of the:		pK_a (in water 20°C)	Half-way reduction potential	μ_{total} (in D)	Angle with respect to the C5–N axis
	Highest filled molecular orbital	Lowest empty molecular orbital	Ring nitrogen	Amino nitrogen				
Acridine	0.49	−0.34	1.20	—	5.60	−0.33	2.71	0
1-Aminoacridine	0.34	−0.38	1.18	1.82	4.40	−0.32	1.12	2.1
2-Aminoacridine	0.42	−0.37	1.24	1.83	8.04	−0.58	4.17	−60.3
3-Aminoacridine	0.39	−0.36	1.20	1.84	5.88	−0.37	4.62	−46.4
4-Aminoacridine	0.36	−0.39	1.23	1.81	6.04	−0.41	6.55	−1.3
5-Aminoacridine	0.35	−0.48	1.33	1.76	9.99	−0.90	7.64	0
Proflavine	0.40	−0.41	1.27	1.83	9.65	−0.63	1.34	0

while increasing in both cases the basic pK of the compounds, corresponds
to an increase of mutagenic activity in the first case and to its decrease in
the second. This last result signifies perhaps some involvement of the
amino groups in the activity (see also Leith, 1963). The situation in this
field is obviously far from being clear. It would, of course, be exceedingly
important to determine the relative aptitude of the aminoacridines to
intercalate, both for the sake of knowing whether, at least among the
mutagenic acridines, there is any relationship between the abilities to
intercalate and to mutate and also for the sake of establishing which of the
different electronic indices listed in Table VI plays the essential role in
favoring the ability to intercalate.

c. *Semiconductivity.* Finally it is not possible to terminate this section
on the electron donor-acceptor properties of the base pairs without discussing the possible significance of these properties for the electronic
semiconductivity of the nucleic acid. This last property, first measured by
Duchesne (1962: Duchesne *et al.*, 1960), has since been confirmed by different groups (Eley and Spivey, 1962; Snart, 1962; Eley, 1962; O'Konski and
Shirai, 1963; O'Konski *et al.*, 1964; Liang and Scalco, 1964), who have
established the energy gap for the semiconductivity of dry DNA as being
2.4 eV. Doubts are, however, left as to the intrinsic or extrinsic nature of
the observed semiconductivity.

The complexity of the structure of the nucleic acids makes, of course,
the theoretical evaluation of the energy gap a difficult task. Very recently,
however, Mesnard and Vasilescu (1963) succeeded in measuring these
energies for the purine and pyrimidine bases, and their study from the
theoretical viewpoint is necessarily easier (Pullman, B., 1964f). It leads also
to some interesting conclusions about the semiconductivity of DNA itself.

The most plausible theory of semiconductivity of organic molecular
solids is based on the formation of charge carriers through a donor-acceptor mechanism (Lyons, 1957; Kommandeur and Hall, 1961; Kearns,
1964). Following this theory, the energy necessary for producing the separation of charges at a distance at which coulombic interactions between
them are negligible is given by Eq. (5), where I: is the ionization

$$E = I_c - E_c = I_D - E_A - P_+ - P_- = I_D - E_A - 2P \quad (5)$$

energy of the crystal, E_c the electron affinity of the crystal, I_D the ionization potential of the molecule that is the electron donor, E_A the electron
affinity of the molecule that is the electron acceptor, and P_+ and P_- the
polarization energies due to the presence of a positive or a negative charge
in the polarizable crystal. These last two energies are frequently considered
equal to the same energy P.

The quantity $I_D - E_A$ thus appears to be of fundamental importance for the determination of the energy gaps for semiconductivity, in particular for the sake of the comparison of these energies in a series of compounds, P generally being fairly constant and oscillating only feebly around the mean value of 1.6 eV (Lyons and Mackie, 1963).

In the absence of any experimental data in this field, these quantities have been evaluated theoretically in two different approximations regarding the values of I_D.

1. In the first approximation, these values have been obtained from the energy coefficients of the highest filled molecular orbital, in the Hückel approximation ("Quantum Biochemistry," p. 217) and the reference curve based upon experimental data for a series of standard compounds due in particular to Wacks and Dibeler ("Quantum Biochemistry," p. 129). Quite similar results are obtained if the reference curve based upon the experimental results of Stevenson ("Quantum Biochemistry," p. 129) is being used, with the only difference that, in this last case, all the I_D values are about 0.5 eV higher

2. In the second approximation, the I_D values have been obtained by a self-consistent field molecular orbital calculation, specifically adapted for the calculation of ionization potentials (Pullman, A., and Rossi, 1964). It is striking to observe that the values of the I_D's obtained in the two procedures are quite close in spite of the fact that, in the first approximation, the reference curve is constructed with data concerning conjugated hydrocarbons and used for heterocycles.

In both approximations, the values of E_A have been obtained from the energy coefficients of the lowest empty molecular orbital of the bases ("Quantum Biochemistry," p. 217) and the reference curve given in "Quantum Biochemistry," p. 134, which is constructed from semiempirical data for the electron affinities of a few standard molecules. These values of electron affinities are probably much more approximate than those of the ionization potentials, although possibly of the correct order of magnitude. Thus, the electron affinities may also be deduced from the halfway reduction potentials of the bases through the approximate relation of Eq. (6), which is apparently valid for a series of heterocycles (Briegleb, 1964).

$$E_A = -E_{1/2}^{red} + 1.41 \tag{6}$$

The particularly well established reduction potential of cytosine (Smith and Elving, 1962b; Janik and Palecek, 1964) is equal at pH 7 to about 1.7 eV. The preceding relation would thus lead to an electron affinity of -0.3 eV which may be considered, in this difficult field, in fairly good

agreement with the value of $+0.1$ eV, deduced from the reference curve.[5]
Moreover, the polarographic reduction potentials also confirm the relative
order of the electron affinities of the bases: Thus, in contrast to cytosine,
uracil, and thymine (and isocytosine, whose coefficient of the energy of the
lowest empty molecular orbital is -0.98, against -0.80 for cytosine) have
shown stability to polarographic reduction (Janik and Palecek, 1964).
Similarly, adenine may be reduced polarographically (although it seems
possible that its wave is a catalytic hydrogen wave), whereas guanine
cannot be reduced under normal polarographic conditions (Smith and
Elving, 1962a). These results confirm, in particular, the *prediction* of the
Hückel method made at the time when no experimental data were available about the great electron affinity of cytosine as compared with the
other bases of the nucleic acid.

The results of the evaluations of I_D, E_A, and $I_D - E_A$ are presented in
Table VII. The principal conclusions which may be drawn from this table
are twofold. First, the theoretical energy gaps which can be obtained by
subtracting $2P = 3.2$ eV from $I_D - E_A$ have the mean value of 5 eV
and are thus much greater than the experimental ones (Mesnard and
Vasilescu, 1963),[6] which are equal to 1.96 eV for guanine, 2.4 eV for cytosine

TABLE VII

$I_D - E_A$ (eV)

	1st Approximation					2nd Approximation			
	G	A	C	T	U	G	A	C	U
I_D	7.2	7.8	8.1	7.8	8.1	7.6	8.4	8.3	9
E_A	-0.5	-0.1	-0.1	-0.2	-0.2	-0.5	-0.1	0.1	-0.2
$I_D - E_A$	7.7	7.9	8.0	8.0	8.3	8.1	8.5	8.2	9.2

[5] In connection with this point it may be remarked that theoretical calculations on
electron affinities of aromatic hydrocarbons usually lead to data appreciably different
from the semiempirical ones utilized in the reference curve that we are employing
(e.g., Briegleb, 1964; Ehrenson, 1962; Hoyland and Goodman, 1962; Becker and Wentworth, 1963). A reference curve based on the purely theoretical calculations would lead,
in the case of the bases, to predictions of absolute values of electron affinities appreciably
greater than those deduced from the polarographic reduction potentials.

[6] Although they are of the order of magnitude of those obtained for the nucleosides
with the exception of guanosine which has a particularly low value of activation energy
(Eley and Leslie, 1963). The order in which the nucleosides may be classified from that
point of view on a relative scale is fairly parallel to that of the bases. In fact the order of
decreasing energy gaps for the nucleosides corresponds exactly to the order of decreasing
$I_D - E_A$ for the first approximation of Table VII.

and thymine, 2.6 eV for adenine, and 2.72 eV for uracil. This disagreement is not surprising, taking into account the approximation of the calculations considered in relation to experiments carried out on compressed pellets and not on crystals. In fact, such disagreements, although not so pronounced, are observed even in studies on the semiconductivity of aromatic hydrocarbons (Lyons, 1957). On the other hand, and this may be the essential conclusion, the relative order of the computed $I_D - E_A$ and, thus, in this approximation, of the energy gaps is fairly parallel to the experimental one. In particular, guanine, which has the smallest activation energy, also has the smallest $I_D - E_A$, whereas uracil, which has the greater activation energy, has also the greatest $I_D - E_A$. Such a situation represents a strong argument in favor of the "donor-acceptor" theory of conductivity.

It may be added that this procedure enables in fact a general classification of biochemicals in the order of predicted increasing semiconductive properties, which is verified in the limit of the available experimental data (Pullman, B., 1965).

The application of these ideas to the case of the nucleic acids themselves leads to at least one important prediction. Following Table V, we may consider the ionization potential of the G-C pair practically equal to that of guanine and its electron affinity equal to that of cytosine; similarly, we may consider the ionization potential of the A-T pair equal to that of adenine and its electron affinity equal to that of thymine. With the numerical values calculated previously for these quantities, we may estimate $I_D - E_A$ to be equal to about 7 eV for the G-C pair and to about 8 eV for the A-T pair (see also Blumenfeld, 1961). If the base pairs are considered the "isolated molecules" and the DNA polymer "the crystal," it may be predicted that the energy gaps for semiconduction should be smaller for a DNA formed exclusively of G-C pairs than for a DNA formed exclusively of A-T pairs. For practical cases it may therefore be *predicted that the energy gap for semiconduction in DNA should decrease with increasing G-C content.* The mean absolute value predicted for the energy gap, which is of the order of 4.5 eV, is naturally greater than the observed one. It must however be stressed that the calculated value refers to intrinsic semiconductivity, whereas, as stated before, there is a strong probability that the observed semiconductivity is associated with the presence of impurity levels.

The problem may also be looked upon from a more "macromolecular" point of view (e.g., Brillouin, 1962). Thus, in the case of regularly stacked structures, such as those of the bases in the nucleic acids, a tempting viewpoint is to consider the *cooperative charge-transfer effects* resulting from the possibility of a large number of charge-transfer structures contributing to the state of the system, thus creating a $\infty : \infty$ complex instead of a 1:1 complex. The resonance between these different types of structures will introduce considerable orbital delocalization both in the ground and especially in the excited state of the crystal, representing a possibility of electron transfer over large fractions of the crystalline array.

D. Molecular Associations

1. Base-Base Interactions

In close connection with the considerations developed in the preceding section are the electronic aspects of the numerous molecular associations involving the nucleic acids or their constituents ("Quantum Biochemistry," pp. 215–223). Among recent developments in this field, one of the most outstanding concerns the base-base interactions studied in particular by Ts'o and collaborators (Ts'o et al., 1962, 1963; Ts'o and Lu, 1964; Ts'o and Chan, 1964; Chan et al., 1964; Ts'o, 1964: for somewhat similar studies, see also Herskovits et al., 1961; Geiduschek and Herskovits, 1961; Hamaguchi and Geiduschek, 1962; Levine et al., 1963). The studies involve the interactions in solution both between the monomeric units, their analogs, or derivatives, and between the monomeric units and the nucleic acid polymer. The principal results may be summarized as follows:

1. The uncharged bases and nucleosides interact extensively in aqueous solution and their tendency of association may be ordered in the following series:

$$\text{Purine-Purine} > \text{Purine-Pyrimidine} > \text{Pyrimidine-Pyrimidine}$$

2. The mode of association of these compounds appears to be one of stacking in a partial overlapping way. This conclusion has been substantiated, in particular, by NMR studies (Jardetzky, 1964; Chan et al., 1964) which indicate that the average distance between the rings in such complexes is 3–4 Å, that the interaction energies are of the order of a few hundred calories per mole, that in the purine stacks the six-membered rings probably stack face to face and that so do the five-membered rings, and, finally, that the association process need not stop at the dimer stage but may continue to higher polymers.

3. Methyl and halogen substitutions seem to increase the self-association tendency of the bases; thus, 6-methylpurine tends to associate more extensively than purine, and 5-bromouridine more extensively than uridine.

4. There is no noticeable interaction between the bases or their nucleosides and the helical form of the nucleic acid. They do, however, interact

significantly with the coil forms, more with DNA than with RNA, the purines again being more efficient than the pyrimidines.

It is obvious from this short summary of the experimental results that these molecular associations involve forces very much akin to those previously considered responsible for the stability of the nucleic acid edifice itself. A detailed evaluation of the different components of these forces is therefore a rather complex task, although obviously easier to perform than for the nucleic acids. In fact, this work is presently being carried out in our laboratory, but unfortunately the final results are not available at the time these pages are being written. A few preliminary remarks may however be made.

The factors contributing to these associations may be considered two essential types: the van der Waals–London interactions and the charge-transfer complexations. As concerns the charge-transfer interactions, we have ssen in Section III, 6, 3, a that, in a series of related compounds, they depend essentially (or at least their relative magnitude in such a series of compounds depends essentially) on the ionization potential of the electron donor and, generally to a somewhat smaller extent, on the electron affinity of the electron acceptor: the charge-transfer complex formation is greater the smaller the ionization potential of the donor and the greater the electron affinity of the acceptor. Generally speaking, as concerns the van der Waals–London forces, we may recall that they involve three essential components: the electrostatic (dipole-dipole) interactions, the polarization or induction (dipole-induced dipole) interactions, and the dispersion interactions. The interaction energy between two dipoles in the most favorable aligned orientation is given by Eq. (7), where μ_1 and μ_2 stand for the

$$E_{\text{electrostatic}} = -2\mu_1\mu_2/\epsilon R^3 \qquad (7)$$

dipole moments and ϵ is some effective value for the dielectric constant of the medium. The average interaction for all orientations is

$$E_{\text{electrostatic}} = -2\mu_1^2\mu_2^2/3KT\epsilon R^6 \qquad (8)$$

The induction interactions are

$$E_{\text{induction}} = -(1/\epsilon^2 r^6)(\mu_1^2\alpha_2 + \mu_2^2\alpha_1) \qquad (9)$$

where α_1 and α_2 stand for the polarizabilities. The dispersion interactions are

$$E_{\text{dispersion}} = -(1/r^6)\tfrac{3}{2}\alpha_1\alpha_2[I_1I_2/(I_1 + I_2)] \qquad (10)$$

where I_1 and I_2 stand for the ionization potentials.

While waiting for the detailed calculations, we may estimate *a priori* that the dipole-dipole interactions, important as they may be numerically, cannot be primarily responsible for the relative ability of the bases to associate.[7] Thus purines seem generally to associate more extensively than pyrimidines, whereas no clear-cut distinction can be made between these two types of bases with respect to the value of their dipole moments. Thus, for example, as we have seen already, guanine or cytosine have greater dipole moments than adenine or thymine. Also, as we shall see in the next section, aromatic hydrocarbons with no dipole moments have a relatively great association constant toward purines, in fact greater association constants than those observed between the bases (Ts'o and Lu, 1964). It therefore seems probable that the electrostatic component cannot, in general, be the essential one in these types of association.

The relative importance of the induction forces is more difficult to ascertain. Thus, although the purines and pyrimidines cannot be divided, as indicated before from the viewpoint of the values of their dipole moments, the polarizabilities are, in general, a few units greater for the pyrines than for the pyrimidines. Thus, for example, evaluated with the aid of the usual additivity rules (Denbigh, 1940), their values are 14.4 Å^3 for guanine, 13.9 Å^3 for adenine, 12.4 Å^3 for purine, 11.0 Å^3 for cytosine, 10.2 Å^3 for uracil, and 12 Å^3 for thymine. The relative values of the resultant dipole-induced dipole components will therefore be determined by the interplay of these two sometimes convergent, sometimes opposed, factors.

The same situation concerns to some extent the dispersion forces. Those will be, roughly speaking, greater, the greater the ionization potentials and the polarizabilities. The ionization potentials, as we have seen, are in general greater for the pyrimidines than for the purines. The polarizabilities are, however, greater for the purines. Moreover, the differences in ionization potentials between these two types of bases are relatively small, whereas the differences in the polarizabilities are relatively great. It may therefore be estimated that the dispersion forces will most probably be appreciably greater among the purines than among the pyrimidines. This component could therefore play an important role in the greater tendency of association of purines over pyrimidines. Numerical results on these interactions are now available (see Pullman, B., et al., 1965a).

On the other hand, planar and aromatic rings seem definitely to be more effective than non planar and saturated rings, and this situation points to the importance of the π-electron effect. This could possibly be due to a charge-transfer effect. Thus, it is worth underlining that, although the dispersion forces are greater the greater the ionization potentials, charge-

[7] Of course, the previously indicated necessity of evaluating rather the monopole-monopole interactions may somewhat change the picture regarding the electrostatic interactions.

transfer complexation is favored by low ionization potentials. The intervention of such an effect could possibly account directly for the greater association tendency of purines over pyrimidines, the purines being better electron donors than the pyrimidines, and the greater association tendency of cytidine over uridine (Chan *et al.*, 1964), cytosine being (based on self-consistent field calculations) both a better electron donor and a better electron acceptor than uracil, and for the enhancement of association upon methyl and bromine substitution, 6-methylpurine and 5-bromouracil being better electron donors than, respectively, purine and uracil (the energy coefficients of the highest filled molecular orbital are 0.69 in purine, 0.66 in 6-methylpurine, 0.60 in uracil, and 0.53 in 5-bromouracil). In connection with this situation, it may be added that, although the dipole moment of 6-methylpurine is predicted to be smaller (3.8 D) than that of purine (4.2 D), the dipole moment of 5-bromouracil (4.5 D) is predicted to be greater than that of uracil (3.0 D). The polarizabilities of the substituted compound are, on the other hand, expected to be greater in both cases than those of the unsubstituted one.

It is expected that it will be possible in the near future to give a more quantitative evaluation of the relative importance of the different forces involved in these interactions.

2. Interactions with Aromatic Hydrocarbons; Significance in Carcinogenesis

Although some aspects of interactions with aromatic hydrocarbons have already been presented in "Quantum Biochemistry" (pp. 219–221), their particular importance especially in connection with the problem of chemical carcinogenesis and recent new developments necessitates rediscussion here.

These recent developments have indicated in particular the probable usefulness of distinguishing between the interactions of aromatic hydrocarbons with the free bases or their nucleosides in solution, on the one hand, and the interactions of the hydrocarbons with the nucleic acids themselves, on the other.

The interactions between the hydrocarbons and the free bases or their nucleosides correspond to the long-known solubilization of aromatic molecules by purines (Weil-Malherbe, 1946), recently reinvestigated by Boyland and Green (1962a, b), solubilization resulting sometimes in the formation of molecular compounds. In connection with the stacking mechanism of interaction considered previously, it may be useful to refer also to the results of X-ray investigations on the molecular geometry of a 1:1 crystalline complex between tetramethyluric acid and pyrene (De Santis *et al.*, 1961). These measurements established a plane-to-plane alternate stacking of the purine and pyrene molecules. If the associations observed in solution are of the same type, their establishment must involve the mixture of intermolecular forces as those in operation in the base-base associations, although, of course, possibly in different proportions.

In fact, the interactions between the hydrocarbons and the purines present, from the theoretical viewpoint, some particularities which make their study advantageous and relatively simple (Pullman, B., et al., 1965). Thus, it may be observed that the unsubstituted aromatic polybenzenoid hydrocarbons to which we shall limit our discussion are, with very few exceptions, devoid of dipole moments (Pullman, B., and Pullman, A., 1952). This situation means that the purely electrostatic dipole-dipole interaction forces cannot play any essential role in the hydrocarbon-purine associations. For the same reason, the dipole-induced dipole interaction forces will be reduced to only one of their components, the one involving the dipole moment of the base and the polarizability of the hydrocarbon. Now it can easily be shown that this factor, whatever its numerical contribution (vide infra), cannot account by itself for the observed order of the solubilizing power of the different purines studied. Thus, results are available which indicate the relative solubilizing (association) power of a series of purines toward a given hydrocarbon, in particular 3,4-benzopyrene. In these conditions, the polarizability, being that of the hydrocarbon, remains constant, and, if the induction forces played a decisive role in ensuring the solubilization, the degree of solubilization would be related to the dipole moments of the bases. This is absolutely

TABLE VIII

DIPOLE-INDUCED DIPOLE INTERACTIONS BETWEEN THE BASES AND 3,4-BENZOPYRENE

Base	Dipole moment of the base (D)	Energy of interaction (kcal/mole)	
		3.4 Å	4 Å
Tetramethyluric acid	3.4	−1.9	−0.7
Caffeine	3.4	−1.9	−0.7
6-Dimethylaminopurine	3.3	−1.8	−0.7
Guanine	6.8	−7.7	−2.9
Adenine	3.2	−1.7	−0.6
Hypoxanthine[a]	5.2	−4.5	−1.7
Thymine	3.6	−2.1	−0.8
Cytosine	7.2	−8.5	−3.2
Uracil	3.9	−2.5	−0.9

[a] Following Weil-Malherbe (1946), this compound has a smaller solubilizing power than adenine; following Boyland and Green (1962b), it has a greater solubilizing power than adenine.

not the case. Thus, for example, the solubilizing power of the purines is quite generally much greater than that of the pyrimidines and, in the purines themselves, increases with methyl substitution. Quite generally also, there is no relationship between this behavior and the values of the corresponding dipole moments.

This is illustrated in Table VIII, which presents the results of the evaluation of the contribution of the dipole-induced dipole interactions to the energy of the association between representative purines and pyrimidines with 3,4-benzopyrene. The purines and pyrimidines are listed in the order of decreasing solubilizing power. The polarizability of the hydrocarbon is taken equal to 35.7 Å³. From an examination of Table VIII, it can be deduced that no correlation exists between the values of these polarization interactions and the solubilizing power of the purines. We shall see shortly that this component is nevertheless significant for the total result.

As far as the classical van der Waals–London forces are concerned, we are thus left with the dispersion forces. An *a priori* evaluation of the significance of these forces is difficult, because they depend on a somewhat complex interplay of different factors, such as the ionization potentials and the polarizabilities of the partners. This situation remains true even if the problem is somewhat simplified by considering again the solubilization of a fixed hydrocarbon, say, 3,4-benzopyrene again, by a series of different bases. As already mentioned in connection with the base-base interactions, the ionization potentials are, as a mean, greater for the pyrimidines than

TABLE IX

DISPERSION INTERACTIONS BETWEEN THE BASES AND 3,4-BENZOPYRENE

Base	Ionization potential (eV)	Polarizability (Å³)	Energy of interaction (kcal/mole)	
			3.4 Å	4 Å
Tetramethyluric acid	5.8	21.8	−55.9	−21.1
Caffeine	6.8	19.3	−53.9	−20.3
6-Dimethylaminopurine	7.2	17.6	−50.7	−19.1
Guanine	7.2	14.4	−41.5	−15.7
Adenine	7.8	13.9	−41.4	−15.6
Hypoxanthine[a]	7.5	13	−38.2	−14.4
Thymine	7.8	12	−33.9	−12.8
Cytosine	8.1	11	−33.6	−12.7
Uracil	8.1	10.2	−31.1	−11.7

[a] See footnote a to Table VIII.

for the purines, but the polarizabilities of the purines are greater than those of the pyrimidines. Only numerical calculations can therefore give an answer to this problem. Such calculations are presented in Table IX. The bases are listed again in the order of decreasing solubilizing power. Their ionization potentials are deduced from the coefficient of their highest filled molecular orbital and the reference curve given in "Quantum Biochemistry," p. 129. This procedure, as seen in Section III, C, 3, c (on semiconductivity), gives results in substantial agreement with those obtainable by an appropriate self-consistent field procedure. (See, however, a later comment on some special cases.) The ionization potential of benzopyrene, obtained in a similar way, is 7.2 eV, in excellent agreement with a semiempirical value deduced from charge-transfer spectroscopy (Birks and Slifkin, 1961).

In distinction to those of Table VIII, the results of Table IX indicate the existence of a good parallel between the solubilizing power of the bases toward 3,4-benzopyrene and the dispersion forces involved in the intermolecular interactions between these entities. Obviously it is the value of the polarizabilities which plays the essential role in determining the relative value of these forces associated with the different bases. In fact, the order of the polarizabilities themselves corresponds to the order of the solubilizing power of the bases.

Table X summarizes the results of Tables VIII and IX and indicates the values of the total energies of interaction between the bases and 3,4-benzopyrene, owing to the summation of the polarization (induction) and dispersion interactions. It may be seen that the correlation observed in Table IX is conserved. In fact, it is even somewhat refined in Table X. Thus, for example, the combination of the polarization and dispersion interactions increases the advantage of guanine over adenine, which is in better agreement with the greater solubilizing power of the first of these bases. Similarly, it brings closer together the values for adenine and hypoxanthine, whose relative solubilizing powers are disputable.

Before closing this discussion on the role of the van der Waals–London forces in the interactions of the purine and pyrimidine bases with 3,4-benzopyrene, a few conservative remarks must be made. The calculations presented here are to some extent preliminary and correspond to the same rough approximation as that utilized by DeVoe and Tinoco in their study of these interactions in the nucleic acids. The numerical values of the forces depend strongly upon the distance between the stacked components. In fact, the distance is small with respect to the molecular dimensions of the components, so that the absolute values of the interactions may be quite different from those obtained by using dipoles and applying the inverse sixth-power law. It must also be stressed that orientation factors

TABLE X

TOTAL VAN DER WAALS–LONDON INTERACTIONS
BETWEEN THE BASES AND 3,4-BENZOPYRENE

Base	Polarization + dispersion interactions (kcal/mole)	
	3.4 Å	4 Å
Tetramethyluric acid	−57.7	−21.8
Caffeine	−55.7	−21.0
6-Dimethylaminopurine	−52.5	−19.8
Guanine	−49.0	−18.5
Adenine	−43.1	−16.2
Hypoxanthine	−42.5	−16.0
Thymine	−35.9	−13.5
Cytosine	−41.8	−15.8
Uracil	−33.4	−12.6

and the influence of the medium have not been taken into account in these calculations. These possible refinements are presently being investigated in our laboratory and have now been published (see Pullman, B., et al., 1965a). However, although they may appreciably influence the numerical values of the results, it seems rather improbable that they would change to a large extent the relative order of the numbers obtained in Table X, particularly since these are essentially determined by the values of the polarizabilities of the bases. We may therefore state, with a large degree of confidence, that the combination of the polarization and dispersion forces must play an important role in the physical interactions between purines and the polybenzenoid aromatic hydrocarbons.

On the other hand, there is also the possibility that charge transfer forces may play an equal role in these associations. In fact, a relationship pointing toward such a participation was established some years ago. Thus, it has been shown (Pullman, A., and Pullman, B., 1958; Pullman, B., 1964a, c) that the solvent power of the bases toward a given hydrocarbon runs parallel to their electron-donor properties, as measured, for example, by the value of the energy coefficient of their highest filled molecular orbital.

These values are shown in Table XI for a few representative purines and pyrimidines. They account not only for the relative solubilizing power of the unsubstituted bases but also for the effect of the methyl substituents. As we have already mentioned, N-methylation increases the solvent power, and, moreover, the analysis of the experimental data

PULLMAN

TABLE XI

ELECTRON-DONOR PROPERTIES OF PURINE AND PYRIMIDINE BASES

Compound	Energy coefficient of the highest occupied molecular orbital (β)
Purine	0.69
Adenine	0.49
Guanine	0.31
Hypoxanthine	0.40
Xanthine	0.44
Uric acid	0.17
1-Methylguanine	0.30
9-Methylguanine	0.30
1-Methylxanthine	0.44
3-Methylxanth'ne	0.40
7-Methylxanthine	0.43
1-Methyluric acid	0.17
3-Methyluric acid	0.15
7-Methyluric acid	0.13
9-Methyluric acid	0.16
Uracil	0.60
Thymine	0.51
Cytosine	0.60

(Weil-Malherbe, 1946) shows that in xanthine the effect of methylation is strongest when the substitution occurs at N_3 (the next strongest effect being due to a substitution at N_7), whereas in uric acid it is the methylation at N_7 which has the strongest effect on the solubilizing power. For uric acid the only available data are for di- or polymethyl derivatives, but their analysis shows that the methylation increases the solvent power of the molecule in the order $N_7 > N_3 > N_9 > N_1$. Moreover, a comparison of related polymethylated xanthines and uric acids indicates that the methylated uric acids have a much greater solubilizing effect than the corresponding xanthines. All these effects of the methyl groups on the solubilizing power parallel their effect on the decrease of the energy of the highest filled orbital.

These results suggest, therefore, the possible involvement of charge transfer as a component in the purine-hydrocarbon association. The numerical importance of this contribution particularly with respect to that of the dispersion forces is unknown at present, and we are carrying out studies in view of its determination.

Until now we have examined essentially the purine-hydrocarbon interactions. The whole situation is much more complicated regarding the interactions of the aromatic hydrocarbons with the nucleic acids themselves. It is claimed by some groups, on the basis of *in vitro*, nonenzymic studies (Boyland and Green, 1962c; Liquori *et al.*, 1962) that they may involve the intercalation of the hydrocarbons in a sandwichlike fashion between the pairs of adjacent complementary purine-pyrimidine bases, a type of interaction that would then be similar to the one considered and apparently substantiated in the case of the aminoacridines.

This concept is, however, strongly criticized by others, in particular by Heidelberger and his collaborators (Giovanella *et al.*, 1964), who estimate they have disproved the evidence produced by the English and Italian workers on the interaction of hydrocarbons with DNA. Following the Madison School, these experiments correspond, in reality, to the formation of a colloidal suspension of hydrocarbon particles. The only role that DNA plays in this phenomenon is to stabilize the colloid to some extent. Another important point in Heidelberger's work is to demonstrate that the DNA in Boyland and Green's experiment must be largely single-stranded, a result which may be compared with the work of Ts'o and Lu (1964), showing that the interaction of hydrocarbons, just as that of the purine bases or nucleosides, is much stronger with the coil than with the helical form of DNA. The English workers refute these objections (Boyland and Green, 1964a, b, c: Boyland, 1964b) and a strong polemic is going on presently on this problem. Very recently, the situation became still more complicated by the discovery by Brookes and Lawley (1964) of the existence of apparently another different type of binding between aromatic hydrocarbons and DNA. The binding observed by these last authors is a strong, possibly "chemical," one, whereas the one observed by Boyland and Green is a weak, possibly "physical," one.

It is difficult and appears much premature to try to derive any definite conclusion as to the issue of this problem at this moment. The only sure inference which springs from all these results is that obviously *the mode of interaction of the aromatic hydrocarbons with the nucleic acids may be quite different from its mode of interaction with the free bases* (or their nucleosides). The significance of such a situation will appear more clearly in the next section, concerned with the similar case of actinomycin.

On the other hand, there remains the crucial problem of the significance of the hydrocarbon-nucleic acid (or purine) interactions for the process of carcinogenesis. With the process involving an actual modification of essential properties of the cell, the production of such a permanent change through a direct alteration of the genetic apparatus of the cell represents the simplest possible mechanism. The over-all data do not seem, however, or at least did not seem until the latest work of Brookes and Lawley, to be in favor of such a simple mechanism. Thus, at least as far as the complexes of the type observed by Boyland are concerned, there are definite indications that they cannot be directly related to the production of cancer. The essectial argument against such a direct relation is based on the *nonspecificity of such interactions* (Pullman, B., 1964a, c). To some extent it may be related also to our theory correlating the carcinogenic activity of aromatic hydrocarbons to specific features of their electronic structure (Pullman, A., and Pullman, B., 1955a, b; Pullman, A., 1964c; Pullman, B., 1964e). Thus, one of the principal characteristics of this theory is that, although explicitly considering that the intact, completely aromatic ring system of the hydrocarbons is necessary for the appearance of carcinogenic activity, it nevertheless links the existence of this activity with the electronic properties of specific regions of the molecules. These are regions which both quantum-mechanical calculations and experimental observations indicate to be of particular importance for certain types of *the chemical reactivity of these compounds*. They are the so-called K and L regions, whose location on the molecular periphery is illustrated in the typical example of 1,2-benzanthracene in Fig. 10. To be more precise, the theory states that, in order to be carcinogenic, the molecule must posses a "reactive" K region (a reactive aromatic bond) but be devoid of a "reactive" L region (reactive *para* positions). These reactivities are expressed quantitatively in terms of the "localization energies" which are the essential varying parts of the activation energies for the chemical reactions that can possibly occur at these two types of regions. The quantitative correlation which has been established in this way is able to account, with very few exceptions, for the activity or inactivity of *all* the polybenzenoid hydrocarbons which have been tested esperimentally and, also, to account for the relative potency of the active molecules. It has also *predicted* successfully the existence of new potent aromatic carcinogens, in particular the exceedingly potent 3,4,9,10-dibenzopyrene.

This type of correlations implies definite conclusions as to the nature of the interactions which may occur between the carcinogens and the cellular receptors and lead to the development of tumors: They suggest, for instance, that *the interaction leading to carcinogenesis must occur through the K region of the molecule and should most probably involve a strong chemical binding* of the type of an addition reaction. On the other hand, they indicate that interactions occurring through the L region should be unfavorable for the appearance of carcinogenicity.

Fɪɢ. 10. The K and L regions of carcinogenesis.

Now, since it is not evident that the electronic characteristics of the particular regions which are related to carcinogenesis play a role in the solubilization experiments governing the *loose* type of association of the bases with the hydrocarbons we must conclude that the mere aptitude of a substance to be involved in such interactions should not be simply directly related to its aptitude to produce cancer. This point of view seems to be confirmed, in the narrow limits of available data, by the fact (visible in the results of both the English and the Italian workers) that *noncarcinogenic* hydrocarbons (e.g. pyrene) seem to be as able to form complexes with purines or to "interact" with the nucleic acids as the related *carcinogenic* ones (e.g., 3,4-benzopyrene or 1,2,3,6-dibenzanthracene) (see also Lerman, 1964). Similar conclusions may also be drawn from the study of the effect of substituents on the solubilization of hydrocarbons by purines (Pullman, B., and Pullman, A., 1959). For example, polymethylation of the hydrocarbons, which generally increases greatly their carcinogenic activity, greatly decreases their solubilization by the purines, probably because of steric interference with the sandwich-type binding, so that 9,10-dimethylbenzanthracene and methylcholanthrene, both very potent carcinogens, are scarcely solubilized at all by the purines. The nonspecificity of the interaction of carcinogenic or noncarcinogenic aromatic hydrocarbons with nucleic acids is also apparent in the nonspecificity of their effect on the transforming activity (Zamenhof, 1957, 1959) or on the "melting" temperature of the nucleic acids (Boyland and Green, 1964c). There is also no relationship between the carinogenic activity of aromatic hydrocarbons and their ability to participate in model charge-transfer complexes (Pullman, B., 1964e; Epstein *et al.*, 1964).

All these results seem therefore to converge toward the conclusions that *the weak, van der Waals–London and charge-transfer-type interactions of aromatic hydrocarbons with purines or with the nucleic acids lack specificity with respect to carcinogenic activity and are therefore probably not involved directly in the processes leading to carcinogenesis.*

In this respect the recently discovered strong interactions found by Brookes and Lawley appear to be of a different texture; although only a few representative compounds have been studied by these authors, the interaction of these compounds with the nucleic acids seems to parallel their carcinogenic potency. This last-minute result incites us to a re-evaluation of the possibility of a direct "carcinogenic action" of a hydrocarbon through its interaction with the nucleic acids. It may be expected that in such a case the interaction would obey the theoretical propositions previously quoted and in particular consist of a *chemical* reaction involving the K region. Brookes and Lawley (1964) believe that this chemical interaction probably involves a metabolic transformation product of the hydrocarbon which, following their opinion, could be an epoxide. In relation to such a

164   PULLMAN

proposition, the recent discovery by Boyland (1964a, b) of the particular
behavior of the K region in metabolic oxidations of the carcinogenic hydrocarbons may be significant.

For those not acquainted with the subject it may be useful to add that
we have omitted, on purpose, from the discussion the problem of the interaction of aromatic hydrocarbons with proteins, which represents the second
important aspect and, according to many, the most important one, of
carcinogenesis by this type of molecule. A summary of the status of the
aspect of the problem, particularly in relation to the electronic theory, and
essential references, may be found in A. Pullman (1964d) and B. Pullman
(1964e).

3. Interactions with Actinomycin

The possible duality of the interactions of a compound with the nucleic
acids or the free bases is particularly well illustrated with the example of
actinomycin (IV). This complex molecule composed of a conjugated hetero-

Schematic representation
of actinomycin
(IV)

aromatic (phenoxazone) ring and of two pentapeptide lactone rings is a
highly toxic antibiotic and, in particular, a potent inhibitor of DNA-
dependent RNA synthesis (Reich et al., 1962; Goldberg et al., 1962; Reich,
1963; Kahan et al., 1963). It associates with the nucleic acids, in particular
with DNA, and also with its constituents, the interaction with DNA being
mediated essentially through the guanine moiety (Kersten, 1961; Kersten
and Kersten, 1962).

Recently, Reich (1964) has made an important contribution to the problem of the nature of the interactions by showing that the mechanism of the
reaction with the free bases (or their nucleosides) differs from that with
DNA to such an extent that "the model reaction appears to have little in
common with that occurring between actinomycin and DNA." The reaction with DNA has been shown by the same author and his colleagues

(Hamilton *et al.*, 1963) to consist of the formation of specific hydrogen bonds between the phenoxazone ring of actinomycin and the NH_2 and N_3 groupings of the guanine moiety of DNA, with a possible complementary stabilization resulting from the interaction of the peptide chains of actinomycin with the phosphate groups of DNA. The reaction with the free purines or their nucleosides seems, on the contrary (following Reich), to lack any obvious specific structural prerequisities in the sense that "no single structural feature of the purine ring appears indispensable for the reaction."

In view of the previously discussed and obviously strong tendency of purines and their nucleosides to form molecular associations of the van der Waals–London charge-transfer type, it is natural to investigate whether this may not also be the basis for the association of actinomycin with the free purines. In fact, an explicit proposition in this sense, at least as far as charge-transfer forces are concerned, has been made by Kersten and Kersten (1962). This proposition has found a supplementary argument first in the theoretical evalution of the strong electron-acceptor properties of the phenoxazone ring, the energy coefficient of its lowest empty molecule orbital being − 0.254 (Pullman, B., 1964a), and more recently (Pullman, B., 1964d) in the finding that the interaction of the model compounds with actinomycin may actually be correlated with the electron-donor properties of the purine rings involved. Thus, the order of reactivity of the purine (and related) ring systems with actinomycin, deducible from the data of Reich seems to be, broadly speaking, the following: thioguanine > guanine >

TABLE XII

DATA FOR ACTINOMYCIN-PURINES INTERACTIONS

Ring system	Energy coefficient of the highest occupied molecular orbital (β)	Dipole moment (D)
Thioguanine	0.16	7.78
Guanine	0.31	6.82
2,6-Diaminopurine	0.40	2.09
6-Dimethylaminopurine	0.41	3.25
6-Methylaminopurine	0.45	3.21
Aminopyrazolopyrimidine	0.49	—
Adenine	0.49	3.17
2-Fluoroadenine	0.49	—
2-Aminopurine	0.49	3.66
Benzimidazole	0.64	4.02
6-Methylpurine	0.66	3.78
Purine	0.69	4.17

2,6-diaminopurine $\approx$ 6-dimethylaminopurine $>$ 6-methylaminopurine $\approx$ aminopyrazolopyrimidine $>$ adenine $\approx$ 2-fluoroadenine $>$ 2-aminopurine $\approx$ benzimidazole $>$ 6-methylpurine $>$ purine. A certain amount of uncertainty persists in this classification because of the varying effect, observed in some cases, of the ribose moiety. The classification represents, however, the general experimental trend. Now, this trend parallels in its broad lines the electron-donor tendency of these ring systems, as evaluated by the energy coefficient of the highest occupied molecular orbital of these compounds (Table XII). This situation suggests that charge transfer may be an important factor in the purine-actinomycin association. In view of the previous discussions on the nature of the forces playing a role in the interaction between purines and aromatics, it seems plausible to suppose that charge transfer will only be a component in the bulk of forces involved[8] and also that the interaction will probably consist of a stacking-type, plane-to-plane association of the aromatic rings (with possible complementary interactions, in some cases, between the sugars of the ribosides and the peptides of actinomycin). Such a situation would be consistent with the weakness of the binding observed and with its continuous thermolability.

A very recent result of Cavalieri and Nemchin (1964) suggests that the pattern of interaction of actinomycin with DNA may, in fact, be more complex than postulated by Reich and his colleagues and may involve both H bonding and intercalation. Thus, these authors seem to distinguish two types of binding in the interaction of actinomycin with DNA: (a) a weak binding, representing about 90% of the total binding, which they attribute to hydrogen-bond formation between the phenoxazone ring of actinomycin and the guanine moiety of DNA, and (b) a strong binding, representing the remaining 10% of the total binding, which they attribute to the intercalation of the aromatic portion of actinomycin between adjacent purine-pyrimidine pairs. It is this last type of binding which these authors consider responsible for the inhibition of RNA polymerase. It may be added that the possibility of such an intercalation is not inconsistent with X-ray data on actinomycin (Bachmann and Müller, 1964).

4. Outstanding Electron Donors and Acceptors

As has been seen, biological purines and pyrimidines may be considered, generally speaking, electron donors rather than electron acceptors. They appear nevertheless as moderate electron donors, with the purines being on

---

[8] As can be seen from the data indicated in the fourth column of Table X, no correlation exists between the extent of interaction of the purines with actinomycin and the dipole moment of the purines. This indicates that, as in the previous case, the purely electrostatic component of the interaction does not determine the order of reactivity. The numerical evaluation of the different components is at present under study in our laboratory.

the average better donors than the pyrimidines. There are, however, exceptions to this general rule and they are of two kinds (Pullman, B., and Pullman, A., 1960; Pullman, A., 1965a). In the first place, at least one of the purines, uric acid (V), is predicted to be an exceptionally good electron donor (energy coefficient of the highest filled molecular orbital, 0.17). On

Uric acid	Barbituric acid	Alloxan
(V)	(VI)	(VII)

the other hand, barbituric acid (VI) and alloxan (VII), although playing in the biochemistry of the pyrimidines a role similar to the one played by uric acid in the biochemistry of the purines, are predicted to be particularly bad electrons donors (energy coefficient of their highest filled molecular orbital is equal in both compounds to 1.03). In fact, alloxan is even *predicted* on the basis of this type of calculation to be, rather, an electron acceptor and a better one than the bases of the nucleic acid (the energy coefficient of its lowest empty molecular orbital is − 0.76).

A number of recent experimental results seem to bring forward evidence confirming these theoretical predictions. Thus, the particularly outstanding electron-donor properties of uric acid may be considered evident of its great capacity, greater than that of other purines, to function as an antioxidant toward the oxidation of unsaturated fatty acids (Matsushita *et al.*, 1963; Glavind and Søndergaard, 1964); this is also visible, perhaps, in the electron-spin-resonance spectra of charge-transfer complexes between purines and chloranil (Lagercrantz, personal communication). On the other hand, the formation of free radicals by electron acceptance has been definitely established for alloxan by electron spin resonance studies of the interactions between this compound and glutathione, ascorbic acid (Lagercrantz and Yhland, 1963), or dithionate in a water-methanol solution (Orr, 1964). Moreover, the structure postulated for this free radical on the basis of the electron spin resonance signal is (VIII) (Orr, 1964).

(VIII)

Figure 11 represents the results of molecular orbital calculations on the distribution of the odd electron in such a radical. The calculations are not expected, of course, to indicate the complete location of the odd electron at one atom. Following the calculations, the electron is expected to be spread out throughout the molecular periphery. They do, however, indicate that by far the largest portion of the electron, in fact, more than half of it, should be located at the position corresponding to the experimental identification.

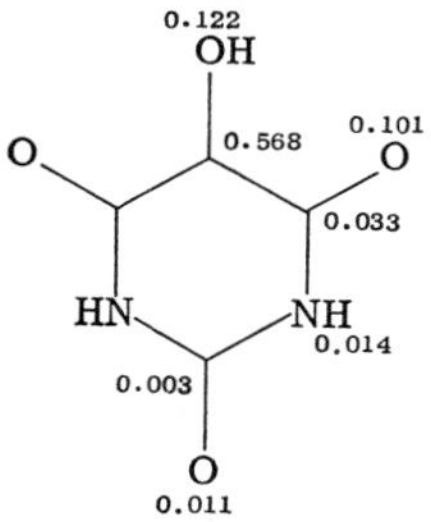

FIG. 11. The distribution of the odd electron in the alloxan free radical.

The relatively strong electron-accepting properties of alloxan have also been confirmed by recent polarographic studies on the system alloxan-alloxantin-dialuric acid (Struck and Elving, 1964).[9]

[9] After this paper was completed, we received a copy of an extensive report by P. J. Elving, W. A. Struck, and D. L. Smith on the electrochemical behavior of purines and pyrimidines (to be published in the 1965 annual volume on organic pharmaceutical analysis issued by the Faculty of Pharmacy of the University of Paris) which brings forward interesting complementary evidence confirming the theoretical evaluations of the electron donor and acceptor properties of the bases. As far as the electron-acceptor properties are concerned, the complementary results indicate that, whereas purine, adenine, hypoxanthine, and 2,6-diaminopurine are reducible at the dropping mercury electrode, guanine, xanthine, and uric acid are not. This is in agreement with the corresponding coefficients of the lowest empty molecular orbital of these compounds which, in the Hückel approximation, range between -0.74 and -0.92 for the four reducible molecules and exceed -1 for the three nonreducible ones. The most interesting results concern, however, the electron-donor properties of the purines and pyrimidines. Those are deducible from the results of oxidation (anodic) waves at the stationary graphite electrode. Simple pyrimidines, i.e., those which, like the bases of the nucleic acids, contain only one or two amino or hydroxy substituents, do not give an oxidation wave. On the contrary, all the purines studied, with the only exception of purine itself, give an oxidation wave. Moreover, the ease of oxidation increases with the number of hydroxy groups, so that uric acid is the most easily oxidized of all the compounds tested. These results are in complete agreement with our calculations which (Table XI) predict just this over-all behavior of the purines and pyrimidines as electron donors. The polarographic results confirm also the prediction that, between the two purines of the nucleic acids, guanine is oxidized more easily than adenine and that, therefore, guanine is the best electron donor among the four bases of the nucleic acids. This last result is also confirmed by studies on charge transfer complexes between the nucleosides and nucleotides of the bases, or the bases themselves, and chloranil (Duchesne et al., 1965; Machmer and Duchesne, 1965).

5. π- and n-Donor Properties

In all the previous discussions concerned with the electron-donor properties of the biochemical purines and pyrimidines, we have considered essentially the donor properties of their π electrons, assuming therefore implicitly that these are the electrons which have the most outstanding of these properties. It must nevertheless be remarked that the purines and pyrimidines contain a large number of heteroatoms, oxygens, and nitrogens, carrying lone-pair electrons. It is therefore important to determine at least the relative values of the ionization potentials of these lone pairs with respect to the π electrons of these molecules. Such an evaluation has been carried out recently (Pullman, A., and Rossi, 1964) using the self-consistent field molecular orbital method in the Pariser–Parr approximation, in which, however, the effect of atomic reorganization energy upon bond formation (Moffitt, 1950) has been taken into account by an empirical diminution of the values of the atomic valence-state ionization potentials. The method has been verified to reproduce correctly the esperimental values of the molecular ionization potentials of 14 fundamental compounds, including pyrimidine, pyridine, pyrrole, aniline, formaldehyde, etc., before being applied to the nucleic acid bases.

The long-pair ionization potentials have been calculated using the expression (Nakajima and Pullman, A., 1958)

$$I_n{}^X = U_n{}^X + \sum_p Q_p(pp,\ nn)$$

where $U_n{}^X$ is the appropriately corrected value of the valence-state ionization potential for the lone-pair orbital of the heteroatom X, Q_p the net π-electronic charge on atom p, and $(pp,\ nn)$ the Coulomb integral between the π-atomic orbital on atom p and the lone-pair atomic orbital considered.

TABLE XIII

π AND LONE PAIR (n) MOLECULAR IONIZATION POTENTIALS (eV)

Compound	n	$n(\mathrm{O})$	$n(\mathrm{N})$	
Guanine	7.6	9.4	N_7	11.2
			N_3	11.6
Adenine	8.4	—	N_1	11.2
			N_3	11.3
			N_7	11.4
Cytosine	8.3	9.8		11.0
Uracil	9.0	10.0 (C_6O)	—	
		10.3 (C_2O)		

The results are summarized in Table XIII. The following principal points emerge from their examination:

1. In all the bases, the lowest ionization potential corresponds to the ionization of a π electron.

2. In all bases the order of increasing ionization potentials is

$$\pi < n(0) < n(N)$$

3. Guanine is both the best π donor and the best $n(0)$ donor.
4. Uracil is both the worst π donor and the worst n donor.
5. Cytosine is the best $n(N)$ donor.

The results confirm therefore the greater electron-donor properties of the π electrons over those of the lone pairs. They do not preclude the possible involvement of the lone pairs of purines and pyrimidines in some types (localized) of charge-transfer complexes.

E. Problems in Radio- and Photobiology

1. Spin Densities in Free Radicals Derived from Nucleic Acid Bases

Among the problems of radio- and photobiology which have received a strong theoretical emphasis recently are the nature and structure of the free radicals derived from the nucleic acid bases and the mechanism of photodimerization of thymine.

The mechanism of photodimerization of thymine, which appears to be one of the most important reactions in photobiology, will be discussed in the next section. In this one, we shall limit ourselves to the problem of the free radicals produced by irradiation of purines and pyrimidines.

One of the most striking results recently obtained points to the possible particular position of thymine in this respect. Thus it appears that the irradiation of the nucleic acids, whether carried out by UV light (Einsinger and Shulman, 1963) or by ionizing radiation, γ-rays of Co^{60} (Salovey et al., 1963, Ehrenberg et al., 1963; Patten and Gordy, 1964; Ehrenberg, 1964), or high-speed electrons (Salovey et al., 1963) yields an electron-spin-resonance signal which seems to correspond to that of the free radical obtained upon the irradiation of thymine. This result, although probably corresponding to a more complex reality (Van de Vorst and Villée, 1964; Lacroix and Williams-Dorlet, 1964), is in agreement with our proposition ("Quantum Biochemistry," pp. 267–283) correlating the radioresistance of conjugated systems with their resonance energy per π electron: Thus from that point of view, thymine should be the most radiosensitive base among the purines and pyrimidines of the nucleic acids. Parenthetically it may be remarked that although some divergent data have been produced recently concerning the relative radioresistance of the nucleic acid bases themselves (Muller,

1963; Muller et al., 1963; Van de Vorst, 1963; Scholes, 1963), the general validity of our correlation seems to be confirmed by the study of a number of organic and biochemical solids (Williams-Dorlet et al., 1964; Pullman, B., 1964; Checcucci et al., 1964). Of particular interest is its possible significance in biochemical evolution and the physicochemical origins of life (Pullman, B., and Pullman A., 1962; Pullman, A., and Pullman, B., 1964).

As concerns the structure of the thymidilic free radical, it seems to correspond to configuration (IX) (Einsinger and Shulman, 1963; Salovey et al.,

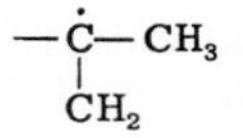

$$-\overset{\displaystyle\cdot}{\underset{\displaystyle \underset{|}{CH_2}}{C}}-CH_3$$

(IX)

1963) in which the odd electron is located at C_5 of thymine, while a hydrogen atom is added to C_6. This experimental finding may be considered in connection with the corresponding molecular orbital calculations. Figure 12

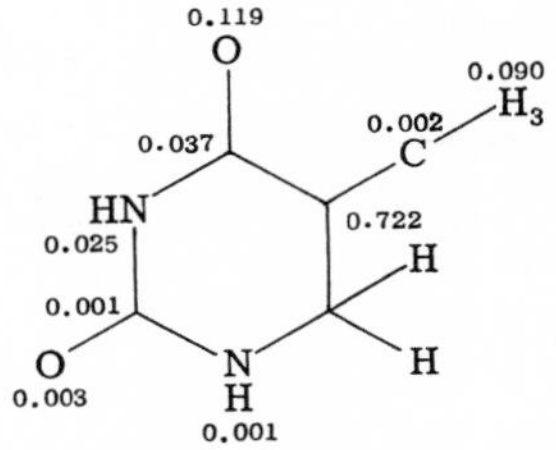

FIG. 12. The distribution of the odd electron in the cationic radical of thymine.

represents the distribution of the odd electron in the free radical obtained from thymine through the departure of an electron from its highest filled molecular orbital (cationic free radical). It can be seen that in such a radical the odd electron should be concentrated to the largest extent, although of course not completely, at C_5 of the thymine skeleton. Figure 13 indicates

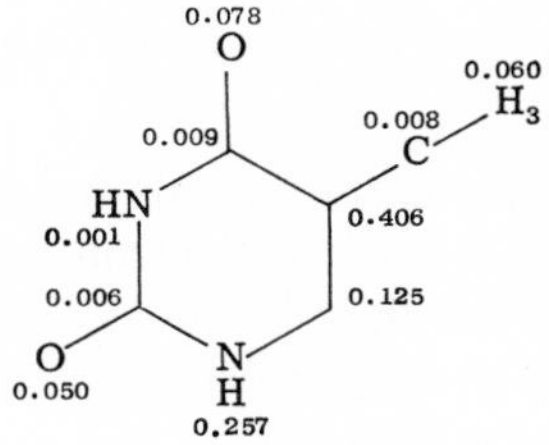

FIG. 13. The distribution of the odd electron in thymidilic free radical.

that this concentration at C_5 should be still greater in the radical in which C_6 has been saturated. Recent experimental work by Pruden and associates (1965) has confirmed the value of 0.70 for the spin density at C_5 of the thymidilic free radical. These results obtained in the Hückel approximation are entirely confirmed by self-consistent field open-shell molecular orbital calculations of spin densities in the corresponding free radical of uracil (Baudet et al., 1962). In connection with the predominance of the thymine signal in the electron-spin-resonance spectra of the nucleic acids, it may be useful to stress that the spin density predicted for C_5 of the thymine cationic radical represents the greatest concentration of spin density which the calculations predict for all the cationic radicals derived from the nucleic acid bases (Fig. 14). The distributions of the spin densities in the cationic free radicals of adenine, guanine, and cytosine have not yet been established experimentally, so that the results of Fig. 14 represent *predictions*.

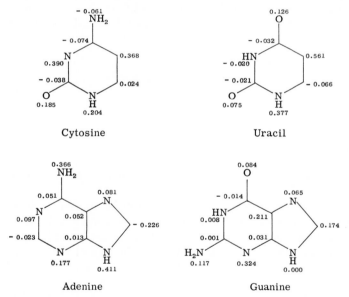

FIG. 14. The distribution of spin densities in the cationic radicals of the nucleic acid bases.

The same situation concerns the anionic free radicals derivable from the nucleic acid bases by addition of an electron to their lowest empty molecular orbital. The predicted distribution of the spin densities in these radicals, evaluated by the molecular orbital method (Baudet et al., 1962) is indicated in Fig. 15.

In connection with the discussions of the next section, one aspect of the results presented in this last figure needs to be stressed. It concerns the

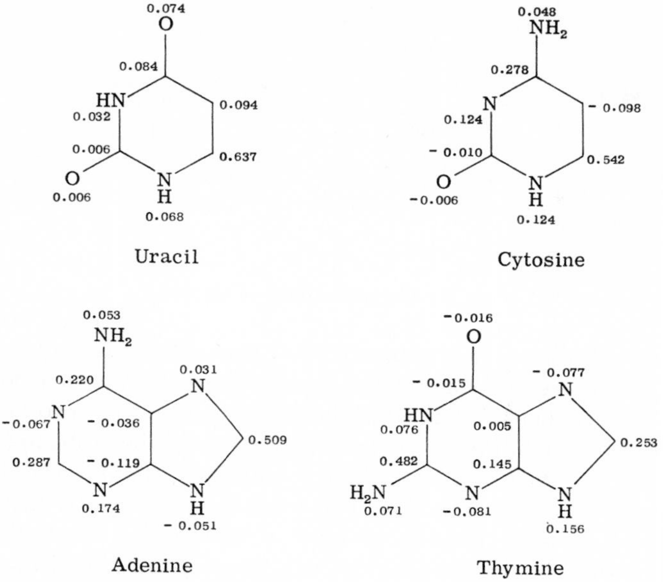

Fig. 15. The distribution of spin densities in the anionic free radicals of the nucleic acid bases.

location of the greatest spin density in the anionic radical of uracil, representing also certainly the situation in thymine: This greatest spin density is concentrated at C_6. It may thus be concluded that, in the biological pyrimidines and in particular in thymine, an electron located at the highest filled molecular orbital has the tendency to concentrate at C_5, whereas an electron placed at the lowest empty molecular orbital has the tendency to concentrate at C_6.

2. The Mechanism of Thymine Photodimerization

The photodimerization reaction, first discovered upon UV irradiation of frozen thymine (Beukers et al., 1958, 1959, 1960; Beukers and Berends, 1960), and afterward upon in vitro (Berends, 1961; Beukers and Berends, 1961) and in vivo (Wacker et al., 1960; Wacker, 1961) irradiation of DNA is presently recognized as one of the most important reactions in photobiology. It takes place through the C_5–C_6 bond of thymine and leads to the formation of a cyclobutane ring. There exist different structural possibilities for the configuration of the dimer, the most probable structure for the dimer formed in DNA probably being the one indicated in Fig. 16 (Wulff, 1963).

We shall not insist here on the biological significance of this reaction. We have summarized this aspect of the problem and given the appropriate references in Mantione and B. Pullman (1964). Suffice to say that the for-

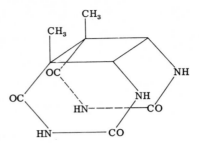

FIG. 16. The photodimer of thymine.

mation of such dimers in irradiated DNA probably constitutes one of the essential factors responsible for the sensitivity of the nucleic acids and the cells to the effects of UV light. On the other hand, we wish to indicate the recent contribution of the molecular orbital study of the problem (Mantione and B. Pullman, 1964; Pullman, B., and Mantione, 1965) to the elucidation of the mechanism of the reaction. This work has been greatly facilitated by the existence of an appreciable amount of information about the relative ability of a series of thymine analogs to undergo photodimerization. (For a summary, see Wacker, 1963).

The starting points for the interpretation of the mechanism of the reaction were, on the one hand, the previously quoted observations on the preferential location at C_5 and C_6 of the lone electrons situated, respectively, on the highest filled and lowest empty molecular orbitals of thymine and, on the other hand, a suggestion (Beukers and Berends, 1961), based on the effect of oxygen and paramagnetic ions, that the photodimerization may involve the first excited triplet state of the molecule. In such an excited state of the substance, there is one electron located at the highest filled molecular orbital and another at the lowest empty molecular orbital, and it appears therefore highly probable that these two uncoupled electrons will tend to concentrate at the C_5–C_6 bond, which is the site of photodimerization. A natural hypothesis is then that the ability to photodimerize may depend upon the concentration of the lone electrons at this particular bond. Such a correlation, if established, would not only confirm the involvement of the triplet state in the reaction but moreover pick out the characteristics of this state responsible for the mechanism of the reaction.

Explicit molecular orbital calculations have completely confirmed this viewpoint. These calculations were first carried out in the Hückel approximation of the method (Mantione and B. Pullman, 1964; B. Pullman and Mantione, 1965). In this particular case, this approximation involves, however, an important technical difficulty. Thus, as is well known, it does not

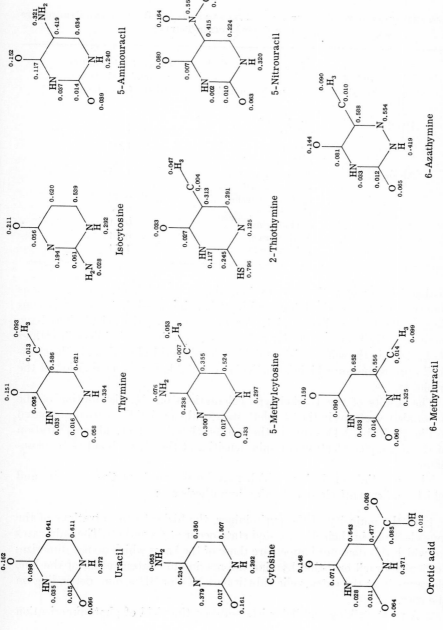

FIG. 17. The distribution of the lone electrons in first excited (triplet) state of pyrimidine bases (in the Hückel approximation).

TABLE XIV

CONCENTRATION OF THE UNCOUPLED ELECTRONS AT THE 5–6 BOND OF THE PYRIMIDINES
IN THEIR FIRST EXCITED TRIPLET

Yield of photodimerization	Compound	Concentration of the uncoupled electrons at the C_5–C_6 bond
Great	Orotic acid	1.12
	Thymine	1.21
	Uracil	1.25
	6-Methyluracil	1.21
Mean	Isocytosine	1.16
	5-Aminouracil	1.05
Small	5-Methylcytosine	0.88
	Cytosine	0.86
None	2-Thiothymine	0.61
	5-Nitrouracil	0.64
	6-Azathymine	1.14

distinguish between the first excited singlet and triplet. Its result thus concerns the first excited state, without it being possible to explicitly consider it the first excited triplet. For these reasons, the calculations have more recently been redone for a few representative pyrimidines (Berthier *et al.*, 1965) in the self-consistent field molecular orbital method, in the open-shell approximation which is particularly suitable for the evaluation of the triplet states.

The results of the Hückel-type calculations on the distribution of the uncoupled electrons in the "triplet" state of the pyrimidines are represented in Fig. 17. Table XIV sums up the results related to the total concentration of the uncoupled electrons or spin densities at the C_5–C_6 bond of the compound.

The essential conclusions which may be drawn from these results and which confirm entirely our starting hypothesis are:

1. In the majority of the pyrimidines, the highest concentrations of the lone electrons in their first excited state occur at C_5 and C_6. The only cases for which this does not happen are those of the bases which do not dimerize: In 5–nitrouracil or 2-thiothymine the maximum concentration of the lone electrons is at the extracyclic substituent NO_2 or SH group, depending on the case.

2. A most striking parallel exists between the yield of photodimerization

and the total concentration of the uncoupled electrons at the C_5–C_6 bond of the pyrimidines in their first excited state.

3. The only exception to the rule just stated is offered by 6-azathymine. Although it is possible that the inability of this molecule to undergo photo-dimerization may be due to its general insensitivity to the effect of UV irradiation or to the difficulty of incorporating a nitrogen atom into a cyclobutane ring, it may be worthwhile indicating that the triplet state of 6-azathymine manifests from the electronic point of view, a characteristic not found in any other compound of Table XII. Thus, if one considers separately the half-occupied orbitals of the triplet state of azathymine, one observes that, as opposed to the photodimerizing compounds, the greatest concentration of the lone electrons does not occur in these individual orbitals either at C_5 or at C_6. It cannot be excluded that this situation creates re-action perturbations interfering with the mechanism of photodimerization.

Calculations on the distribution of the spin densities in the first excited triplet state of a few representative biological pyrimidines have also been carried out in the self-consistent field approximation of the molecular orbital method. In this case they explicitly refer to the excited triplet. The

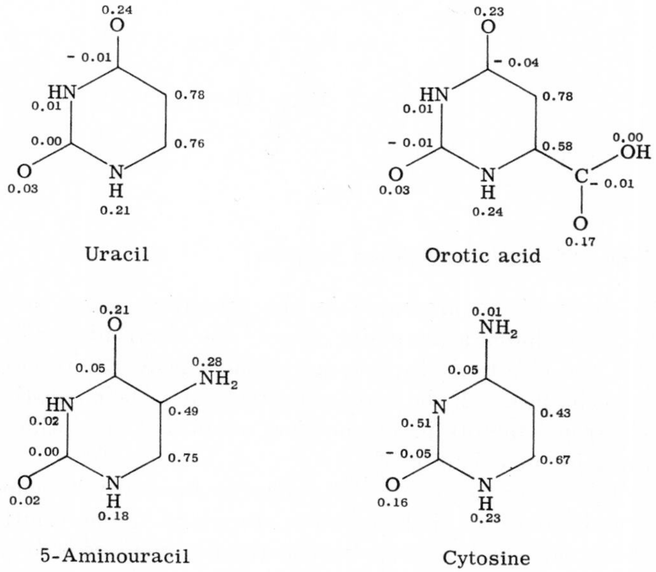

FIG. 18. Spin densities in the first triplet state of representative pyrimidines (self-consistent field open-shell method).

results obtained are presented in Fig. 18, and it can be seen that, although the numerical values obtained in this approximation for the different spin concentrations are, of course, different from those obtained in the Hückel approximation, these refined calcuations confirm our general theory. In particular they confirm the high concentration of the spin densities at the C_5C_6 bond in the triplet state of the pyrimidines and the parallel between this concentration and the yield of photodimerization.

In connection with this problem of photodimerization and the previously mentioned problem of carcinogenic activity of aromatic hydrocarbons, it may be useful to mention some results obtained recently by Rice (1964) about the photochemical addition of 3,4-benzopyrene to pyrimidine derivatives. Although this is a photochemical reaction and thus is probably not related to carcinogenesis, the nature of the product which Rice postulates to be formed in this reaction is particularly interesting both from the point of view of the theory of the K region of carcinogens and the theory of the photodimerization of the biological pyrimidines: the postulated photoproduct between, say, benzopyrene and cytosine has the structure (IX).

(IX)

F. General Remarks on Related Subjects

Besides the subjects presented in the preceding pages, my course in Squaw Valley included a discussion on: (1) the electronic factors in mutagenesis, (2) the electronic factors in carcinogenesis, (3) recent results in quantum-mechanical calculations on proteins and their constituents, and (4) the electronic factors in biochemical evolution susceptible to having played a role in the origin of life.

These different problems have been discussed recently in general reviews from our laboratory. We shall therefore not repeat the description of these subjects here, but shall indicate instead the pertinent references together, in some cases, with a few supplementary references to recent experimental publications in close relation to the hypothesis or predictions involved in the theorical treatments.

1. Electronic Factors in Mutagenesis

A general description of the work accomplished on this subject has been given by A. Pullman (1964a). To this general review may be added the demonstration by Berthod and A. Pullman (1965) of the greater stability of the lactam and amino tautomeric forms of the nucleic acid bases through explicit calculation of the σ and π energies of the tautomeric forms, the development of a perturbation procedure for the evaluation of the influence of heteroatoms and substituents on the tautomeric equilibria of biochemical purines and pyrimidines (Pullman, A., 1964b), and the calculation of the electronic characteristics of the miscoupled base pairs (Pullman, B., 1963). Among the experimental papers directly related to the theoretical investigations, we would like to quote particularly Grossman's (1963) demonstration that the formation of photoproducts may be responsible for coding transitions, and the findings by Howard and Tessman (1964) that cytosine is the primary target of the UV-induced mutations. Although this last work refers to single-stranded DNA, the result is in striking agreement with our theoretical prediction (Pullman, A., 1964a; Pullman, A., and Pullman, B., 1963).

2. Electronic Factors in Carcinogenesis

As mentioned previously, we have dealt in these pages with only one particular aspect of this important problem in connection with the study of the nature of the interactions of aromatic hydrocarbons with the purines and pyrimidines of the nucleic acids. For recent, more exhaustive, reviews of the remaining aspects of the problem (such as the structure activity correlations, the nature of the interaction of aromatic carcinogens with proteins, the case of other types of carcinogens, the relationship of mutagenesis to carcinogenesis) one may refer to the reviews by A. Pullman (1964d) and B. Pullman (1964a, e), and consult among others the procedings of the Oak Ridge symposium on "The Molecular Aspects of Mutagenesis and Carcinogenesis," which were published as a special supplement to the *Journal of Cellular and Comparative Physiology* in 1964.

3. Electronic Structure of Proteins and Their Constituents

An important development in this field is the extension of the quantum-mechanical calculations to all the α-amino acids of proteins in their neutral, anionic, cationic, and zwitterionic forms (Del Re *et al.*, 1963; Yonezawa *et al.*, 1964; Del Re, 1964) and the successful study in particular of the chemical shifts observed in nuclear magnetic resonance, in different solvents in relation to their charge distribution. Reviews on the present status of the particularly exciting and controversial problem of the existence of energy bands in proteins in connection with their semiconductivity have been given by A. Pullman (1964a, 1965b).

4. Electronic Aspects of Biochemical Evolution and the Origins of Life

A general review of this problem has been presented by B. Pullman (1964g).

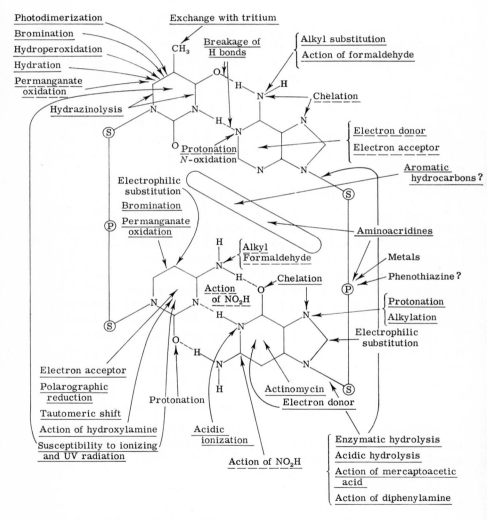

Fig. 19. Principal chemical and physicochemical properties of the nitrogenous bases of the nucleic acids.

Before drawing the final conclusion of this series of lectures, we would like to add one more remark. In the preceding discussion concerning some aspects of the biochemistry and biophysics of the nucleic acids, use has been made of only a few of the theoretical results presented in the form of the calculated electronic indices in Fig. 4. Of course, the indices not discussed here have also been utilized in connection with other aspects of the behavior of the nucleic acids and their constituents. A schematic representation of all these miscellaneous applications is given in Fig. 19, which indicates the sites of the principal physicochemical properties of the nucleic acids, related to the electronic indices presented in Fig. 4. The two figures when considered together illustrate the wide and successful applicability of the theoretical evaluations.

G. Conclusion

There are a number of essential conclusions which, it seems to us, spring from the preceding discussion.

1. The first, perhaps most important, conclusion concerns *the complete confirmation by refined calculations carried out by the self-consistent field molecular orbital method in a rationalized approximation of all the essential results obtained previously by the semiempirical Hückel approximation.* The situation is illustrated in the most striking way by the results of the self-consistent field calculations for the purine-pyrimidine complementary pairs of the nucleic acids and their agreement with the previous Hückel calculations. Thus, both groups of calculations could have been employed without distinction for the construction of Fig. 4, which represents the quintessence of the results obtained.

In fact, we have never doubted this issue. Our conviction in this field was based on the very semiempirical nature of the previous approximation, which was so carefully related to known experimental data and used in such a restrained way that it could hardly be misleading. Thus, it was essentially utilized for the *comparative* study of the electronic structure of biomolecules, for the classification on a *relative* scale of compounds, or molecular regions on their constituent atoms, with respect to a number of electronic properties. In these conditions, the inherent shortcomings of the method were eliminated to the maximum. Moreover, the utilization of the semiempirical procedure was limited, at least in our laboratory, essentially to the properties of the ground states, which are known from general quantum chemistry to be more satisfactory to deal with than those of the excited states. The fact that the self-consistent field calculations confirm the earlier calculations so extensively shows that the previous approach was justified. Of course, the extreme success of the previous approach in discussing an extensive variety of properties related to the nucleic acids or their constituents warranted in itself such an issue.

2. The next point which needs to be stressed is the *extreme abundance* of predictions inherent in the list of the quantum-mechanical results presented here, some of which have already been verified experimentally. It must thus be realized that nearly everything that is said in these pages about the role of resonance energies or ionization potentials or electron affinities in the biochemistry and biophysics of the nucleic acid or their constituents, represents a set of *predictions*, practically no experimental information whatsoever existing about these physicochemical characteristics of these compounds. Among the predictions of the theory, which in the problems mentioned here have already been verified, we may quote, for example, the location at N_7 in guanine of the most basic center of the nucleic acids, the discovery of the greater stability of the nucleic acids rich in guanine-cytosine over those rich in adenine-thymine, the nonexistence of a G-C pairing involving N_7 of guanine (instead of N_1), the polarographic reducibility of cytosine and adenine in opposition to the polarographic inactivity of thymine, uracil, and guanine, the relatively great electron affinity of alloxan, the preferential involvement of the G-C pair in spontaneous mutations, the nonspecificity of the "physical" interactions of the aromatic hydrocarbon with nucleic acids with respect to the carcinogenic activity of the hydrocarbons, the location at C_5 of the greatest spin density of the thymine cationic free radical, etc. Among the specific predictions awaiting experimental verification are, for example, the absolute or even relative values of resonance energies, ionization potentials, and electron affinities of the nucleic acid bases, the prediction that the first ionization potential of the bases is due to their π electrons, the distribution of spin densities in the free radicals derivable from all the bases, the great concentration of spin densities at the C_5–C_6 bond in the first excited triplet state of the pyrimidines and the relation of this concentration to the yield of photodimerization, the relatively high value of the dipole moments of guanine and cytosine, the stacking-type association between the phenoxazone ring of actinomycin and the purines in solution, the greater semiconductivity of nucleic acids rich in guanine-cytosine over those rich in adenine-thymine, etc.

This predictive character of the theoretical considerations may be added to its explicative character which has in itself the obvious fundamental importance, common to the general application of quatum theories to chemistry and physics, of interpreting the biochemical and biophysical phenomena in terms appropriate to electronic structure. If we stress this predictive character, it is because of some rather thoughtless statements found sometimes in this respect, such as reproaching quantum biochemistry for not having led to the discovery of the Krebs or Calvin cycles. This is not of course, the type of discovery that may be expected from quantum bio-chemistry. Furthermore, modern biochemistry and biophysics are tens of years old and occupy hundreds if not thousands of research workers. The application of quantum theories to biochemistry and biophysics dates back only a few years and is still the concern of a few isolated individuals. It can, of course, also be observed that there are many more experimentalists who did not discover the Krebs or Calvin cycles than theoreticians.

3. Our last conclusion concerns the status of the quantum-mechanical applications to biochemistry and biophysics in relation to other techniques. In this field, too, inconsistent remarks may sometimes (although, in fact, very rarely) be found, such as the following: "Most of the phenomena confronting the biologist differ only in complexity and not in essence from those which occur in nonliving matter, and *it is usually more fruitful to look for simple physical analogies than to engage in purely quantum mechnical discussion*." Strangely enough, or maybe naturally, this phrase is from a quantum chemist. How can anybody well aware of the decisive contributions of quantum theories to our understanding of chemistry and physics derive from the first statement the astonishing conclusion italicized is hard to comprehend. It reminds us somewhat of the situation some 40 years ago, when the advent of quantum chemistry was received by somewhat similar statements, those coming, however, from some classical chemists. Maybe it represents a romantic nostalgia for arrows and dots. Whatever, it be, if life is just a very complex physicochemical phenomenon, and this we all believe, is there not in this assertion the strongest argument for the most extensive utilization of quantum-mechanical calculations for the study of the processes of life? The least one can deny to quantum mechanics is that it be a method of physical chemistry, particularly advantageous for evaluation of electronic distributions and energy levels. Of course, its calculations and results may be, as indicated, more or less approximate and need always (as is the case with any human theory) to be verified by experiment, but it is the noble privilege of quantum mechanics to be frequently ahead of experiment or to guide it. If, say, the ionization potentials of the purine and pyrimidine bases were known, the value of the theoretical calculations in this field (although in no way that of the correlations involving these quantities) would be much less significant. But it so happens that these quantities are still unknown, and our only knowledge about them, even if approximate, comes from the quantum-mechanical calculations. And I hope to have shown that this is the case in a number of instances.

The paradox inherent in the phrase quoted before can also be visualized in the following way: What the right-wing conservative of quantum chemistry objects to is the use of this science for the study of the process of life. Should adenine be an ordinary, insignificant compound, he would not object to applying quantum-mechanical methods, for improving our knowledge about its electronic structure and the elucidation of the significance of its structure for its properties. He has done this type of work himself, as has any quantum chemist. It is because adenine is important for the extra-complex phenomenon which is life that we should abandon the technical advantages of quantum mechanics and go back to "simple physical analogies!" Quantum mechanics being reserved for the study of the biologically unimportant isomeric 8-aminopurine!

One final remark. If the contribution and the possible future contribution of quantum mechanics to the understanding of the processes of living matter are not to be underestimated, they should not, of course, be overestimated nor their scope misunderstood either. Most biological phenomena probably involve ground-state chemistry and physics. They belong therefore *ipso facto* to the realm of the general quantum-mechanical interpretation of the phenomena of these sciences. Some of them involve excited-state chemistry and physics or may possibly be related to solid-state physics. Those are, par excellence, subjects for the quantum-mechanical approch. In all this there is, however, no place for anything other than chemistry and physics—very complex chemistry and physics, but only chemistry and physics. What is sometimes referred to, carefully by some and carelessly by others as quantum effects in biology is a way of speaking about physicochemical phenomena which are hard or impossible to describe in the language or within the concepts of classical chemistry and physics. This is due to the erroneous character or limitations of the classical concepts and languages but refers still to phenomena of physical chemistry stated in the appropriate mathematical language and using new concepts.

Also, I personally do not like talking, and never do, about quantum biology, but only about quantum biochemistry or quantum biophysics. These are the fields in which present quantum theory operates, introducing into it its profound and enlightened vision of the molecular and submolecular reality in the appropriate terms of internucleic and interelectronic relations. Quantum biology may, and probably will, come but that time is somewhat distant.

REFERENCES

Bachmann, H. G., and Müller, W. (1964). *Nature* **201**, 261.
Baudet, J., Berthier, G., and Pullman, B. (1962). *Compt. Rend.* **254**, 762.
Becker, R. S., and Wentworth, W. E. (1963). *J. Am. Chem. Soc.* **85**, 2210.
Berthier, G., Baudet, J., and Pullman, B. (1965). *J. Chim. Phys.* (in press).
Berthod, H., and Pullman, A. (1963). *Compt. Rend.* **257**, 2738.
Berthod, H., and Pullman, A. (1964). *Compt. Rend.* **259**, 2711.
Berthod, H., and Pullman, A. (1965a). *Biopolymers* **2**, 483.
Berthod, H., and Pullman, A. (1965b). *J. Chim. Phys.* (in press).
Berends, W. (1961). *J. Chim. Phys.* **58**, 1034.

Beukers, R., and Berends, W. (1960). *Biochim. Biophys. Acta* **41**, 550.
Beukers, R., and Berends, W. (1961). *Biochim. Biophys. Acta* **49**, 181.
Beukers, R., Ijlstra, J., and Berends, W. (1958). *Rec. Trav. Chim.* **77**, 729.
Beukers, R., Ijlstra, J., and Berends, W. (1959). *Rec. Trav. Chim.* **78**, 879, 883.
Beukers, R., Ijlstra, J., and Berends, W. (1960). *Rec. Trav. Chim.* **79**, 101.
Birks, J. B., and Slifkin, M. A. (1961). *Nature* **191**, 761.
Blumenfeld, L. A. (1961). *Mem. Acad. Roy. Belg.* **33**, 93.
Boettcher, B. (1963). *J. Theoret. Biol.* **5**, 108.
Boyland, E. (1964a). *In* "Electronic Aspects of Biochemistry" (B. Pullman, ed.), p. 155. Academic Press, New York.
Boyland, E. (1964b). *Brit. Med. Bull.* **20**, 121.
Boyland, E., and Green, B. (1962a). *Biochem. J.* **84**, 54p.
Boyland, E., and Green, B. (1962b). *Brit. J. Cancer* **16**, 347.
Boyland, E., and Green, B. (1962c). *Brit. J. Cancer* **16**, 507.
Boyland, E., and Green, B. (1964a). *J. Mol. Biol.* **9**, 589.
Boyland, E., and Green, B. (1964b). *Biochim. Biophys. Acta* **87**, 653.
Boyland, E., and Green, B. (1964c). *Biochem. J.* **92**, 4c.
Bradley, D. F., and Felsenfeld, G. (1959). *Nature* **184**, 1920.
Bradley, D. F., and Wolf, M. K. (1959). *Proc. Natl. Acad. Sci. U.S.* **45**, 944.
Bradley, D. F., Lifson, S., and Honig, B. (1964). *In* "Electronic Aspects of Biochemistry" (B. Pullman, ed.), p. 77. Academic Press, New York.
Brenner, S., Barnett, L., Crick, F. H. C., and Orgel, A. (1961). *J. Mol. Biol.* **3**, 121.
Briegleb, G. (1961). "Electron Donator-Acceptor Komplexe." Springer, Berlin.
Briegleb, G. (1964). *Angew. Chem. Intern. Ed. Engl.* **3**, 617.
Brillouin, L. (1962). *In* "Horizons in Biochemistry" (M. Kasha and B. Pullman, eds.), p. 295. Academic Press, New York.
Brookes, P., and Lawley, P. D. (1964). *Nature* **202**, 781.
Cavalieri, L. F., and Nemchin, R. G. (1964). *Biochim. Biophys. Acta* **87**, 641.
Chambron, J., Daune, M., and Sadron, C. (1964). *Compt. Rend.* **258**, 4867.
Chan, S. I., Schweitzer, M. P., Ts'o, P. O. P., and Helmkamp, G. K. (1964). *J. Am. Chem. Soc.* **86**, 4182.
Checcucci, A., Depireux, J., and Duchesne, J. (1964). *Compt. Rend.* **259**, 1669.
Checcucci, A., Depireux, J., and Duchesne, J. (1965). *Nature* (in press).
Crothers, D. M., and Zimm, B. H. (1964). *J. Mol. Biol.* **9**, 1.
Del Re, G. (1958). *J. Chem. Soc.* p. 4031.
Del Re, G. (1964). *In* "Electronic Aspects of Biochemistry" (B. Pullman, ed.), p. 221. Academic Press, New York.
Del Re, G., Pullman, B., and Yonezawa, T. (1963). *Biochim. Biophys. Acta* **75**, 153.
Denbigh, K. (1940). *Trans. Faraday Soc.* **36**, 936.
De Santis, P., Giglio, E., Liquori, A. M., and Ripamonti, A. (1961). *Nature* **191**, 900.
DeVoe, H., and Tinoco, I., Jr. (1962). *J. Mol. Biol.* **4**, 500.
Doty, P., Boedtker, H., Fresco, J. R., Hall, B. D., and Haselkorn, R. (1959). *Ann. N.Y. Acad. Sci.* **81**, 693.
Duchesne, J. (1962). *In* "Horizons in Biochemistry" (M. Kasha and B. Pullman, eds.), p. 335. Academic Press, New York.
Duchesne, J., Depireux, J., Bertinchamps, A., Cornet, N., and Van Der Kaa, J. M. (1960). *Nature* **188**, 405.
Duchesne, J., Machmer, P., and Read, M. (1965). *Compt. Rend.* **260**, 2081.
Ehrenberg, A. (1964). *In* "The Structure and Properties of Biomolecules and Biological Systems" (J. Duchesne, ed.), p. 602. Wiley (Interscience), New York.
Ehrenberg, A., Ehrenberg, L., and Lofroth, G. (1963). *Nature* **200**, 376.

Ehrenson, S. (1962). *J. Phys. Chem.* **66,** 706.

Einsinger, J., and Shulman, R. G. (1963). *Proc. Natl. Acad. Sci. U.S.* **50,** 694.

Eley, D. D. (1962). *In* "Horizons in Biochemistry" (M. Kasha and B. Pullman, eds.), p. 341. Academic Press, New York.

Eley, D. D., and Leslie, R. B. (1963). *Nature* **197,** 898.

Eley, D. D., and Spivey, D. I. (1962). *Trans. Faraday Soc.* **58,** 411.

Epstein, S. S., Bulon, I., Kaplan, J., Small, M., and Mantel, N. (1964). *Nature* **204,** 750.

Falk, M., Hartman, K. A., Jr., and Lord, R. C. (1963). *J. Am. Chem. Soc.* **85,** 391.

Fernandez-Alonso, J. I. (1961). *In* "Quimica Fisiologica" (J. Garcia-Blanco, ed.), Vol. II, p. 657. Saber, Valencia.

Fernandez-Alonso, J. I. (1964). *In* "The Structure and Properties of Biomolecules and Biological Systems" (J. Duchesne, ed.), p. 3. Wiley (Interscience), New York.

Fernandez-Alonso, J. I., and Domingo, R. (1960). *Anales Real. Soc. Espan. Fis. Quim. (Madrid)* **56B,** 687.

Geiduschek, E. P., and Herskovits, T. T. (1961). *Arch. Biochem. Biophys.* **95,** 114.

Gergely, J. (1962). *In* "Symposium of Electrical Conductivity in Organic Solids" (H. Kallman and M. Silver, eds.) p. 369. Wiley (Interscience), New York.

Giovanella, B. C., McKinney, L. E., and Heidelberger, C. (1964). *J. Mol. Biol.* **8,** 20.

Glavind, J., and Søndergaard, E. (1964). *Acta Chem. Scand.* **18,** 2173.

Goldberg, I. H., Rabinowitz, M., and Reich, E. (1962). *Proc. Natl. Acad. Sci. U.S.* **48,** 2094.

Gomel, M., and Lumbroso, H. (1962). *Bull. Soc. Chim. France* p. 2206.

Grossman, L. (1963). *Proc. Natl. Acad. Sci. U.S.* **50,** 657.

Hamaguchi, K., and Geiduschek, E. P. (1962). *J. Am. Chem. Soc.* **84,** 1329.

Hamilton, L. D., Fuller, W., and Reich, E. (1963). *Nature* **196,** 538.

Haschemeyer, A. E. V., and Sobell, H. M. (1963). *Proc. Natl. Acad. Sci. U.S.* **50,** 872.

Haschemeyer, A. E. V., and Sobell, H. M. (1964). *Nature* **202,** 969.

Hayes, W. (1964). "The Genetics of Bacteria and Their Viruses." Blackwell, Oxford.

Helmkamp, G. K., and Ts'o, P. O. P. (1961). *J. Am. Chem. Soc.* **83,** 138.

Herskovits, T. T., Singer, S. J., and Geiduschek, E. P. (1961). *Arch. Biochem. Biophys.* **94,** 99.

Hinze, J., and Jaffé, H. H. (1962). *J. Am. Chem. Soc.* **84,** 540.

Hirschfelder, J. O. (1957). *In* "Molecular Structure and Biological Specificity" (L. Pauling and H. A. Itano, eds.), p. 84. American Institute of Biological Sciences, Washington, D.C.

Hirschfelder, J. O., Curtiss, C. F., and Bird, R. B. (1954). *Molecular Theory of Gases and Liquids.* Wiley, New York.

Hoogsteen, K. (1959). *Acta Cryst.* **12,** 822.

Hoogsteen, K. (1963a). *Acta Cryst.* **16,** 28.

Hoogsteen, K. (1963b). *Acta Cryst.* **16,** 907.

Howard, B. D., and Tessman, I. (1964). *J. Mol. Biol.* **9,** 372.

Hoyland, J. R., and Goodman, L. (1962). *J. Chem. Phys.* **36,** 21.

Isenberg, I., Leslie, R. B., Baird, S. L., Jr., Rosenbluth, R., and Bersohn, R. (1964). *Proc. Natl. Acad. Sci. U.S.* **52,** 379.

Janik, B., and Palecek, E. (1964). *Arch. Biochem. Biophys.* **105,** 225.

Jardetzky, O. (1964). *Biopolymers Symp.* **1,** 501.

Kahan, E., Kahan, F. M., and Hurwitz, J. (1963). *J. Biol. Chem.* **238,** 2491.

Kearns, D. R. (1964). *In* "The Structure and Properties of Biomolecules and Biological Systems" (J. Duchesne, ed.), p. 282. Wiley (Interscience), New York.

Kersten, W. (1961). *Biochim. Biophys. Acta* **47,** 610.

Kersten, W., and Kersten, H. (1962). *Z. Physiol. Chem.* **330,** 21.
Kommandeur, J., and Hall, F. R. (1961). *J. Chem. Phys.* **34,** 129.
Lacroix, M., and Williams-Dorlet, C. (1964). *Compt. Rend.* **259,** 1771.
Ladik, J. (1964a). *Nature* **202,** 1208.
Ladik, J. (1964b). *In* "Electronic Aspects of Biochemistry" (B. Pullman, ed.), p. 203. Academic Press, New York.
Ladik, J., and Hoffman, T. A. (1964). *Biopolymers Symp.* **1,** 117.
Lagercrantz, C., and Yhland, M. (1963). *Acta Chem. Scand.* **17,** 904, 1677.
Lawley, P. D., and Brookes, P. (1963). *Biochem. J.* **89,** 127.
Leith, J. D., Jr. (1963). *Biochim. Biophys. Acta* **72,** 643.
Lerman, L. S. (1961). *J. Mol. Biol.* **3,** 18.
Lerman, L. S. (1963). *Proc. Natl. Acad. Sci. U.S.* **49,** 94.
Lerman, L. S. (1964). *J. Cellular Comp. Physiol.* **64,** (Suppl. 1), 1.
Levine, L., Gordon, J. A., and Jencks, W. P. (1963). *Biochemistry* **2,** 168.
Liang, C. Y., and Scalco, E. G. (1964). *J. Chem. Phys.* **40,** 912.
Liquori, A. M., De Lerma, B., Ascoli, F., Botré, C., and Trasciatti, M. (1962). *J. Mol. Biol.* **5,** 527.
Litman, R. F. (1961). *J. Chim. Phys.* **58,** 997.
Luzzati, V., Mason, F., and Lerman, L. S. (1961). *J. Mol. Biol.* **3,** 634.
Lyons, L. E. (1957). *J. Chem. Soc.* p. 5001.
Lyons, L. E., and Mackie, J. C. (1962). *Proc. Chem. Soc.* p. 71.
Lyons, L. E., and Mackie, J. C. (1963). *Nature* **197,** 589.
McConnell, J. F., Sharma, B. D., and Marsh, R. E. (1964). *Nature* **203,** 399.
McGlynn, S. P. (1958). *Chem. Rev.* **58,** 1113.
McGlynn, S. P. (1960). *Radiation Res. Suppl.* **2,** 300.
Machmer, P., and Duchesne, J. (1965). *Nature,* **206,** 618.
Mahler, H. R., and Mehrotra, D. D. (1962). *Biochim. Biophys. Acta* **55,** 789.
Mantione, M. J., and Pullman, B. (1964). *Biochim. Biophys. Acta* **91,** 387.
Marmur, J., and Doty, P. (1959). *Nature* **183,** 1427.
Marmur, J., Rownd, R., and Schildkraut, C. L. (1963). *Progr. Nucleic Acid Res.* **1,** 231.
Mathews, F. S., and Rich, A. (1964). *Mol. Biol.* **8,** 89.
Matsushita, S., Ibuki, F., and Aoki, A. (1963). *Arch. Biochem. Biophys.* **102,** 446.
Mesnard, G., and Vasilescu, D. (1963). *Compt. Rend.* **257,** 4177.
Moffitt, W. (1950). *Proc. Roy. Soc. (London)* **A202,** 548.
Molinar, G., and Lata, G. F. (1962). *Arch. Biochem. Biophys.* **96,** 486.
Muller, A. (1963). *Intern. J. Radiation Biol.* **6,** 137.
Muller, A., Kohnlein, W., and Zimmer, K. G. (1963). *J. Mol. Biol.* **7,** 92.
Mulliken, R. S. (1952). *J. Phys. Chem.* **56,** 801.
Mulliken, R. S. (1956). *Rec. Trav. Chim.* **75,** 845.
Mulliken, R. S. (1964). *J. Chim. Phys.* **61,** 20.
Nagata, C., Imamura, A., Saito, H., and Fukui, K. (1963). *Gann* **54,** 109.
Nakajima, T., and Pullman, A. (1958). *J. Chim. Phys.* **55,** 793.
Nesbet, R. K. (1964). *Biopolymers Symp.* **1,** 129.
Neville, D. M., Jr., and Bradley, D. F. (1961). *Biochim. Biophys. Acta* **50,** 397.
O'Brien, E. J. (1963). *J. Mol. Biol.* **7,** 107.
O'Konski, C. T., and Shirai, M. (1963). *Biopolymers* **1,** 557.
O'Konski, C. T., Moser, P., and Shirai, M. (1964). *Biopolymers Symp.* **1,** 479.
Orgel, A., and Brenner, S. (1961). *J. Mol. Biol.* **3,** 762.
Orgel, L. E., Cottrell, T. L., Dirk, W., and Sutton, L. E. (1951). *Trans. Faraday Soc.* **47,** 113.
Orr, J. C. (1964). *Nature* **201,** 816.

Patten, R. A., and Gordy, W. (1964). *Nature* **201**, 361.

Pauling, L., and Corey, R. B. (1956). *Archiv. Biochem. Biophys.* **65**, 164.

Pimentel, G. C., and McClellan, A. L. (1960). "The Hydrogen Bond," p. 229. Freeman, San Francisco.

Pruden, B., Snipes, W., and Gordy, W. (1965). *Proc. Natl. Acad. Sci. U. S.* (in press).

Pullman, A. (1963). *Compt. Rend.* **256**, 5435.

Pullman, A. (1964a). *In* "Electronic Aspects of Biochemistry" (B. Pullman, ed.), p. 135. Academic Press, New York.

Pullman, A. (1964b). *Biochim. Biophys. Acta* **87**, 365.

Pullman, A. (1964c). *Biopolymers Symp.* **1**, 29.

Pullman, A. (1964d). *Biopolymers Symp.* **1**, 47.

Pullman, A. (1965a). *J. Chim. Phys.* (in press).

Pullman, A. (1965b). "Modern Quantum Chemistry—Istanbul Lectures" (O. Sinanoğlu, ed.). Academic Press, New York (in press).

Pullman, A., and Pullman, B. (1955a). *Advan. Cancer Res.* **3**, 117.

Pullman, A., and Pullman, B. (1955b). "La Cancérisation par les substances chimiques et la structure moléculaire." Masson, Paris.

Pullman, A., and Pullman, B. (1958). *Bull. Soc. Chim. France* p. 766.

Pullman, A., and Pullman, B. (1959). *Bull. Soc. Chim. France* p. 591.

Pullman, A., and Pullman, B. (1963). *Biochim. Biophys. Acta* **75**, 269.

Pullman, A., and Pullman, B. (1964). *In* "Molecular Orbitals in Chemistry, Physics, and Biology" (B. Pullman and P. O. Löwdin, eds.), p. 547. Academic Press, New York.

Pullman, A., and Rossi, M. (1964). *Biochim. Biophys. Acta* **88**, 211.

Pullman, B. (1962). *Compt. Rend.* **255**, 3255.

Pullman, B. (1963). *Israel J. Chem.* **1**, 412.

Pullman, B. (1964a). *Biopolymers Symp.* **1**, 141.

Pullman, B. (1964b). *In* "Electronic Aspects of Biochemistry" (B. Pullman, ed.), p. 131. Academic Press, New York.

Pullman, B. (1964c). *In* "Electronic Aspects of Biochemistry" (B. Pullman, ed.), p. 559. Academic Press, New York.

Pullman, B. (1964d). *Biochim. Biophys. Acta* **88**, 440.

Pullman, B. (1964e). *J. Cellular Comp. Physiol.* **64**, (Suppl. 1), 91.

Pullman, B. (1964f). *Compt. Rend.* **259**, 2711.

Pullman, B. (1964g). *In* "Molecular Orbitals in Chemistry, Physics, and Biology (B. Pullman and P. O. Löwdin, eds.), p. 547. Academic Press, New York.

Pullman, B. (1965). *Compt. Rend.* **259**, 3101.

Pullman, B., and Mantione, M. J. (1965). *Biochim. Biophys. Acta* **91**, 387.

Pullman, B., and Pullman, A. (1952). "Les Théories electroniques de la chimie organique." Masson, Paris.

Pullman, B., and Pullman, A. (1959). *Biochim. Biophys. Acta* **36**, 343.

Pullman, B., and Pullman, A. (1960). *Rev. Mod. Phys.* **32**, 428.

Pullman, B., and Pullman, A. (1961). *Nature* **189**, 725.

Pullman, B., and Pullman, A. (1962a). *Nature* **196**, 1137.

Pullman, B., and Pullman, A. (1962b). *Biochim. Biophys. Acta* **64**, 403.

Pullman, B., and Pullman, A. (1963a). "Quantum Biochemistry." Wiley (Interscience), New York.

Pullman, B., and Pullman, A. (1963b). *Nature* **199**, 467.

Pullman, B., Claverie, P., and Caillet, J. (1965). *Science* **147**, 1305.

Pullman, B., Claverie, P., and Caillet, J. (1965a). *Compt. Rend.* (in press).

Reich, E. (1963). *Cancer Res.* **23**, 1428.
Reich, E. (1964). *Science* **143**, 684.
Reich, E., Goldberg, I. H., and Rabinowitz, M. (1962). *Nature* **196**, 743.
Rice, J. M. (1964). *J. Am. Chem. Soc.* **86**, 1444.
Rich, A. (1962). *In* "Horizons in Biochemistry" (M. Kasha and B. Pullman, eds.), p. 103. Academic Press, New York.
Salovey, R., Shulman, R. G., and Walsh, W. M. (1963). *J. Chem. Phys.* **39**, 839.
Scholes, G. (1963). *Prog. Biophys. Mol. Biol.* **13**, 59.
Sinanoğlu, O., and Abdulnar, S. (1964). *J. Photochem. Photobiol.* **3**, 333.
Sinanoğlu, O., Abdulnar, S., and Kestner, N. R. (1964). *In* "Electronic Aspects of Biochemistry" (B. Pullman, ed.), p. 301. Academic Press, New York.
Singer, L. S., and Kommandeur, J. (1961). *J. Chem. Phys.* **34**, 133.
Smith, D. L., and Elving, P. J. (1962a). *J. Am. Chem. Soc.* **84**, 1412.
Smith, D. L., and Elving, P. J. (1962b). *J. Am. Chem. Soc.* **84**, 2741.
Snart, R. S. (1963). *Trans. Faraday Soc.* **59**, 754.
Sobell, H. M., Tomita, K. I., and Rich, A. (1963). *Proc. Natl. Acad. Sci. U.S.* **49**, 885.
Stone, A. L., and Bradley, D. F. (1961). *J. Am. Chem. Soc.* **83**, 3627.
Struck, W. A., and Elving, P. J. (1964). *J. Am. Chem. Soc.* **86**, 1229.
Suard, M. (1962). *Biochim. Biophys. Acta* **64**, 400.
Sutton, L. E. (1951). *Trans. Faraday Soc.* **47**, 113.
Szybalski, W. (1962). "The Molecular Basis of Neoplasia," p. 147. Univ. Texas Press, Austin.
Ts'o, P. O. P. (1964). "The Nucleohistones" (J. Bonner and P. O. P. Ts'o, eds.), p. 149. Holden-Day, San Francisco.
Ts'o, P. O. P., and Chan, S. I. (1964). *J. Am. Chem. Soc.* **86**, 4176.
Ts'o, P. O. P., and Lu, P. (1964). *Proc. Natl. Acad. Sci. U.S.* **51**, 17.
Ts'o, P. O. P., Helmkamp, G. K., and Sander, C. (1962). *Proc. Natl. Acad. Sci. U.S.* **48**, 686.
Ts'o, P. O. P., Melvin, J. S., and Olson, A. C. (1963). *J. Am. Chem. Soc.* **85**, 1289.
Tubbs, R. K., Ditmars, W. E., and Van Winkle, Q. (1964). *J. Mol. Biol.* **9**, 545.
Van de Vorst, A. (1963). Etude par résonance paramagnétique électronique de l'action des rayonnements ionisants sur les acides nucléiques et leurs constituants. Ph.D. Thesis, Université dé Liège.
Van de Vorst, A., and Villée, F. (1964). *Compt. Rend.* **259**, 928.
Veillard, A., and Pullman, B. (1963). *J. Theoret. Biol.* **4**, 37.
Wacker, A. (1961). *J. Chim. Phys.* **58**, 1041.
Wacker, A. (1963). *Prog. Nucleic Acid Res.* **1**, 369.
Wacker, A., Dellweg, H., and Weinblum, D. (1960). *Naturwiss.* **20**, 477.
Webb, R. B., and Kubitschek, H. E. (1963). *Biochem. Biophys. Res. Commun.* **13**, 90.
Weill, G., and Calvin, M. (1963). *Biopolymers* **1**, 401.
Weil-Malherbe, H. (1946). *Biochem. J.* **40**, 351.
Williams-Dorlet, C., Duchesne, J., and Lacroix, M. (1964). *In* "Electronic Aspects of Biochemistry" (B. Pullman, ed.), p. 127. Academic Press, New York.
Wulff, D. L. (1963). *J. Mol. Biol.* **7**, 431.
Yonezawa, T., Del Re, G., and Pullman, B. (1964). *Bull. Chem. Soc. Japan*, **37**, 985.
Zamenhof, S. (1957). *In* "The Chemical Basis of Heredity" (W. D. McElroy and B. Glass, eds.), p. 351. John Hopkins Press, Baltimore.
Zamenhof, S. (1959). "The Chemistry of Heredity." Blackwell, Oxford.
Zimm, B. H. (1960). *J. Chem. Phys.* **33**, 1349.
Zimm, B. H., and Kallenbach, N. B. (1962). *Ann. Rev. Phys. Chem.* **13**, 171.

Electron Spin Resonance (ESR) in Certain Biologically Important Iron Compounds

J. S. GRIFFITH[1]

Department of Mathematics,
Manchester College of Science and Technology,
Manchester, England

I. Ions

Before considering electron spin resonance itself, we shall give a brief description of some background material about the behavior of iron atoms, ions, and simple compounds.

Iron has atomic number 26, which is 8 more than the preceding inert gas argon. Of its 26 electrons, 18 form a relatively inert inner core and the remaining 8 give the normal chemical and physicochemical properties. From the study of atomic spectroscopy, it is known that in the gas phase the ground states of the iron atom and its first three ions are:

$$Fe^0: \quad 1s^2 2s^2 2p^6 3s^2 3p^6 3d^6 4s^2 : \quad {}^5D$$

$$Fe^+: \quad 1s^2 2s^2 2p^6 3s^2 3p^6 3d^6 4s : \quad {}^6D$$

$$Fe^{2+}: \quad 1s^2 2s^2 2p^6 3s^2 3p^6 3d^6 \quad : \quad {}^5D \tag{1}$$

$$Fe^{3+}: \quad 1s^2 2s^2 2p^6 3s^2 3p^6 3d^5 \quad : \quad {}^6S$$

The description of the electronic structure in terms of occupancy of orbitals is only an approximation; however, it is difficult to give a much more accurate one, and it serves to give a qualitative and some quantitative understanding of many properties. At the right in (1) are shown the Russell–Saunders coupling designations, called terms; these contain information about the total spin S. The superscript is $2S + 1$ and hence, for example, Fe^{2+} has spin 2. Capital letters represent the total orbital angular momen-

---

[1] Present address: Department of Mathematics, Bedford College, London, England.

tum L, in accordance with the conventional rule that

$$S, P, D, F, \cdots$$

means

$$L = 0, 1, 2, 3, \cdots$$

The number of independent substates may be deduced from the Russell–Saunders symbol; it is in fact $(2S + 1)(2L + 1)$. It is customary to say that there is a spin degeneracy of $2S + 1$ and a spatial degeneracy of $2L + 1$. Even the Russell–Saunders classification, although it is derived comparatively directly from experimental measurements, is an approximation, and when spin-orbit coupling is included, the total spin and the total orbital angular momenta do not accurately remain good quantum numbers. However, the main effect of the spin-orbit coupling is merely to remove the degeneracy of the states of the term. These then split into subsets, called levels, having total angular momenta J, with J running from $L + S$ down to $\mid L - S \mid$.

The spectrum of the ions in the gas phase is well known, in considerable detail, for the ions Fe^0, Fe^+, and Fe^{2+} (Moore, 1952). The spectrum is known hardly at all for Fe^{3+}, but there is no reasonable doubt whatever that the ground term is ^6S of the $3d^5$ configuration. In compounds it is usual and almost certainly invariable for Fe^{2+} and Fe^{3+} to retain the same $3d^n$ configuration. Owing to the different effects of the environment on $3d$ and $4s$ orbitals, it is probable, in the rare cases when Fe^+ occurs in molecular conditions, that it also has this type of configuration, i.e., $3d^7$ (Hayes, 1958; Hall et al., 1963).

TABLE I

ABUNDANCE OF ISOTOPES OF IRON[a]

A	$\%$	I	μ
54	5.84	(0)	
56	91.68	(0)	
57	2.17	$\frac{1}{2}$	<0.05
58	0.31	(0)	—

[a] A = mass number, I = nuclear spin, μ = magnetic moment in nuclear magnetons. Data from Strominger et al. (1958).

Iron has four naturally occurring isotopes. Their abundances and some other properties are shown in Table I. It is evident from this table that iron cannot show any nuclear quadrupole coupling interaction and that even its hyperfine interaction would be very difficult to observe.

II. Iron in Compounds

Iron forms divalent or trivalent compounds, although other valencies are sometimes observed (see, e.g., Sidgwick, 1950). It is usually octahedrally coordinated, although tetrahedral and other coordinations are known. Here the term *octahedral coordination* is used by the chemist to mean that there are six atoms directly linked to the central metal atom, so that they lie approximately along the positive and negative directions of three rectangular coordinate axes. However, octahedral coordination does not mean that the symmetry around the central atom is necessarily accurately octahedral, although of course it may be. With either regular octahedral or tetrahedral coordination (that is, with octahedral or tetrahedral symmetry), the d orbitals split into two equi-energetic sets, as shown in Fig. 1.

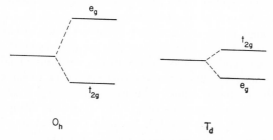

FIG. 1. Splitting of d orbitals in octahedral (O_h) and tetrahedral (T_d) symmetries.

The notation used in Fig. 1 is the conventional group-theoretic one. We shall not be concerned here with group theory, and it will not be necessary for the understanding of the remainder of this lecture. Therefore we may think of the group-theoretic symbols as being merely useful names for classification purposes. With this understanding, we may regard the symbol O_h as indicating octahedral symmetry and the symbol T_d as symbolizing tetrahedral symmetry. Furthermore, the symbol t_{2g} means that we have a triply degenerate set of orbitals, whereas e_g means that we have a doubly degenerate set of orbitals. Splitting between the e_g and t_{2g} orbitals is typically smaller for tetrahedral coordination than for octahedral. Evidently it would be possible to ask what would be the relationship between these two splittings in case we were to compare six ligands arranged octahedrally and four of the same kind arranged tetrahedrally. According to simple models, the theoretical relationship here is that the splitting for the tetrahedral situation is $\frac{4}{9}$ that for the octahedral one (see, e.g., Griffith, 1961, Section 8.3).

If the environment has a lower symmetry, then, generally speaking, orbitals split up further energetically. For a sufficiently irregular environment, one even obtains five separate energies. Although we shall not discuss this here, it is important to bear in mind that the interaction of the iron ion with its environment is an extremely complicated one, and, in particular, it is no longer accurate to suppose that the d orbitals have the same wave functions as they do in the gas phase (Stevens. 1953; Tanabe and Sugano, 1956; Sugano and Shulman, 1963).

III. High-Spin and Low-Spin Compounds

The compounds we want to discuss are octahedrally coordinated. It is convenient to describe their electronic configuration in terms of the occupancy of the t_{2g} and e_g orbitals. There are two main contributions to the electronic energy, which oppose each other. These are the orbital energy and the electrostatic energy. The first is obviously a minimum when the electrons are crowded as far as possible into the lowest (t_{2g}) orbitals. The second tries to push them as far apart as possible and to put only one electron in each orbital. In addition to this simple classical electrostatic repulsion, there are also specifically quantum mechanical contributions, called exchange energies, which make electrons prefer to have their spins parallel, other things being equal. The exchange energies are responsible for Hund's rule in atomic spectroscopy. They favor the situation in which each electron has a separate orbital, because two electrons in the same orbital must have their spins opposed (Pauli principle).

The electronic configuration which is observed for the ground state depends, therefore, on the balance of these opposing forces. This gives two limiting possible ground states, which are shown in Table II. For obvious reasons one of these is called high-spin and the other low-spin. It should be noted that the spin of the high-spin state is the same as the spin of the

TABLE II
Arrangement of Electrons in the Ground States
of Ferrous and Ferric Ions in an Octahedral Field

Orbitals	Ferrous		Ferric	
	High-spin	Low-spin	High-spin	Low-spin
e_g	$\uparrow$ $\uparrow$		$\uparrow$ $\uparrow$	
t_{2g}	$\uparrow\downarrow$ $\uparrow$ $\uparrow$	$\uparrow\downarrow$ $\uparrow\downarrow$ $\uparrow\downarrow$	$\uparrow$ $\uparrow$ $\uparrow$	$\uparrow\downarrow$ $\uparrow\downarrow$ $\uparrow$
	${}^5T_{2g}({}^5D)$	${}^1A_{1g}$	${}^6A_{1g}({}^6S)$	${}^2T_{2g}$
Spin	2	0	$2\frac{1}{2}$	$\frac{1}{2}$

free ion. It is obvious that this should be so, as in the free ion the energy difference between the t_{2g} and e_g orbitals is zero. Again we have shown conventional group-theoretic notation for the four kinds of states, and in the high-spin cases have given the free-ion term to which the state is closely related. We see also that, for both the ferrous and the ferric ion, there is a theoretical possibility of an intermediate value for the spin, that is, 1 or $1\frac{1}{2}$, respectively. Such intermediate spins may be shown theoretically to be extremely unlikely for the ground state in regular octahedral (or tetrahedral) symmetry (Griffith, 1956a). They are not known for these but probably occur in rare cases for lower symmetry (Griffith, 1961, Section 12.4.12).

IV. Magnetic Behavior

We now describe briefly the magnetic behavior of ferrous and ferric iron in typical inorganic compounds. Because of the occurrence of high-spin and low-spin versions of each of these ions, there are four distinct cases to be considered. These are summed up in Table III.

TABLE III

MAGNETIC BEHAVIOR OF TYPICAL IRON COMPOUNDS

Ion	Type	μ_{eff}	ESR
Ferrous	High-spin	5.2–5.5 (4.90)	None or very complicated
Ferrous	Low-spin	0 (0)	None
Ferric	High-spin	5.9 (5.92)	Yes, see text
Ferric	Low-spin	2.3–2.5 (1.73)	Anisotropic

Paramagnetic susceptibilities are conveniently displayed in terms of the so-called effective Bohr magneton number μ_{eff}, which is related to the susceptibility by the formula

$$\chi = \frac{N\beta^2\mu^2_{eff}}{3kT} \tag{2}$$

In Table III typical experimental values of μ_{eff} at room temperature are given, with the spin-only value in parentheses. The latter is the theoretical value, calculated assuming that only the spin magnetic moment makes any contribution to the susceptibility. That value agrees well with the experimental value in two cases but not so well in the others. This is because in these two cases there is no spatial degeneracy, whereas in the other two there is a triple spatial degeneracy which allows the development of considerable orbital magnetic moment.

The electron spin resonance (ESR) measurements are fairly well understood. When we pass to biological iron compounds, the paramagnetic susceptibilities are in the same general ranges, and nothing new or curious occurs, so long, at least, as they are compounds with comparatively well-separated ions. The same is true for ESR in three of the cases, but for the ferric high-spin compounds there is a dramatically different behavior in hemoglobin and myoglobin from that in most simpler compounds. In the next section we shall discuss what ESR behavior is to be expected for ferric high-spin compounds and then pass on, in Section VI, to discuss the behavior found for hemoglobin, myoglobin, and some other biological iron compounds.

V. ESR of High-Spin Compounds

In the electron spin resonance method, the specimen is placed between the poles of an electromagnet, giving a static and substantially uniform magnetic field (Bleaney and Stevens, 1953). Plane-polarized radiofrequency waves are directed into the specimen and arrangements made to determine the occurrence of absorption. This absorption is typically in the centimeter region and is derived from induced transitions between states of paramagnetic ions which are degenerate, or at least close together, in the absence of the magnetic field, but which are split apart by it.

We are going to discuss only the high-spin ferric ion. In the gas phase, the static magnetic field would split the ^6S ground term into six equally spaced levels with a separation between adjacent levels of $2\beta H$. This is illustrated in Fig. 2, in which are given also the magnitudes of the components of the total spin lying along the magnetic field (M_s). Owing to the quantum mechanical selection rules, the transitions should be only between levels differing by one unit of M_s. This means that the only possible energies of transitions are $2\beta H$, and hence one would expect absorption of the radiation to occur only for the frequency ν corresponding to $h\nu = 2\beta H$.

In our calculation, the transition energy turned out to be proportional to H. In any such case it is customary to write $h\nu = g\beta H$. Since ν and H can be determined experimentally, we may sum up the result of experimental measurement by giving the value of the dimensionless constant g. We have shown theoretically that $g = 2$ for the high-spin ferric ion. For inorganic high-spin ferric ions, a g value of slightly less than 2 is usually observed. This is in accord with our theoretical calculation, and the small deviation from $g = 2$ is due to a spin-orbit coupling interaction of the ^6S ground term with an excited term.

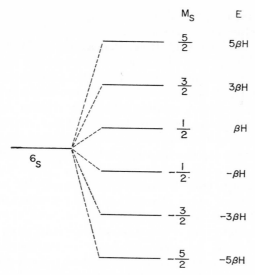

Fig. 2. Splitting of a ^6S term in a magnetic field.

VI. ESR of High-Spin Hemoglobin and Myoglobin

Hemoglobin is responsible for carrying oxygen in the blood from the lungs to the tissues. It has four sites at each of which it can bind an oxygen molecule or water molecule. By using these, it operates a sort of shuttle service by which it carries oxygen molecules from the lungs to the tissues and then comes back again carrying water molecules. It is red and forms part of the red blood cells, which also carry carbon dioxide back into the lungs. The four sites can also carry other molecules, and in case of carbon monoxide poisoning these sites have been taken up by the more readily bound CO molecules. Myoglobin is a somewhat similar molecule and serves a similar purpose within the tissues. It has only one binding site in each molecule, although this difference is not important for us.

Hemoglobin and myoglobin are both predominantly protein, but each has a nonprotein component. The nonprotein component is a large flat conjugated system with a ferrous ion in the center. It is called heme and its structure is illustrated in Fig. 3. Hemoglobin has four of these heme groups, whereas myoglobin has just one. In addition to the four nitrogen atoms of the heme system, there is also a nitrogen atom of histidine, an amino acid from the protein, linked directly to the iron atom. From the point of view of octahedral coordination, this leaves a further possible linkage to the iron on the other side of the heme ring. It is believed that it is at this position that the oxygen or water is bound. The exact geometric configuration of the oxygen molecule, relative to the heme, is not known. I have discussed elsewhere various possibilities for this configuration from a theoretical point of view, slightly favoring a structure in which the oxygen molecule lies with its axis parallel to the heme plane in a sort of π complex, and I still think this structure to be the most probable, although by no means certain (Griffith, 1965b). It is made more likely by the recent discovery that an inorganic, iridium-containing oxygen carrier has this type of structure (Vaska, 1963; Ibers and La Placa, 1964). A final point about the structure of the ring system is that it has recently been shown that the ferrous ion is not strictly coplanar with the main ring but is slightly out to one side.

In the laboratory, both hemoglobin and myoglobin may be readily oxidized to the ferric state. Furthermore, many other small molecules (in particular, fluoride, azide, and cyanide) as well as oxygen, carbon monoxide, and water, may be made to combine with them.

ESR measurements on high-spin ferric hemoglobin and myoglobin derivatives give, approximately, $g = 6$ (Bennett et al., 1955; for further references see the survey by Griffith, 1964a; see also Aasa et al., 1963; Schoffa, 1964). This is entirely at variance with the behavior observed for typical inorganic compounds of this type, and, curiously enough, it is relatively difficult to observe this behavior in inorganic materials at all (although, see Castner et al., 1960). Measurements were made at three separate frequencies, and the resonance frequency was found to be accurately proportional to the magnetic field. This means that we have a pair of states which separate in a magnetic field with energies $\pm 3\beta H$, as illustrated in Fig. 4. It is important to emphasize this, for ESR is very often done at only one frequency because, at least until very recently, most commercial instruments have only operated at one frequency.

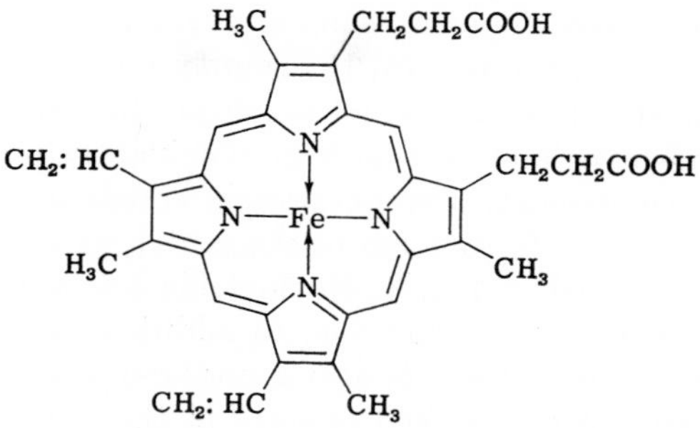

FIG. 3. Heme, the prosthetic group of hemoglobin. One classical chemical structure is shown; the ring system has the symmetry of its nuclei to a good approximation. (From Griffith, 1956b, 1961, by kind permission of Cambridge University Press.)

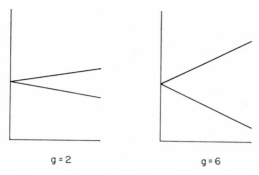

g = 2   g = 6

FIG. 4. Energy of a doublet in a magnetic field for $g = 2$ and $g = 6$.

The resonance at $g = 6$ may be observed at room temperature and in polycrystalline specimens, but work at low temperatures has shown that the g value is anisotropic with $g_\perp = 5.95$ and $g_{||} \simeq 2$. Here the symbols $\perp$ and $||$ refer to the axis of approximately fourfold symmetry which runs through the ferrous ion at right angles to the heme plane. In a polycrystalline specimen, different heme planes will lie at different angles to the external magnetic field, randomly, and as a result of this, one gets a distribution of absorption frequencies. Hence, for simple geometric reasons, the majority of the absorption is clustered near the $g_\perp$ value, and in a polycrystalline specimen one observes a line peaked at 5.95 and trailing away toward $g = 2$.

The correct interpretation of these findings is almost certainly in terms of the existence of a fine-structure, or zero-field, splitting (Griffith, 1956b). This would mean that even in the absence of a magnetic field the states of the ^6S term are somewhat separated in energy. This is illustrated in Fig. 5(a), where the relative energies are given on the left in the usual notation. It will be seen that the six states are no longer degenerate but form three separate doublets. The M_s values are given at the right of Fig. 5(a) and refer to the component of the spin along the axis at right angles to the heme plane, not to an externally defined axis.

If we make the assumption of the existence of this zero-field splitting and, furthermore, assume it to be large compared with the energy of interaction with the static magnetic field, then it is a simple quantum mechanical calculation to determine the g values associated with each of these three doublets. These g values will depend upon the relative angle of the external magnetic field and the approximately fourfold axis of the heme plane. When H is parallel to this axis, we obtain the splittings shown in Fig. 5(b), whereas when it is at right angles to that axis we obtain those shown in Fig. 5(c). Comparing the behavior of the lowest-energy doublet with that shown in

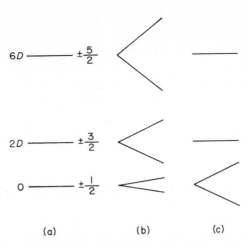

$6D$ ———— $\pm\frac{5}{2}$

$2D$ ———— $\pm\frac{3}{2}$

0 ———— $\pm\frac{1}{2}$

(a)   (b)   (c)

FIG. 5. Behavior of ^6S ground term of Fe^{3+} with an axial fine-structure splitting. (a) No magnetic field, (b) magnetic field along fourfold axis (OZ), (c) magnetic field along OX or OY.

Fig. 4 demonstrates that with this model we should expect $g_\perp = 6$ and $g_{||} = 2$. The value $g_\perp$ is actually slightly less than this, presumably because of the spin-orbit coupling interaction with an excited term.

High-spin hemoglobin and myoglobin compounds have susceptibilities at room-temperature which are not significantly different from those of typical inorganic high-spin compounds. This does not conflict with our present interpretation, because, as was shown long ago by Van Vleck, the effect of small zero-field splittings on paramagnetic susceptibilities is very small, providing these splittings are small compared with kT. The fact that the yardstick of energy here is the thermal one rather than the smaller energy of interaction with the magnetic field, arises from the statistical averaging needed to obtain a susceptibility. Small effects on the susceptibility do remain, however, and have been observed by George and Beetlestone. They have been reported and discussed elsewhere (Griffith, 1964a; George, 1964).

VII. Technical Discussion

We now give a more technical discussion of the probable origin of the fine structure. The g value at 5.95 is only proportional to the magnetic field, theoretically, so long as the matrix element of the magnetic field between the ground doublet and the next higher one is unimportant. The experimental observation of this proportionality, therefore, means that D cannot be very small (at least more than 5 cm^{-1}). This is a very large fine-structure splitting, which is therefore presumably due mainly to the lowest-order effect of the spin-orbit coupling interaction between the ^6S ground term and one or more excited terms. It has been shown that in such a case the zero-field splitting may be represented in a spin-Hamiltonian by a quadratic form (Griffith, 1960). Let us refer this quadratic form to principal axes and choose our zero of energy to be at the center of gravity of the six states. Then the form becomes

$$\mathcal{H}(S) = D(S_z^2 - \tfrac{35}{12}) + E(S_x^2 - S_y^2) \tag{3}$$

in the usual terminology. The symmetry around the iron ion is approximately fourfold with the fourfold axis at right angles to the heme plane. The spin-Hamiltonian may then be taken to have the same symmetry, which means that it is simply of the form

$$\mathcal{H}(S) = D(S_z^2 - \tfrac{35}{12}) \tag{4}$$

Here the z axis is at right angles to the heme plane, and it is apparent that the fine-structure Hamiltonian of Eq. (4) gives the zero-field splittings of Fig. 5(a).

We now have two things left to explain: why does D have a positive sign and why is it as large as it is? It is necessary for D to be positive, because otherwise the intensity of the transition would decay with the Boltzmann factor toward zero temperature in a way which is not observed. The theoretical derivation of D has been discussed elsewhere (Griffith, 1964a). Here I shall merely say that in the free ion the selection rules show that there is only spin-orbit interaction between ^6S and one other term, that is the ^4P of $3d^5$. In octahedral symmetry there is interaction with the three $^4T_1$ terms into which this ^4P is distributed. Because the symmetry is actually lower than octahedral, although retaining an approximate fourfold axis, these $^4T_1$ each split into a spatially nondegenerate and a spatially doubly degenerate term. It is through this splitting that the zero-field splitting arises, and the most reasonable guess at the way in which the lowest $^4T_1$ term would split gives a positive D. This D is roughly $\zeta^2/5\Delta E$; where ΔE is the energy separation between the ^6S and the lowest part of the split $^4T_1$.

It is interesting here to mention that another peculiar resonance behavior has been found, which has been interpreted as arising from a spin-Hamiltonian, as in Eq. (3) but with $D = 0$, $E \neq 0$ (Castner et al., 1960). If we again assume that the energies associated with the fine-structure splitting are large compared with those associated with the magnetic field, we can obtain theoretical g values for this situation. In the absence of the magnetic field, it is easy to show that the ^6S splits into three equally separated doublets with a spacing of $2E(7)^{\frac{1}{2}}$. Then the theoretical g value for the middle one of these three doublets is isotropic at $30/7$. A g value very close to this has been observed for the ferric ion in interstitial materials and also in various biological materials. The temperature dependence of its intensity is in accord with the view that it is not arising from the lowest doublet, and can also give an estimate of E (Castner et al., 1960).

It is not easy to see how the situation $D = 0$, $E \neq 0$ could arise. The symmetry of a spin-Hamiltonian must reflect the symmetry of the environment, but no environment has a symmetry which would give this spin-Hamiltonian. In fact, environmental symmetry could only enforce, rigorously, either $D = E = 0$ or $E = 0$ but not $D = 0$ alone. Of course it can be that $D = 0$ accidentally, but this would not be a very satisfactory explanation, since this g value occurs in a number of situations (see also Schoffa, 1964; Walsh et al., 1963).

It has been shown, however, that certain environments, in particular FeA_2B_2 or octahedral FeA_3B_3 having C_{2v} symmetry, will split the excited $^4T_1$ term into three equally separated components. This occurs for a rather involved reason, for which the reader is referred elsewhere (Griffith, 1964b). However, the calculation shows that, if the center of gravity of the $^4T_1$ term lies at m above the ^6S and if the $^4T_1$ term has an over-all splitting of $2a$, then

$$D = -\frac{a^2\zeta^2}{5m(m^2 - a^2)}; \qquad E = -\frac{a\zeta^2}{5(m^2 - a^2)} \qquad (5)$$

Although D is, evidently, not equal to 0, nevertheless it is very much smaller than E. As

$$D/E = a/m$$

one sees that this ratio is typically of the order of $\frac{1}{10}$. It is not certain that this interpretation is correct, because the structure is not known for any compound giving this g value. It is to be hoped that someone will prepare a compound having one of these structures and will see whether it has the predicted ESR behavior.

REFERENCES

Aasa, R., Malmström, B. G., Saltman, P., and Vänngård, T. (1963). Biochim. Biophys. Acta. 75, 203.

Bennett, J. E., Ingram, D. J. E., George, P., and Griffith, J. S. (1955). Nature 170, 394; true g value of 6.

Bleaney, B., and Stevens, K. W. H. (1953). Rept. Progr. Phys. 16, 108.

Castner, T., Newell, G. S., Holton, W. C., and Slichter, C. P. (1960). J. Chem. Phys. 32, 668; elementary theory of $g = 4.3$.

George, P. (1964). Symposium on quantum aspects of polynucleotides and polypeptides, Stanford, California, 1963. Biopolymers Symp. 1, 45.

Griffith, J. S. (1956a). J. Inorg. Nucl. Chem. 2, 1.

Griffith, J. S. (1956b). Proc. Roy. Soc. (London) A 235, 23; elementary theory of $g = 6$.

Griffith, J. S. (1960). *Mol. Phys.* **3**, 79.

Griffith, J. S. (1961). "The Theory of Transition-Metal Ions." Cambridge University Press, New York.

Griffith, J. S. (1964a). "The magnetic properties of haemoglobin and myglobin derivatives" (Symposium on quantum aspects of polynucleotides and polypeptides, Stanford, California, 1963). *Biopolymers Symp.* **1**, 35; general survey to 1963.

Griffith, J. S. (1964b). *Mol Phys.* **8**, 213; detailed theory of $g = 4.3$.

Hall, T. P. P., Stevenson, R. W. H., and Wilkens, J. (1963). *J. Chem. Phys.* **39**, 35.

Hayes, W. (1958). *Discussions Faraday Soc.* **26**, 58.

Ibers, J. A., and La Placa, S. J. (1964). *Science* **145**, 920.

Moore, C. E. (1952). "Atomic energy levels." *Natl. Bur. Std. (U.S.) Circular No.* **467**.

Schoffa, G. (1964). *Nature* **203**, 640.

Sidgwick, N. V. (1950). "The Chemical Elements and their Compounds," Vol. 2. Clarendon Press, Oxford.

Stevens, K. W. H. (1953). *Proc. Roy. Soc. (London)* **A 219**, 542.

Strominger, D., Hollander, J. M., and Seaborg, G. T. (1958). *Rev. Mod. Phys.* **30**, 585.

Sugano, S., and Shulman, R. G. (1963). *Phys. Rev.* **130**, 517.

Tanabe, Y., and Sugano, S. (1956). *J. Phys. Soc. Japan* **11**, 864

Vaska, L. (1963). *Science* **140**, 809.

Walsh, W. M., Rupp, L. W., and Wyluda, B. J. (1963). "Paramagnetic Resonance" (W. Low, ed.), p. 836. Academic Press, New York.

Electron Spin Resonance in Molecular Triplet States[1]

M. WEISSBLUTH

Biophysics Laboratory,
Stanford University,
Stanford, California

I. Introduction

Triplet states first entered into organic chemistry when they were invoked to explain the origin of phosphorescence in conjugated molecules as arising from radiative transitions between the first (lowest energy) triplet state and the ground singlet state (Lewis and Kasha, 1944). Since triplet states are electronic states with a total spin $S = 1$ and an accompanying magnetic moment of two Bohr magnetons, one would expect an equilibrium population of molecules residing in the triplet state to exhibit paramagnetism. Indeed, magnetic effects were observed by Lewis *et al.* (1949), but it was not until the pioneering work of Hutchison and Mangum (1961) that the study of triplet states in organic molecules became susceptible to observation by electron spin resonance (ESR) methods.

The present review will be confined to ESR studies of triplet states in organic molecules having π electrons, and whose ground states are singlets, that is, $S = 0$. Molecules such as O_2 with triplet ground states are not considered.

[1] This work was supported by National Science Foundation Grant GB 1409 and by U. S. Office of Naval Research Contract Nonr 225(36).

The following properties of the triplet state will be recalled.

1. Triplet states, whether in atoms or molecules, are electronic states in which two electrons have parallel spins resulting in a total spin $S = 1$ and a multiplicity $2S + 1 = 3$. The state derives its name from the multiplicity.

2. In conjugated molecules the two electrons characterizing the triplet state are π electrons. In terms of a molecular orbital description the electron configurations corresponding to the lowest (ground) singlet state (S_0), the first excited singlet state (S_1), and the first excited triplet state (T_1) are as shown in Fig. 1(a), 1(b), and 1(c), respectively.

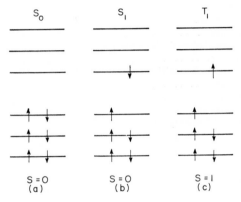

FIG. 1. Molecular orbitals for the π-electron system in Hückel approximation. (a) Ground singlet state, S_0, with $S = 0$; (b) first excited singlet state, S_1, with $S = 0$; (c) first excited triplet state, T_1, with $S = 1$.

3. Triplet states lie lower in energy than their corresponding singlet states, the latter being states with the same spatial wave function. The difference in energy between singlets and triplets arises as a consequence of the antisymmetry requirement on the total wave function describing the molecular state, and is expressed in terms of an exchange integral.

4. In terms of molecular states, as distinct from molecular orbitals, the energy level diagram representing the states S_0, S_1, and T_1 are as shown in Fig. 2. Higher excited singlet and triplet states, although they exist, are not shown in the diagram; neither is the vibrational structure of the electronic states shown.

5. Referring to Fig. 2, we note the following: (a) The long wavelength (photon) absorption band of the molecule is associated with the transition $S_0 \rightarrow S_1$; most often, the wavelengths lie in the ultraviolet region of the spectrum. (b) The radiative transition $S_1 \rightarrow S_0$ is known as fluorescence and is characterized by lifetimes of the order of 10^{-8} sec. (c) The transition

$S_1 \rightarrow S_0$ may also occur by nonradiative processes; this is known as internal conversion. (d) Triplet states are generally not accessible by direct photon absorption, and the predominant mode for populating states such as T_1 is by a nonradiative transition $S_1 \rightarrow T_1$. (e) The radiative transition $T_1 \rightarrow S_0$ is spin forbidden; nevertheless, there is, in a large number of cases, sufficient spin-orbit coupling so that the state T_1 is more accurately described as a mixture of triplet and singlet states. Radiative transitions then become allowed to an extent depending on the degree of admixture

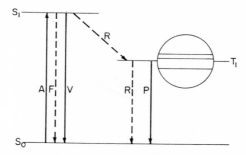

FIG. 2. Energies of the molecular states S_0, S_1, and T_1. A, absorption; F, fluorescence; V, internal conversion; R, intersystem crossing; P, phosphorescence. Zero-field splitting of the triplet state is shown in the inset. The vibrational structure of the states is not shown.

of singlet states. The radiative transition $T_1 \rightarrow S_0$ is known as phosphorescence and is characterized by lifetimes ranging from 10^{-4}–10^{1} sec. (f) The transition $T_1 \rightarrow S_0$ may also occur by nonradiative processes; nonradiative transitions such as $S_1 \rightarrow T_1$ and $T_1 \rightarrow S_0$ are known as intersystem crossings. Recent discussions of nonradiative transitions have been given by Gouterman (1962); Hadley et al. (1963); and Robinson and Frosch (1962, 1963). The phosphorescence of amino acids and proteins has been studied by Steele and Szent-Györgyi (1958) and by Vladimirov and Litvin (1960).

Normally, chemical reactions occur while the participating molecules are in their ground states. The lifetimes of excited states are generally too short for them to contribute significantly to chemical reactions. The important exception is T_1, the lowest lying triplet state whose lifetime is sufficiently long for the molecule to undergo a chemical reaction or to transfer its energy while it is still in the triplet state (Hammond and Turro, 1963).

The triplet state in a spherically symmetric system such as an atom is threefold degenerate. Upon application of a magnetic field, an axis of quantization is established and the degeneracy is lifted. In a molecule axes of symmetry may exist which can serve as axes of quantization. It is, therefore, to be expected that, in a molecule with symmetry axes, the degeneracy may be partially or totally lifted, even in the absence of a magnetic field. If there is a trigonal axis, as in benzene, the triplet state consists of a singlet and a doublet; for molecules of lower symmetry, as for naphthalene, the triplet state consists of three singlets. We refer to such a situation as zero-field splitting (zfs), and the interaction responsible for it in molecules such as the aromatic hydrocarbons is the spin-spin interaction between the two electrons making up the triplet state. Spin-orbit interactions have been shown to be negligible in their contribution to the zfs (Hameka and Oosterhoff, 1958). Typical splittings in aromatic hydrocarbons are of the order of 0.1 cm^{-1}, which of course cannot be resolved by

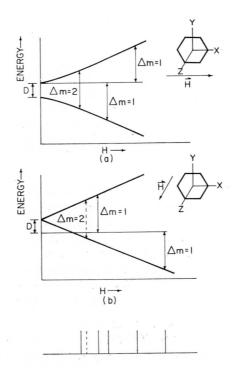

Fig. 3. Energies of the triplet state in a magnetic field for a molecule with trigonal symmetry. (a) Magnetic field parallel to x axis (or y axis); (b) magnetic field parallel to z axis. The dashed transition is strictly forbidden.

phosphorescence studies but whose effect is readily discerned by ESR methods in which the microwave photons have energies of the same order of magnitude. Application of a static magnetic field causes the zfs levels to diverge, and at certain values of the magnetic field the separation between two of the three levels will be equal in energy to the energy of the microwave photon. Provided the transition is allowed, an ESR signal may be observable. Generally, there will be several values of the magnetic field where this condition is satisfied.

As shown by Hutchison and Mangum (1961), the values of magnetic field at which the conditions for an ESR signal are satisfied will depend markedly on the orientation of the molecule relative to the magnetic field. This is illustrated in Fig. 3 for a molecule with a trigonal axis of symmetry. The zero-field splitting consists of a singlet and a doublet separated by an energy D. Upon application of a magnetic field there is a general divergence of the levels, the exact form of which depends on the orientation of the molecule relative to the magnetic field. For a magnetic field along one of the molecular axes, there are generally three values of the field for which the energetic conditions for resonance are satisfied.

It is this anisotropy which frustrated the work of previous investigators in their attempts to observe ESR signals of the triplet state in solutions where the molecules were randomly oriented. A further point noted by van der Waals and de Groot (1959) was that there existed a low field resonance, which was far less anisotropic and in fact was observable in solution. Many organic compounds have now been observed in this way and the original hypothesis of Lewis and Kasha has been considerably strengthened by the ESR observations.

II. Spin-Spin Interactions

A. The Hamiltonian

The Hamiltonian for the spin-spin interaction between two electrons is

$$\mathcal{3C}' = \frac{g^2\beta^2}{r^3}\left[\mathbf{S}(1)\cdot\mathbf{S}(2) - 3\frac{[\mathbf{S}(1)\cdot\mathbf{r}][\mathbf{S}(2)\cdot\mathbf{r}]}{r^2}\right] \tag{1}$$

in which g is the gyromagnetic ratio, β is the Bohr magneton, r is the distance between the two electrons, $\mathbf{S}(1)$ and $\mathbf{S}(2)$ are the spin operators for electrons 1 and 2. It is understood that $\mathbf{S}(1)$, for instance, has the components $[S_1(1),\ S_2(1),\ S_3(1)]$.

A straightforward expansion of the operator gives

$$\mathcal{3C}' = \frac{g^2\beta^2}{r^3}\left[S_1(1)\,S_1(2)\left(1 - \frac{3x_1^2}{r^2}\right) + S_2(1)\,S_2(2)\left(1 - \frac{3x_2^2}{r^2}\right)\right.$$

$$+ S_3(1)\,S_3(2)\left(1 - \frac{3x_3^2}{r^2}\right) - 3[S_1(1)\,S_2(2) + S_2(1)\,S_1(2)]\frac{x_1x_2}{r^2}$$

$$- 3[S_1(1)\,S_3(2) + S_3(1)\,S_1(2)]\frac{x_1x_3}{r^2}$$

$$\left. - 3[S_2(1)\,S_3(2) + S_3(1)\,S_2(2)]\frac{x_2x_3}{r^2}\right] \quad (2)$$

This is a tensor operator, as may be seen by writing

$$\mathcal{3C}' = g^2\beta^2\mathbf{S}(1)\cdot Q\cdot\mathbf{S}(2) \quad (3)$$

in which Q is the symmetric tensor with zero trace

$$Q = \begin{bmatrix} \dfrac{r^2 - 3x_1^2}{r^5} & -\dfrac{3x_1x_2}{r^5} & -\dfrac{3x_1x_3}{r^5} \\[2mm] -\dfrac{3x_2x_1}{r^5} & \dfrac{r^2 - 3x_2^2}{r^5} & -\dfrac{3x_2x_3}{r^5} \\[2mm] -\dfrac{3x_3x_1}{r^5} & -\dfrac{3x_3x_2}{r^5} & \dfrac{r^2 - 3x_3^2}{r^5} \end{bmatrix}$$

or

$$Q = (r^2\delta_{ik} - 3x_ix_k)/r^5 \quad (4)$$

Expansion of the diagonal terms in Eq. (2) and a rearrangement of terms lead to

$$\mathcal{3C}' = \frac{g^2\beta^2}{r^3}\left\{\tfrac{1}{2}[3S_3(1)\,S_3(2) - \mathbf{S}(1)\cdot\mathbf{S}(2)]\left(1 - \frac{3x_3^2}{r^2}\right) - \tfrac{3}{2}[S_1(1)\,S_1(2)\right.$$

$$- S_2(1)\,S_2(2)]\left(\frac{x_1^2 - x_2^2}{r^2}\right) - 3[S_1(1)\,S_2(2) + S_2(1)\,S_1(2)]\frac{x_1x_2}{r^2}$$

$$- 3[S_1(1)\,S_3(2) + S_3(1)\,S_1(2)]\frac{x_1x_3}{r^2}$$

$$\left. - 3[S_2(1)\,S_3(2) + S_3(2)\,S_2(1)]\frac{x_2x_3}{r^2}\right\} \quad (5)$$

Another form is

$$\mathcal{K}' = \frac{g^2\beta^2}{r^3}\left[\tfrac{1}{2}[3 S_3(1)\, S_3(2) \;-\; \mathbf{S}(1)\cdot\mathbf{S}(2)]\left(1 - \frac{3x_3^2}{r^2}\right)\right.$$

$$- \tfrac{3}{2}[S_+(1)\, S_3(2) \;+\; S_3(1)\, S_+(2)]\,\frac{(x_1 - ix_2)x_3}{r^2}$$

$$- \tfrac{3}{2}[S_-(1)\, S_3(2) \;+\; S_3(1)\, S_-(2)]\,\frac{(x_1 + ix_2)x_3}{r^2}$$

$$\left.- \tfrac{3}{4}S_+(1)\, S_+(2)\,\frac{(x_1 - ix_2)^2}{r^2} - \tfrac{3}{4}S_-(1)\, S_-(2)\,\frac{(x_1 + ix_2)^2}{r^2}\right] \qquad (6)$$

with

$$S_\pm(1) = S_1(1) \pm i S_2(1)$$

$$S_\pm(2) = S_1(2) \pm i S_2(2) \qquad (7)$$

This form is particularly useful in discussions involving the transformation properties of the Hamiltonian. First we note that the spatial factors are components of the spherical harmonic $Y_m^{(2)}(\theta,\ \varphi)$ which, of course, belongs to the $D^{(2)}$ representation of the rotation group. The spin parts also belong to the $D^{(2)}$ representation, as will now be shown.

Consider the vectors $\mathbf{S}(1)$ and $\mathbf{S}(2)$ with components $S_1(1)$, $S_2(1)$, $S_3(1)$ and $S_1(2)$, $S_2(2)$, $S_3(2)$, respectively. The components may also be expressed in the spherical basis by defining

$$S_{+1}(1) = -\frac{S_1(1) + i S_2(1)}{\sqrt{2}}$$

$$S_0(1) = S_3(1) \qquad (8)$$

$$S_{-1}(1) = \frac{S_1(1) - i S_2(1)}{\sqrt{2}}$$

with analogous definitions for $S_{+1}(2)$, $S_0(2)$, $S_{-1}(2)$. The spherical components of each vector transform as the components of $Y_m^{(1)}(\theta,\ \varphi)$; therefore, each vector belongs to the $D^{(1)}$ representation. There are nine possible products of the components of $\mathbf{S}(1)$ and $\mathbf{S}(2)$, and they belong to the product representation $D^{(1)} \times D^{(1)}$. The product representation is reducible:

$$D^{(1)} \times D^{(1)} = D^{(0)} + D^{(1)} + D^{(2)} \qquad (9)$$

and it is possible to find the linear combinations which constitute a basis of, or belong to, each of the representations $D^{(0)}$, $D^{(1)}$, $D^{(2)}$. This is accomplished with the aid of the Wigner or vector-coupling coefficients.

In particular the linear combinations belonging to $D^{(2)}$ are

$$W_0^{(2)} = (6)^{-1/2}[3S_3(1)S_3(2) - \mathbf{S}(1)\cdot\mathbf{S}(2)]$$

$$W_{+1}^{(2)} = -\tfrac{1}{2}[S_+(1)S_3(2) + S_3(1)S_+(2)]$$

$$W_{-1}^{(2)} = \tfrac{1}{2}[S_3(1)S_-(2) + S_-(1)S_3(2)] \tag{10}$$

$$W_{+2}^{(2)} = \tfrac{1}{2}S_+(1)S_+(2)$$

$$W_{-2}^{(2)} = \tfrac{1}{2}S_-(1)S_-(2)$$

Comparing the spin factors in Eq. (6) with Eq. (10), we see that they transform according to $D^{(2)}$. We may therefore write the Hamiltonian, Eq. (1), in terms of irreducible tensors of rank 2:

$$\mathfrak{K}' = -(g^2\beta^2/r^3)(\tfrac{24}{5}\pi)^{1/2}\sum_m Y_m^{(2)*}(\theta, \varphi)W_m^{(2)}[\mathbf{S}(1), \mathbf{S}(2)] \tag{11}$$

This form is particularly suitable for the application of the Wigner–Eckart theorem in the evaluation of matrix elements (Jarrett, 1963), as well as in the development of the spin Hamiltonian.

The spin-spin operator, because of its tensor character, may be transformed to principal axes x, y, z in order to eliminate off-diagonal terms. Calling the transformed operator $\mathfrak{K}_p'$ we have, from Eq. (2),

$$\mathfrak{K}_p' = \frac{g^2\beta^2}{r^3}\left[S_x(1)S_x(2)\left(1 - \frac{3x^2}{r^2}\right) + S_y(1)S_y(2)\left(1 - \frac{3y^2}{r^2}\right)\right.$$

$$\left. + S_z(1)S_z(2)\left(1 - \frac{3z^2}{r^2}\right)\right] \tag{12}$$

Rearrangement of Eq. (5) gives another form for the Hamiltonian referred to principal axes:

$$\mathfrak{K}_p' = \frac{g^2\beta^2}{r^3}\left[(\tfrac{3}{2}S_z(1)S_z(2) - \tfrac{1}{2}\mathbf{S}(1)\cdot\mathbf{S}(2))\left(1 - \frac{3z^2}{r^2}\right)\right.$$

$$\left. + \tfrac{3}{2}(S_x(1)S_x(2) - S_y(1)S_y(2))\left(\frac{y^2 - x^2}{r^2}\right)\right] \tag{13}$$

B. Zero-Field Splitting

A molecular state is described by an antisymmetrized N-electron wave function $\psi(1, 2, \cdots, N)$. Only π electrons will be considered as contributing to the formation of the triplet state. With a Hamiltonian operator consisting of Coulomb terms only,

$$\psi(1, 2, \cdots, N) = \sum_i c_i \Delta_i \qquad (14)$$

where the Δ_i are Slater determinants of order N constructed from a complete set of molecular spin-orbitals; the c_i are coefficients. A function of this form automatically satisfies the Pauli principle. Most molecules have closed-shell configurations in their ground states resulting in these states being singlets, i.e., with all spins paired. An approximate ground state wave function may then be written in terms of a single Slater determinant:

$$\psi_0(1, 2, \cdots, N) = |\, \varphi_1\alpha\varphi_1\beta\cdots\varphi_n\alpha\varphi_n\beta \,| \qquad (15)$$

with $N = 2n$. The lowest n molecular orbitals are occupied and an equal number are vacant. The term ψ is an eigenfunction of S^2 and S_z with zero eigenvalue in each case.

For excited states, a single electron is raised from a ground state orbital, say φ_i, to a vacant molecular orbital, say φ_k, as illustrated in Fig. 1. Approximate wave functions corresponding to the four possible spin orientations are of the form

$$\psi_{ik}(1, 2, \ldots, N) = \left|\, \varphi_1\alpha\varphi_1\beta\ldots\varphi_{i-1}\varphi_{i-1}\beta \left\{ \begin{array}{c} \varphi_i\alpha\varphi_k\alpha \\[6pt] \varphi_i\alpha\varphi_k\beta \\[6pt] \varphi_i\beta\varphi_k\alpha \\[6pt] \varphi_i\beta\varphi_k\beta \end{array} \right\} \varphi_{i+1}\alpha\varphi_{i+1}\beta\ldots\varphi_n\alpha\varphi_n\beta \,\right|$$

$$(16)$$

These functions are eigenfunctions of S_z but not of S^2; however, they may be grouped into linear combinations which become eigenfunctions of S^2 with eigenvalues 0 and 2 corresponding to $S = 0$ (singlet) and $S = 1$ (triplet). These combinations are

$$^1\psi_{ik}(1, 2, \ldots, N) = \sqrt{2}^{-1}[|\, \varphi_1\alpha\varphi_1\beta\ldots\varphi_i\alpha\varphi_k\beta\ldots\varphi_n\alpha\varphi_n\beta \,|$$
$$- |\, \varphi_1\alpha\varphi_1\beta\ldots\varphi_i\beta\varphi_k\alpha\ldots\varphi_n\alpha\varphi_n\beta \,|] \qquad (17)$$

$$^3\psi_{ik}(1, 2, \ldots, N) = \left\{ \begin{array}{l} |\, \varphi_1\alpha\varphi_1\beta\ldots\varphi_i\alpha\varphi_k\alpha\ldots\varphi_n\alpha\varphi_n\beta \,| \\[10pt] \sqrt{2}^{-1}[|\, \varphi_1\alpha\varphi_1\beta\ldots\varphi_i\alpha\varphi_k\beta\ldots\varphi_n\alpha\varphi_n\beta \,| \\[6pt] \qquad + |\, \varphi_1\alpha\varphi_1\beta\ldots\varphi_i\beta\varphi_k\alpha\ldots\varphi_n\alpha\varphi_n\beta \,|] \\[10pt] |\, \varphi_1\alpha\varphi_1\beta\ldots\varphi_i\beta\varphi_k\beta\ldots\varphi_n\alpha\varphi_n\beta \,| \end{array} \right. \qquad (18)$$

Situations arise in which φ_i or φ_k or both belong to degenerate sets or in which two or more configurations lie close to one another in energy and belong to the same representation of the symmetry group. In such cases it may be necessary to construct linear combinations of functions of the type of Eqs. (17) or (18) to obtain a good approximation to the exact wave function. This is known as configurational mixing.

The present discussion will be based on triplet functions of the type of Eq. (18). An important simplification arises from the fact that closed shells do not contribute to zero-field splitting (McConnell, 1959). In the absence of orbital degeneracies, the simplest triplet state wave function for two electrons outside of closed shells may be written

$$^3\psi = \begin{cases} | \varphi_1(1)\alpha(1)\varphi_2(2)\alpha(2) | \\ \sqrt{2}^{-1}[| \varphi_1(1)\alpha(1)\varphi_2(2)\beta(2) | + | \varphi_2(1)\beta(1)\varphi_1(2)\alpha(2) |] \\ | \varphi_1(1)\beta(1)\varphi_2(2)\beta(2) | \end{cases} \quad (19)$$

These may be factored into products of spatial and spin functions

$$^3\psi = \begin{cases} \varphi_a(1, 2)\alpha(1)\alpha(2) \\ \varphi_a(1, 2)\sqrt{2}^{-1}[\alpha(1)\beta(2) + \beta(1)\alpha(2)] \\ \varphi_a(1, 2)\beta(1)\beta(2) \end{cases} \quad (20)$$

in which $\varphi_a(1, 2)$ is an antisymmetric function of two electrons:

$$\varphi_a(1, 2) = \sqrt{2}^{-1}[\varphi_1(1)\varphi_2(2) - \varphi_2(1)\varphi_1(2)] \quad (21)$$

If, further, we define

$$\begin{align} T_{+1} &= \alpha(1)\alpha(2) \\ T_0 &= \sqrt{2}^{-1}[\alpha(1)\beta(2) + \beta(1)\alpha(2)] \\ T_{-1} &= \beta(1)\beta(2) \end{align} \quad (22)$$

the triplet state, Eq. (20), becomes

$$^3\psi = \begin{cases} \varphi_a(1, 2) T_{+1} \\ \varphi_a(1, 2) T_0 \\ \varphi_a(1, 2) T_{-1} \end{cases} \quad (23)$$

The effect of various spin operators on T_1, T_0, T_{-1} is shown in Table I; matrix elements of $\mathcal{3C}'$ are shown in Table II, where we have made use of

TABLE I

EFFECT OF SPIN OPERATORS ON T_{+1}, T_0, AND T_{-1}

Spin operator	T_{+1}	T_0	T_{-1}
$S_1 = S_1(1) + S_1(2)$	$\sqrt2^{-1}T_0$	$\sqrt2^{-1}(T_{+1} + T_{-1})$	$\sqrt2^{-1}T_0$
$S_2 = S_2(1) + S_2(2)$	$(i/\sqrt2)T_0$	$-(i/\sqrt2)(T_{+1} - T_{-1})$	$-(i/\sqrt2)T_0$
$S_3 = S_3(1) + S_3(2)$	T_{+1}	0	$-T_{-1}$
$S_1(1)S_1(2)$	$\tfrac14 T_{-1}$	$\tfrac14 T_0$	$\tfrac14 T_{+1}$
$S_2(1)S_2(2)$	$-\tfrac14 T_{-1}$	$\tfrac14 T_0$	$-\tfrac14 T_{+1}$
$S_3(1)S_3(2)$	$\tfrac14 T_{+1}$	$-\tfrac14 T_0$	$\tfrac14 T_{-1}$
$S_1^2 = [S_1(1) + S_1(2)]^2$	$\tfrac12(T_{+1} + T_{-1})$	T_0	$\tfrac12(T_{+1} + T_{-1})$
$S_2^2 = [S_2(1) + S_2(2)]^2$	$\tfrac12(T_{+1} - T_{-1})$	T_0	$-\tfrac12(T_{+1} - T_{-1})$
$S_3^2 = [S_3(1) + S_3(2)]^2$	T_{+1}	0	T_{-1}
$S^2 = S_1^2 + S_2^2 + S_3^2$	$2T_{+1}$	$2T_0$	$2T_{-1}$
$\mathbf{S}(1)\cdot\mathbf{S}(2)$	$\tfrac14 T_{+1}$	$\tfrac14 T_0$	$\tfrac14 T_{-1}$
$S_+ = S_+(1) + S_+(2)$	0	$\sqrt2\,T_{+1}$	$2T_{-1}$
$S_- = S_-(1) + S_-(2)$	$\sqrt2\,T_0$	$\sqrt2\,T_{-1}$	$\tfrac14 T_{-1}$
S_+S_-	$2T_1$	$2T_0$	$\sqrt2\,T_0$
$S_+(1)S_+(2)$	0	0	T_{+1}
$S_-(1)S_-(2)$	T_{-1}	0	0
$S_+(1)S_3(2) + S_3(1)S_+(2)$	0	$\sqrt2^{-1}T_{+1}$	$-\sqrt2^{-1}T_0$
$S_-(1)S_3(2) + S_3(1)S_-(2)$	$\sqrt2^{-1}T_0$	$-\sqrt2^{-1}T_{-1}$	0
$\mathcal{H}'$	$\dfrac12 g^2\beta^2\left[\dfrac12 T_{+1}\left(1 - \dfrac{3x_3^2}{r^2}\right)\right.$ $-\dfrac{3}{\sqrt2}T_0\dfrac{(x_1 + ix_2)x_3}{r^2}$ $\left.-\dfrac32 T_{-1}\dfrac{(x_1 + ix_2)^2}{r^2}\right]$	$\dfrac12 g^2\beta^2\left[-\dfrac{3}{\sqrt2}T_{+1}\dfrac{(x_1 - ix_2)x_3}{r^2}\right.$ $-T_0\left(1 - \dfrac{3x_3^2}{r^2}\right)$ $\left.+\dfrac{3}{\sqrt2}T_{-1}\dfrac{(x_1 + ix_2)x_3}{r^2}\right]$	$\dfrac12 g^2\beta^2\left[-\dfrac32 T_{+1}\dfrac{(x_1 - ix_2)^2}{r^2}\right.$ $+\dfrac{3}{\sqrt2}T_0\dfrac{(x_1 - ix_2)x_3}{r^2}$ $\left.+\dfrac12 T_{-1}\left(1 - \dfrac{3x_3^2}{r^2}\right)\right]$

TABLE II

Matrix Elements of the Spin-Spin Hamiltonian $\mathcal{H}'$ in the Basis $(\varphi_a(1, 2)T_{+1}, \varphi_a(1, 2)T_0, \varphi_a(1, 2)T_{-1})$

	$\varphi_a(1, 2)T_{+1}$	$\varphi_a(1, 2)T_0$	$\varphi_a(1, 2)T_{-1}$
$\varphi_a(1, 2)T_{+1}$	$\frac{1}{4}g^2\beta^2\langle\varphi_a(1, 2)\mid(r^2 - 3x_3^2)/r^5\mid\varphi_a(1, 2)\rangle$	0	$-\frac{3}{4}g^2\beta^2\langle\varphi_a(1, 2)\mid(x_1^2 - x_2^2)/r^5\mid\varphi_a(1, 2)\rangle$
$\varphi_a(1, 2)T_0$	0	$-\frac{1}{2}g^2\beta^2\langle\varphi_a(1, 2)\mid(r^2 - 3x_3^2)/r^5\mid\varphi_a(1, 2)\rangle$	0
$\varphi_a(1, 2)T_{-1}$	$-\frac{3}{4}g^2\beta^2\langle\varphi_a(1, 2)\mid(x_1^2 - x_2^2)/r^5\mid\varphi_a(1, 2)\rangle$	0	$\frac{1}{4}g^2\beta^2\langle\varphi_a(1, 2)\mid(r^2 - 3x_3^2)/r^5\mid\varphi_a(1, 2)\rangle$

the orthonormality property of T_1, T_0, T_{-1}, as well as the property that spatial integrals over odd functions vanish. In this basis set the Hamiltonian $\mathcal{H}'$ is not diagonal; however, a new basis set may be found in which $\mathcal{H}'$ is diagonal. This set consists of the following linear combinations:

$$
\begin{aligned}
T_1 &= -\sqrt{2}^{-1}(T_{+1} - T_{-1}) \\
&= \sqrt{2}^{-1}[\beta(1)\beta(2) - \alpha(1)\alpha(2)] \\
T_2 &= (i/\sqrt{2})(T_{+1} + T_{-1}) \\
&= (i/\sqrt{2})[\beta(1)\beta(2) + \alpha(1)\alpha(2)] \\
T_3 &= T_0 \\
&= \sqrt{2}^{-1}[\alpha(1)\beta(2) + \beta(1)\alpha(2)]
\end{aligned}
\tag{24}
$$

with the inverse relations

$$
\begin{aligned}
T_{+1} &= -\sqrt{2}^{-1}[T_1 + iT_2] \\
T_0 &= T_3 \\
T_{-1} &= \sqrt{2}^{-1}[T_1 - iT_2]
\end{aligned}
\tag{25}
$$

The properties of the functions T_1, T_2, T_3 are displayed in Table III. We note that both (T_{+1}, T_0, T_{-1}) and (T_1, T_2, T_3) are eigenfunctions of S^2 and $\mathbf{S}(1) \cdot \mathbf{S}(2)$ with eigenvalues of 2 and $\frac{1}{4}$, respectively. An important difference arises with respect to S_3; the functions T_{+1}, T_0, T_{-1} are eigenfunctions of S_3 with eigenvalues 1, 0, -1, respectively, whereas T_1 and T_2 are no longer eigenfunctions of S_3. Indeed S_3 operating on T_1 or T_2 gives a mixture of T_{+1} and T_{-1}; clearly the states described by T_1 and T_2 do not have sharp values of the magnetic quantum number m_s, and the latter is no longer a constant of motion. Another mode of expression is to say that the spin-spin operator $\mathcal{H}'$ mixes "spin-up" and "spin-down" states. T_3 and T_0 are of course identical and the properties of that state remain unaffected.

Several operator identities, which may be verified with the aid of Table I or III, are:

$$
S_i(1) S_i(2) = \tfrac{1}{2} S_i^2 - \tfrac{1}{4}
\tag{26}
$$

$$
\mathbf{S}(1) \cdot \mathbf{S}(2) = \tfrac{1}{4}
\tag{27}
$$

Using the basis set $(\varphi_a(1, 2) T_1,\ \varphi_a(1, 2) T_2,\ \varphi_a(1, 2) T_3)$, the Hamiltonian matrix is diagonal, as shown in Table IV. The eigenvalues are

$$
\begin{aligned}
X &= \tfrac{1}{2} g^2 \beta^2 \langle \varphi_a(1, 2) \mid (3x_1^2 - r^2)/r^5 \mid \varphi_a(1, 2) \rangle \\
Y &= \tfrac{1}{2} g^2 \beta^2 \langle \varphi_a(1, 2) \mid (3x_2^2 - r^2)/r^5 \mid \varphi_a(1, 2) \rangle \\
Z &= \tfrac{1}{2} g^2 \beta^2 \langle \varphi_a(1, 2) \mid (3x_3^2 - r^2)/r^5 \mid \varphi_a(1, 2) \rangle
\end{aligned}
\tag{28}
$$

and

$$
X + Y + Z = 0
\tag{29}
$$

TABLE III

EFFECT OF SPIN OPERATORS ON T_1, T_2, AND T_3

Spin operator	T_1	T_2	T_3
$S_1 = S_1(1) + S_1(2)$	0	iT_3	$-iT_2$
$S_2 = S_2(1) + S_2(2)$	$-iT_3$	0	iT_1
$S_3 = S_3(1) + S_3(2)$	iT_2	$-iT_1$	0
$S_1(1)S_1(2)$	$-\frac14 T_1$	$\frac14 T_2$	$\frac14 T_3$
$S_2(1)S_2(2)$	$\frac14 T_1$	$-\frac14 T_2$	$\frac14 T_3$
$S_3(1)S_3(2)$	$\frac14 T_1$	$\frac14 T_2$	$-\frac14 T_3$
$S_1{}^2 = [S_1(1) + S_1(2)]^2$	0	T_2	T_3
$S_2{}^2 = [S_2(1) + S_2(2)]^2$	T_1	0	T_3
$S_3{}^2 = [S_3(1) + S_3(2)]^2$	T_1	T_2	0
$S^2 = S_1{}^2 + S_2{}^2 + S_3{}^2$	$2T_1$	$2T_2$	$2T_3$
$\mathbf{S}(1)\cdot\mathbf{S}(2)$	$\frac14 T_1$	$\frac14 T_2$	$\frac14 T_3$
$S_+ = S_+(1) + S_+(2)$	T_3	iT_3	$-(T_1 + iT_2) = -T_+$
$S_- = S_-(1) + S_-(2)$	$-T_3$	iT_3	$T_1 - iT_2 = T_-$
$S_+ S_-$	$T_1 + iT_2 = T_+$	$-i(T_1 + iT_2) = -iT_+$	$2T_3$
$S_+(1)S_+(2)$	$\frac12(T_1 + iT_2) = \frac12 T_+$	$-\frac12 i(T_1 + iT_2) = -\frac12(i)T_+$	0
$S_-(1)S_-(2)$	$-\frac12(T_1 - iT_2) = -\frac12 T_-$	$\frac12 i(T_1 - iT_2) = \frac12(i)T_-$	0
$S_+(1)S_3(2) + S_3(1)S_+(2)$	$-\frac12 T_3$	$-\frac12(i)T_3$	$-\frac12(T_1 + iT_2) = -\frac12 T_+$
$S_-(1)S_3(2) + S_3(1)S_-(2)$	$-\frac12 T_3$	$\frac12(i)T_3$	$-\frac12(T_1 - iT_2) = -\frac12 T_-$
$\mathcal{H}'$	$\frac12 \frac{g^2\beta^2}{r^3}\left[\left(\frac{3x_1{}^2}{r^2} - 1\right)T_1 + \frac{3x_1x_2}{r^2}T_2 + \frac{3x_1x_3}{r^2}T_3\right]$	$\frac12 \frac{g^2\beta^2}{r^3}\left[\frac{3x_2x_1}{r^2}T_1 + \left(\frac{3x_2{}^2}{r^2} - 1\right)T_2 + \frac{3x_2x_3}{r^2}T_3\right]$	$\frac12 \frac{g^2\beta^2}{r^3}\left[\frac{3x_3x_1}{r^2}T_1 + \frac{3x_3x_2}{r^2}T_2 + \left(\frac{3x_3{}^2}{r^2} - 1\right)T_3\right]$

TABLE IV

Matrix Elements of the Spin–Spin Hamiltonian $\mathcal{H}'$ in the Basis $(\varphi_a(1,2)T_1,\ \varphi_a(1,2)T_2,\ \varphi_a(1,2)T_3)$

	$\varphi_a(1,2)T_1$	$\varphi_a(1,2)T_2$	$\varphi_a(1,2)T_3$
$\varphi_a(1,2)T_1$	$\frac{1}{2}g^2\beta^2\langle\varphi_a(1,2)\mid(3x_1^2 - r^2)/r^5\mid\varphi_a(1,2)\rangle$	0	0
$\varphi_a(1,2)T_2$	0	$\frac{1}{2}g^2\beta^2\langle\varphi_a(1,2)\mid(3x_2^2 - r^2)/r^5\mid\varphi_a(1,2)\rangle$	0
$\varphi_a(1,2)T_3$	0	0	$\frac{1}{2}g^2\beta^2\langle\varphi_a(1,2)\mid(3x_3^2 - r^2)/r^5\mid\varphi_a(1,2)\rangle$

For systems of symmetry lower than cubic, the terms X, Y, Z are not equal and the triplet state consists of two or three separated levels. Thus, a molecule whose charge distribution is anisotropic with respect to the x_1, x_2, x_3 axes may exhibit zero-field splitting. In Hückel approximation, for example, the highly anisotropic $2p_z$ orbitals are often used for aromatic molecules. In contrast, for spherically symmetric systems such as atoms, x_1, x_2, and x_3 are equivalent directions resulting in $X = Y = Z$ or a threefold degenerate state.

C. Spin Hamiltonian

One form of the spin-spin Hamiltonian was given in Eq. (12). Applying the identities Eqs. (26) and (27), we obtain

$$\mathcal{H}_p' = g^2\beta^2\left[(\tfrac{1}{2}S_x^2 - \tfrac{1}{4})\left(\frac{r^2 - 3x^2}{r^5}\right) + (\tfrac{1}{2}S_y^2 - \tfrac{1}{4})\left(\frac{r^2 - 3y^2}{r^5}\right)\right.$$

$$\left. + (\tfrac{1}{2}S_z^2 - \tfrac{1}{4})\left(\frac{r^2 - 3z^2}{r^5}\right)\right] \quad (30)$$

The spin Hamiltonian is obtained by integrating over the space variables, leaving an operator which acts only on spin functions

$$\mathcal{H}_{\text{spin}} = \langle\varphi_a(1, 2) \mid \mathcal{H}' \mid \varphi_a(1, 2)\rangle$$

$$= -[X S_x^2 + Y S_y^2 + Z S_z^2] \quad (31)$$

where X, Y, Z are the same quantities given in Eq. (28). The constant terms do not contribute to the zero-field splitting and have been omitted.

Repeating the process beginning with Eq. (13), we are led to another form:

$$\mathcal{H}_p' = g^2\beta^2\left[(\tfrac{3}{4}S_z^2 - \tfrac{1}{2})\left(\frac{r^2 - 3z^2}{r^5}\right) + \tfrac{3}{4}(S_x^2 - S_y^2)\left(\frac{y^2 - x^2}{r^5}\right)\right] \quad (32)$$

and the spin Hamiltonian becomes

$$\mathcal{H}_{\text{spin}} = \langle\varphi_a(1, 2) \mid \mathcal{H}_p' \mid \varphi_a(1, 2)\rangle$$

$$= D(S_z^2 - \tfrac{1}{3}S^2) + E(S_x^2 - S_y^2) \quad (33)$$

where

$$D = \tfrac{3}{4}g^2\beta^2\langle\varphi_a(1, 2) \mid (r^2 - 3z^2)/r^5 \mid \varphi_a(1, 2)\rangle$$

$$E = \tfrac{3}{4}g^2\beta^2\langle\varphi_a(1, 2) \mid (y^2 - x^2)/r^5 \mid \varphi_a(1, 2)\rangle \quad (34)$$

The term $-\tfrac{1}{3}DS^2$ is a constant and does not contribute to the zero-field splitting; it is included in order to put the center of gravity of the split levels at zero energy. Both D and E depend on the spatial distribution of the two electrons responsible for the triplet state and are therefore sensitive to the local environment. Molecules having a trigonal or higher axis of symmetry belong to the group D_3 (or to a group containing D_3 as a subgroup), which consists of two one-dimensional and one two-dimensional irreducible representations. Terms x and y transform according to the two-dimensional representation and are therefore equivalent directions. Since T_x and T_y transform as x and y, they too belong to the same representation and therefore constitute a pair of degenerate eigenfunctions. As a result, $E = 0$, the energy levels consist of a singlet and a doublet, and a single parameter, namely D, suffices to describe the zero-field splitting.

With the aid of Table III and Eq. (29), the eigenvalue equations for the two forms of the spin Hamiltonian may be obtained. We note that the relations given in Table III are valid in any coordinate system and, in particular, hold for the principal axis system x, y, z.

$$\mathcal{H}_{\text{spin}} T_x = -(Y + Z) T_x$$
$$= X T_x$$
$$= (\tfrac{1}{3}D - E) T_x$$
$$\mathcal{H}_{\text{spin}} T_y = -(X + Z) T_y$$
$$= Y T_y \qquad (35)$$
$$= (\tfrac{1}{3}D + E) T_y$$
$$\mathcal{H}_{\text{spin}} T_z = -(X + Y) T_z$$
$$= Z T_z$$
$$= -\tfrac{2}{3}D T_z$$

From Eq. (35) we obtain

$$X = \tfrac{1}{3}D - E$$
$$Y = \tfrac{1}{3}D + E$$
$$Z = -\tfrac{2}{3}D \qquad (36)$$
$$D = \tfrac{1}{2}(X + Y) - Z$$
$$E = \tfrac{1}{2}(Y - X)$$

The same relations are obtained by comparing Eqs. (28) with (34). Such consistency is not obtained if the constant term in Eq. (33) is omitted.

A relation to be needed later is

$$D^{*2} = D^2 + 3E^2 = \tfrac{3}{2}(X^2 + Y^2 + Z^2)$$
$$= -3(XY + XZ + YZ) \qquad (37)$$

It is useful to point out that ESR measurements are usually interpreted in terms of the zfs parameters D, E, or X, Y, Z. Similarly, the object of the theory is to calculate these parameters from suitable molecular wave functions. It may therefore be said that it is in the spin Hamiltonian that theory and experiment meet.

In the two-electron cases, the spatial part of the wave function is anti-symmetric and has a node at the origin. Therefore, the probability that two electrons will be close to one another is small. An important conse-quence of this is that an approximate electronic wave function for the two electrons will still give reasonable values of zero-field splitting, even if the approximation is not very good at distances of close approach. McConnell (1959) generalized this property to N-electron systems and showed that the zero-field splittings depend only on those components of the two-particle density matrix that are antisymmetric in their space variables. The basic physical principle is, of course, the Pauli principle, which pre-vents two electrons with parallel spins from coming close together.

The same result follows from McLachlan's spin-correlation function (McLachlan, 1963), as well as from McWeeny's "coupling anisotropy function" (McWeeny, 1961).

III. Interaction with an External Magnetic Field

A. Resonance Fields

In aromatic molecules, the spin-spin interaction and the interaction with the magnetic field in a typical ESR experiment are of the same order of magnitude and must be considered together in the Hamiltonian. It is convenient to picture the two effects as a simultaneous quantization along axes of symmetry, as well as along the direction of the field. It is therefore to be expected that large anisotropies would arise. This was first demon-strated by Hutchison and Mangum (1961) when they observed that the resonance fields, that is, the magnetic fields at which ESR signals were detected, depended markedly on the orientation of the molecules in the field.

The application of a magnetic field adds another term to the Hamiltonian:

$$\mathcal{3C} = \mathcal{3C}' + \beta \mathbf{H} \cdot g \cdot \mathbf{S} \qquad (38)$$

or, using Eq. (33),

$$\mathcal{H} = \beta \mathbf{H} \cdot g \cdot \mathbf{S} + D(S_z^2 - \tfrac{1}{3}S^2) + E(S_x^2 - S_y^2) \tag{39}$$

Experimentally it is found that g deviates very little from the free spin value; hence we may use the simpler form

$$\mathcal{H} = g\beta \mathbf{S} \cdot \mathbf{H} + D(S_z^2 - \tfrac{1}{3}S^2) + E(S_x^2 - S_y^2) \tag{40}$$

or the equivalent form based on Eq. (31):

$$\mathcal{H} = g\beta \mathbf{S} \cdot \mathbf{H} - (XS_x^2 + YS_y^2 + ZS_z^2) \tag{41}$$

Spin-order coupling has been neglected; this is justified both on theoretical grounds and on the basis of experimentally measured lifetimes of the phosphorescent state.

In order that we may deal with molecules having arbitrary orientations with respect to an external magnetic field, it is necessary to define the following coordinate systems (Kottis and Lefebvre, 1963):

The x_1, x_2, x_3 describe a set of fixed axes, i.e., the laboratory system. The static magnetic field H will be taken in the x_3 direction (Fig. 4). Subse-

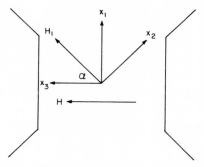

FIG. 4. Laboratory coordinate system. The static magnetic field, H, is along x_3; the microwave oscillating field, H_1, lies in the x_1x_3 plane, at an angle α with respect to H.

quently, for purposes of ESR experiments, we shall need an oscillating magnetic field; the latter, H_1, will be assumed to lie in the x_1x_3 plane at an angle α to the static field.

The xyz describe a set of molecular axes, i.e., a set of axes attached to the molecule. In this system the static magnetic field is in the direction (θ, φ), where θ and φ are the polar and azimuth angles, respectively. Moreover x, y, z, are so oriented within the molecule as to diagonalize the spin-spin tensor whose principal values are X, Y, Z. In other words, the molecular axes x, y, z are assumed to coincide with the principal axes of the spin-spin Hamiltonian. Usually, the symmetry of the molecule will determine the orientation of the axes. Thus in naphthalene there are three symmetry axes, and the only arbitrariness left is in the labeling. If the symmetry is not sufficient to determine the axes, they are chosen so as to diagonalize the spin-spin tensor.

We shall from now on express all quantities in the molecular system of axes x, y, z; the spin eigenfunctions are T_x, T_y, T_z. For a magnetic field arbitrarily oriented relative to the molecular axes, the components are

$$H_x = H \sin \theta \cos \varphi$$
$$H_y = H \sin \theta \sin \varphi \qquad (42)$$
$$H_z = H \cos \theta$$

and the Hamiltonian matrix, in the basis set T_x, T_y, and T_z becomes, according to Eqs. (35) and Table III,

$$\mathcal{K} = \begin{pmatrix} \frac{1}{3}D - E & -ig\beta H \cos \theta & ig\beta H \sin \theta \sin \varphi \\ ig\beta H \cos \theta & \frac{1}{3}D + E & -ig\beta H \sin \theta \cos \varphi \\ -ig\beta H \sin \theta \sin \varphi & ig\beta H \sin \theta \cos \varphi & -\frac{2}{3}D \end{pmatrix}$$

$$(43)$$

or

$$\mathcal{K} = \begin{pmatrix} X & -ig\beta H \cos \theta & ig\beta H \sin \theta \sin \varphi \\ ig\beta H \cos \theta & Y & -ig\beta H \sin \theta \cos \varphi \\ -ig\beta H \sin \theta \sin \varphi & ig\beta H \sin \theta \cos \varphi & Z \end{pmatrix}$$

$$(44)$$

Remembering that

$$X + Y + Z = 0$$

the secular equation based on the Hamiltonian matrix Eq. (44) is

$$\epsilon^3 - \epsilon[(g\beta H)^2 - (XY + XZ + YZ)]$$
$$+ (g\beta H)^2[X \sin^2 \theta \cos^2 \varphi + Y \sin^2 \theta \sin^2 \varphi + Z \cos^2 \theta] - XYZ = 0 \quad (45)$$

Equation (45) gives the complete development of the triplet state in a magnetic field, as illustrated in Fig. 3. For special purposes the solutions may be expressed in various ways:

1. For a given orientation of the magnetic field, that is, for given θ and φ, the roots ϵ_1, ϵ_2, ϵ_3 give the energies of the three triplet states as a function of magnetic field.

2. ESR spectrometers usually operate at a fixed microwave frequency and varying magnetic field. Hence for given θ, φ, the magnetic fields at which resonance occurs are obtained from the solutions of Eq. (45) subject to the condition

$$\epsilon_i - \epsilon_j = \delta \tag{46}$$

where ϵ_i and ϵ_j are two roots and δ is the energy of a microwave photon at the frequency of the spectrometer.

3. It is often useful to know the values of ϵ_i and ϵ_j, which are roots of Eq. (45), for given θ and φ and are also subject to condition Eq. (46).

We shall now consider these forms separately.

1′. The solution of Eq. (45) for various cases presents no special problems. It is seen immediately that, for a given magnetic field strength H the triplet state energies ϵ_i will depend on the orientation of the field, that is, the values of θ and φ. For a magnetic field oriented parallel to the x axis of the molecule, equivalent to $\theta = \pi/2$, $\varphi = 0$, the secular equation reduces to

$$\epsilon^3 - \epsilon[(g\beta H)^2 - (XY + XZ + YZ)] + (g\beta H)^2 X - XYZ = 0 \tag{47}$$

with solutions

$$\epsilon_1 = X$$

$$\epsilon_{2,3} = \tfrac{1}{2}(Y + Z) \pm \{[\tfrac{1}{2}(Y - Z)]^2 + (g\beta H)^2\}^{1/2} \tag{48}$$

Analogous solutions are readily obtained for the magnetic field along the y or z axes. These are given in Table V.

2′. The general solution of Eq. (45) subject to the condition of Eq. (46) was obtained by Kottis and Lefebvre (1963), who give the following relation:

$$X \sin^2 \theta \cos^2 \varphi + Y \sin^2 \theta \sin^2 \varphi + Z \cos^2 \theta$$

$$= \frac{XYZ}{(g\beta H)^2} \pm (\tfrac{1}{3})^{3/2} \left[\frac{\delta^2 + XY + XZ + YZ}{(g\beta H)^2} - 1 \right]$$

$$\times [4(g\beta H)^2 - \delta^2 - 4(XY + XZ + YZ)]^{1/2} \tag{49}$$

An equivalent form of Eq. (49) is (de Groot and van der Waals, 1963c)

$$X \sin^2 \theta \cos^2 \varphi + Y \sin^2 \theta \sin^2 \varphi + Z \cos^2 \theta$$

$$= (g\beta H)^{-2}[XYZ \pm \tfrac{1}{9}\{\delta^2 - (g\beta H)^2 - \tfrac{1}{3}D^{*2}\}$$

$$\times \{12(g\beta H)^2 - 3\delta^2 + 4D^{*2}\}^{1/2}] \tag{50}$$

TABLE V

ENERGIES AND EIGENFUNCTIONS OF TRIPLET LEVELS IN MAGNETIC FIELDS

Energy	H_x	H_y	H_z
ϵ_1	$-X$	$\frac{1}{2}(X+Z) + [\frac{1}{2}(X-Z)^2 + (g\beta H)^2]^{1/2}$ $= \frac{1}{2}(X+Z) + \frac{1}{2}\delta$	$\frac{1}{2}(X+Y) + [\frac{1}{2}(X-Y)^2 + (g\beta H)^2]^{1/2}$ $= \frac{1}{2}(X+Y) + \frac{1}{2}\delta$
V_1	T_x	$\sqrt{2}^{-1}\left[\left(1 + \frac{X-Z}{\delta}\right)^{1/2} T_x + i\left(1 - \frac{X-Z}{\delta}\right)^{1/2} T_z\right]$	$\sqrt{2}^{-1}\left[\left(1 + \frac{X-Y}{\delta}\right)^{1/2} T_x + i\left(1 - \frac{X-Y}{\delta}\right)^{1/2} T_y\right]$
ϵ_2	$\frac{1}{2}(Y+Z) + [\frac{1}{2}(Y-Z)^2 + (g\beta H)^2]^{1/2}$ $= \frac{1}{2}(Y+Z) + \frac{1}{2}\delta$	Y	$\frac{1}{2}(X+Y) - [\frac{1}{2}(X-Y)^2 + (g\beta H)^2]^{1/2}$ $= \frac{1}{2}(X+Y) - \frac{1}{2}\delta$
V_2	$\sqrt{2}^{-1}\left[\left(1 + \frac{Y-Z}{\delta}\right)^{1/2} T_y + i\left(1 - \frac{Y-Z}{\delta}\right)^{1/2} T_z\right]$	T_y	$\sqrt{2}^{-1}\left[i\left(1 - \frac{X-Y}{\delta}\right)^{1/2} T_x + \left(1 + \frac{X-Y}{\delta}\right)^{1/2} T_y\right]$
ϵ_3	$\frac{1}{2}(Y+Z) - [\frac{1}{2}(Y-Z)^2 + (g\beta H)^2]^{1/2}$ $= \frac{1}{2}(Y+Z) - \frac{1}{2}\delta$	$\frac{1}{2}(X+Z) - [\frac{1}{2}(X-Z)^2 + (g\beta H)^2]^{1/2}$ $= \frac{1}{2}(X+Z) - \frac{1}{2}\delta$	Z
V_3	$\sqrt{2}^{-1}\left[i\left(1 - \frac{Y-Z}{\delta}\right)^{1/2} T_y + \left(1 + \frac{Y-Z}{\delta}\right)^{1/2} T_z\right]$	$\sqrt{2}^{-1}\left[i\left(1 - \frac{X-Z}{\delta}\right)^{1/2} T_x + \left(1 + \frac{X-Z}{\delta}\right)^{1/2} T_z\right]$	T_z

in which

$$D^{*2} = D^2 + 3E^2 = \tfrac{3}{2}(X^2 + Y^2 + Z^2)$$

$$= -3(XY + XZ + YZ) \tag{51}$$

Equations (49) or (50) are best handled graphically. This is illustrated in Fig. 5, where the right-hand side of Eq. (49) is plotted against H for

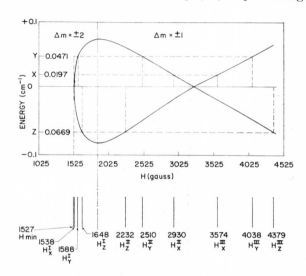

FIG. 5. Resonance fields for naphthalene at 9279 Mc/sec (after Kottis and Lefebvre, 1963). H_{min} is the lowest field at which resonance occurs. $H_x{}^{I} \cdots H_z{}^{III}$ are the resonance fields for canonical orientations.

specified values of X, Y, Z, and δ. The resonance fields for canonical orientations of the magnetic field are shown in this figure. It is seen that in each direction there are three resonance fields spread over a large range of magnetic fields. Moreover, the spread in resonance fields along the three directions is less in the low-field region than in the high-field region. It may further be shown that the resonance fields considered a function of orientation have stationary values along the canonical directions.

For a magnetic field parallel to the x axis of the molecule or $\theta = \pi/2$, $\varphi = 0$, the condition of Eq. (49) or Eq. (50) is satisfied when

$$H_x{}^{I} = (2g\beta)^{-1}[\delta^2 - (Y - Z)^2]^{1/2}$$

$$H_x{}^{II} = (2g\beta)^{-1}[(2\delta - 3X)^2 - (Y - Z)^2]^{1/2} \tag{52}$$

$$H_x{}^{III} = (2g\beta)^{-1}[(2\delta + 3X)^2 - (Y - Z)^2]^{1/2}$$

WEISSBLUTH

TABLE VI
RESONANCE FIELDS

Magnetic field	$2g\beta H^{I}$ ($\Delta m = \pm 2$)	$2g\beta H^{II}$ ($\Delta m = \pm 1$)	$2g\beta H^{III}$ ($\Delta m = \pm 1$)
H_x	$[\delta^2 - (Y - Z)^2]^{1/2}$	$[(2\delta - 3X)^2 - (Y - Z)^2]^{1/2}$	$[(2\delta + 3X)^2 - (Y - Z)^2]^{1/2}$
H_y	$[\delta^2 - (Z - X)^2]^{1/2}$	$[(2\delta - 3Y)^2 - (Z - X)^2]^{1/2}$	$[(2\delta + 3Y)^2 - (Z - X)^2]^{1/2}$
H_z	$[\delta^2 - (X - Y)^2]^{1/2}$	$[(2\delta - 3Z)^2 - (X - Y)^2]^{1/2}$	$[(2\delta + 3Z)^2 - (X - Y)^2]^{1/2}$

These are the three values of magnetic field, applied in the x direction, at which resonance may be observed. For magnetic fields applied in other directions, the resonance values are listed in Table VI.

It should be further noted that the distribution of resonance fields depends in a complicated way on the microwave frequency of the spectrometer. It is therefore not possible to describe resonances in terms of g values, which imply a linear relation between microwave frequency and magnetic field.

Equations (52) may be obtained from Eq. (48); thus

$$\epsilon_2 - \epsilon_3 = \delta = 2[\tfrac{1}{2}(Y - Z)^2 + (g\beta H)^2]^{1/2}$$

and

$$H = (2g\beta)^{-1}[\delta^2 - (Y - Z)^2]^{1/2} = H_x{}^{\mathrm{I}} \tag{53}$$

Similarly,

$$\epsilon_1 - \epsilon_3 = \delta = X - \tfrac{1}{2}(Y + Z) + [\tfrac{1}{2}(Y - Z)^2 + (g\beta H)^2]^{1/2}$$

$$H = (2g\beta)^{-1}[(2\delta - 3X)^2 - (Y - Z)^2]^{1/2} = H_x{}^{\mathrm{II}} \tag{54}$$

and

$$\epsilon_2 - \epsilon_1 = \delta = \tfrac{1}{2}(Y + Z) + [\tfrac{1}{2}(Y - Z)^2 + (g\beta H)^2]^{1/2} - X$$

$$H = (2g\beta)^{-1}[(2\delta + 3X)^2 - (Y - Z)^2]^{1/2} = H_x{}^{\mathrm{III}} \tag{55}$$

3′. In a magnetic field which produces resonance, that is, a field of the proper magnitude and orientation to cause two of the three triplet levels to be separated by an energy δ, the energies of the two levels may readily be found. Thus, let the two levels correspond to the two roots ϵ_i and ϵ_j of the cubic Eq. (45) with the condition that

$$\epsilon_i - \epsilon_j = \delta$$

By substituting, in turn, $\epsilon = \epsilon_i$ and $\epsilon = \epsilon_i - \delta$ into Eq. (45) and subtracting one from the other, one gets

$$3\epsilon_i^2 - 3\delta\epsilon_i + \{\delta^2 - [(g\beta H)^2 - (XY + XZ + YZ)]\} = 0 \tag{56}$$

The solutions are

$$\epsilon_i = \tfrac{1}{2}\delta \pm (1/2\sqrt{3})[(2g\beta H)^2 - \delta^2 - 4(XY + XZ + YZ)]^{1/2}$$

$$\epsilon_j = \epsilon_i - \delta \tag{57}$$

or

$$\epsilon_i = \tfrac{1}{2}\delta \pm \tfrac{1}{6}[12(g\beta H)^2 - 3\delta^2 + 4D^{*2}]^{1/2}$$

$$D^{*2} = D^2 + 3E^2 \tag{58}$$

As an example of the use of these equations, we may let H correspond to a resonance field, say,

$$2g\beta H = 2g\beta H_x{}^{\mathrm{I}} = [\delta^2 - (Y - Z)^2]^{1/2} \tag{53}$$

Substitution into Eq. (57) yields

$$\epsilon_i = \tfrac{1}{2}(Y + Z) + \tfrac{1}{2}\delta \tag{59}$$

$$\epsilon_j = \tfrac{1}{2}(Y + Z) - \tfrac{1}{2}\delta$$

Additional expressions are given in Table V.

B. Eigenfunctions and Transitions

In the absence of a magnetic field the spin eigenfunctions are T_x, T_y, T_z. When a magnetic field is applied, the new eigenfunctions are given by linear combinations of T_x, T_y, T_z:

$$V = c_x T_x + c_y T_y + c_z T_z \tag{60}$$

The new functions V must satisfy the Schrodinger equation

$$\mathfrak{K}V = \epsilon V \tag{61}$$

in which

$$\mathfrak{K} = g\beta \mathbf{S}\cdot\mathbf{H} - [X S_x{}^2 + Y S_y{}^2 + Z S_z{}^2]$$

or any of the equivalent forms discussed previously.

This requirement leads to the set of homogeneous equations

$$c_x(X - \epsilon) - i c_y g\beta H_z + i c_z g\beta H_y = 0$$

$$i c_x g\beta H_z + c_y(Y - \epsilon) - i c_z g\beta H_x = 0 \tag{62}$$

$$-i c_x g\beta H_y + i c_y g\beta H_x + c_z(Z - \epsilon) = 0$$

The roots of the secular Eq. (45), when substituted in turn into Eqs. (62), yield the coefficients which define V_1, V_2, V_3 and which are the eigenfunction of the Hamiltonian with eigenvalues ϵ_1, ϵ_2, ϵ_3.

For a magnetic field applied in the x direction, the eigenvalues are

$$\epsilon_1 = X; \qquad \epsilon_{2,3} = \tfrac{1}{2}(Y + Z) \pm \tfrac{1}{2}\delta \tag{63}$$

Substituting these in turn into Eq. (62), we get

$$V_1 = T_x$$

$$V_2 = \frac{1}{\sqrt{2}}\left\{ \left(1 + \frac{Y - Z}{\delta}\right)^{1/2} T_y + i\left(1 - \frac{Y - Z}{\delta}\right)^{1/2} T_z \right\} \tag{64}$$

$$V_3 = \frac{1}{\sqrt{2}}\left\{ i\left(1 - \frac{Y - Z}{\delta}\right)^{1/2} T_y + \left(1 + \frac{Y - Z}{\delta}\right)^{1/2} T_z \right\}$$

Eigenfunctions for other orientations are given in Table V; solutions for the general case are given by Kottis and Lefebvre (1963).

The matrix element associated with a transition between two of the three levels is

$$\langle V_i \mid \mathbf{\mu} \cdot \mathbf{H}_1 \mid V_j \rangle \qquad (65)$$

in which $\mathbf{\mu}$ is the magnetic moment operator

$$\mathbf{\mu} = g\beta\mathbf{S} \qquad (66)$$

and $\mathbf{H}_1$ is the oscillating magnetic field associated with the microwave energy. Thus the matrix elements to be evaluated are of the form

$$\langle V_i \mid \mathbf{H}_1 \cdot \mathbf{S} \mid V_j \rangle \qquad (67)$$

With the aid of Table III, it may be verified that the only nonvanishing matrix elements are

$$\langle T_x \mid S_y \mid T_z \rangle; \qquad \langle T_y \mid S_z \mid T_x \rangle; \qquad \langle T_z \mid S_x \mid T_y \rangle$$

each of which has the value i. For the first two matrix elements, the microwave magnetic field is perpendicular to x, whereas for the third it is parallel to x. Quite generally, we may write

$$V_1 = c_{1x}T_x + c_{1y}T_y + c_{1z}T_z$$
$$V_2 = c_{2x}T_x + c_{2y}T_y + c_{2z}T_z \qquad (68)$$
$$V_3 = c_{3x}T_x + c_{3y}T_y + c_{3z}T_z$$

As shown by de Groot and van der Waals (1960)

$$\langle V_1 \mid \mathbf{S} \mid V_2 \rangle = -i(\mathbf{c}_1 \times \mathbf{c}_2)$$
$$\langle V_1 \mid \mathbf{S} \mid V_3 \rangle = -i(\mathbf{c}_1 \times \mathbf{c}_3) \qquad (69)$$
$$\langle V_2 \mid \mathbf{S} \mid V_3 \rangle = -i(\mathbf{c}_2 \times \mathbf{c}_3)$$

in which $\mathbf{c}_i$ is a vector with components (c_{ix}, c_{iy}, c_{iz}).

The general case in which the static magnetic field H is arbitrarily oriented relative to the molecular axes and in which the oscillating magnetic field H_1 may have variable orientation is treated by Kottis and Lefebvre (1963).

The levels ϵ_i may be described in terms of their properties in the limit of high magnetic field, where the coupling of the spins to the constant field is much stronger than the spin-spin interaction. In this limit, the magnetic quantum number m becomes a constant of motion, and the levels may be labeled, as in the atomic case, by $m = \pm 1, 0, -1$. The allowed transitions are those corresponding to $\Delta m = \pm 1$, whereas those corresponding to $\Delta m = \pm 2$ are strictly forbidden. Thus, Eqs. (48), for example, become

$$\epsilon_1 = 0; \qquad m = 0$$

$$\epsilon_2 = g\beta H; \qquad m = +1 \qquad\qquad (70)$$

$$\epsilon_3 = -g\beta H; \qquad m = -1$$

and the allowed transitions are $\epsilon_2 \leftrightarrow \epsilon_1$ and $\epsilon_3 \leftrightarrow \epsilon_1$, each with energy separations of $g\beta H$ or resonance fields of $\delta/g\beta$.

For less intense magnetic fields, the level separations resulting from the spin-magnetic field interaction and the zero-field splitting are comparable in magnitude. The levels can no longer be described in terms of precise values of m, since the latter is no longer an appropriate or "good" quantum number. Transitions may now occur among the three levels wherever they are energetically possible, with no regard to selection rules. Nevertheless, it is often useful to retain the high-field terminology throughout the range of magnetic fields and to describe the transitions as corresponding to $\Delta m = \pm 1$ or $\Delta m = \pm 2$. As may be seen from Figs. 3 and 5, the $\Delta m = \pm 2$ transitions, for a fixed microwave frequency, occur at a lower value of magnetic field than the $\Delta m = \pm 1$ transitions. This is also evident from Eqs. (70), where the $\Delta m = \pm 2$ transition corresponds to $\epsilon_2 \leftrightarrow \epsilon_3$ and occurs at a field given by $\delta/2g\beta$. For this reason, we may speak of "low-field" transitions corresponding to $\Delta m = \pm 2$ and "high-field" transitions corresponding to $\Delta m = \pm 1$ with the understanding that both "low" and "high" fields are in the region where the zero-field splitting is not negligible. A summary of the polarizations and pertinent matrix elements is given in Table VII.

TABLE VII

TRANSITIONS

Transition	Polarization of H_1	Contribution matrix elements	
Low field, $\Delta m = \pm 2$			
$H_x{}^{\mathrm{I}}$	$\parallel$ to x and H	$\langle T_z \mid S_x \mid T_y \rangle$	
$H_y{}^{\mathrm{I}}$	$\parallel$ to y and H	$\langle T_x \mid S_y \mid T_z \rangle$	
$H_z{}^{\mathrm{I}}$	$\parallel$ to z and H	$\langle T_y \mid S_z \mid T_x \rangle$	
High field, $\Delta m = \pm 1$			
$H_x{}^{\mathrm{II}}, \quad H_x{}^{\mathrm{III}}$	$\perp$ to x and H	$\langle T_x \mid S_y \mid T_z \rangle,$	$\langle T_y \mid S_z \mid T_x \rangle$
$H_y{}^{\mathrm{II}}, \quad H_y{}^{\mathrm{III}}$	$\perp$ to y and H	$\langle T_z \mid S_x \mid T_y \rangle,$	$\langle T_y \mid S_z \mid T_x \rangle$
$H_z{}^{\mathrm{II}}, \quad H_z{}^{\mathrm{III}}$	$\perp$ to z and H	$\langle T_z \mid S_x \mid T_y \rangle,$	$\langle T_x \mid S_y \mid T_z \rangle$

C. Trigonal Symmetry

For molecules with a trigonal or higher axis of symmetry, x and y are equivalent directions resulting in

$$E = 0; \quad X = Y = \tfrac{1}{3}D; \quad Z = -\tfrac{2}{3}D; \quad D^* = D \quad (71)$$

Also, there will be no orientation effects which depend on the azimuth angle φ. For convenience, φ may be taken equal to zero.

Substitution of Eqs. (71) into Eq. (50) gives

$$\cos^2 \theta \ (H)$$

$$= \frac{2D^3 + 9D(g\beta H)^2 \pm \{3\delta^2 - D^2 - 3(g\beta H)^2\}[-3\delta^2 + 4D^2 + 12(g\beta H)^2]^{1/2}}{27D(g\beta H)^2}$$

$$(72)$$

with

$$0 \leq \cos \theta \leq 1$$

a result obtained by de Groot and van der Waals (1960).

The resonance fields may be easily obtained from Table VI by insertion of Eqs. (71):

$$\Delta m = \pm 2: \quad 2g\beta H_x{}^{\mathrm{I}} = 2g\beta H_y{}^{\mathrm{I}} = [\delta^2 - D^2]^{1/2}$$

$$2g\beta H_z{}^{\mathrm{I}} = \delta$$

$$\Delta m = \pm 1: \quad 2g\beta H_x{}^{\mathrm{II}} = 2g\beta H_y{}^{\mathrm{II}} = [2\delta(2\delta - D)]^{1/2} \quad (73)$$

$$g\beta H_z{}^{\mathrm{II}} = (\delta + D)$$

$$\Delta m = \pm 1: \quad 2g\beta H_x{}^{\mathrm{III}} = 2g\beta H_y{}^{\mathrm{III}} = [2\delta(2\delta + D)]^{1/2}$$

$$g\beta H_z{}^{\mathrm{III}} = (\delta - D)$$

It is seen that the resonance field $H_z{}^{\mathrm{I}}$ is independent of D, the zero-field splitting parameter. We might expect that, since $H_z{}^{\mathrm{I}}$ corresponds to a $\Delta m = \pm 2$ resonance it will, for this case, be forbidden. This may be verified by inserting the conditions of Eqs. (71) into Table VII. For $H = H_z$,

$$V_1 = \sqrt{2}^{-1}(T_x + iT_y)$$

$$V_2 = (i/\sqrt{2})(T_x - iT_y) \quad (74)$$

and

$$\langle V_1 \mid \mathbf{S} \mid V_2 \rangle = 0$$

For the states V_1 and V_2, the m is a good quantum number and is equal to $+1$ and -1, respectively; the transition between the two levels is strictly forbidden.

IV. Solution Spectra

A. Random Orientations

The electron spin resonance work of the triplet state of molecules in solution has gone through several stages. At first, attempts to observe such signals were unsuccessful; the reasons for such failures were unclear, and some doubts were expressed regarding the existence of triplet states and the Lewis–Kasha hypothesis. There followed the work of Hutchison and Mangum (1958, 1961) on naphthalene oriented in a host crystal of durene. The resonances they observed were highly anisotropic and were spread over a region of about 2000 gauss. It became apparent that in solution, with molecules having random orientations, the spectra were due to numerous overlapping resonances and were simply too broad to be observed.

It was soon realized by van der Waals and de Groot (1959) that, in addition to the usual magnetic transition with the selection rule $\Delta m = \pm 1$, aromatic molecules may undergo transitions corresponding to $\Delta m = \pm 2$. Moreover, the latter transitions were far less dependent on the orientation of the molecule relative to the magnetic field than the $\Delta m = \pm 1$ transitions, as is evident from Fig. 5. In naphthalene, for example, the anisotropy of the $\Delta m = \pm 2$ transitions, as measured by the range of magnetic field over which resonances were observed, was smaller, by a factor of about 20, than the $\Delta m = \pm 1$ transitions. It was therefore not unreasonable to look for resonances in solution in the low-field or $\Delta m = \pm 2$ region. This they did and succeeded. A line-shape analysis by de Groot and van der Waals (1960) and by Kottis and Lefebvre (1963) demonstrated how zero-field splitting parameters may be obtained from solution spectra.

Paradoxically, now that ESR resonances were observed in solutions in the low-field region, it was found by Yager et al. (1962), as well as by de Groot and van der Waals (1963c), that it was possible to recognize resonances in the high-field region as well. These resonances, associated with $\Delta m = \pm 1$ transitions, although considerably weaker than the $\Delta m = \pm 2$ transitions, could also yield precise information regarding the zero-field splitting parameters (Wasserman et al., 1964; Kottis and Lefebvre, 1964).

The most prominent resonance in solution occurs in the $\Delta m = \pm 2$ (low-field) region and is located at H_{min}, the lowest value of magnetic field at which it is energetically possible to absorb a microwave photon. This occurs when the right side of Eqs. (49) or (50) is no longer real or when the discriminant vanishes,

$$4(g\beta H_{min})^2 - \delta^2 - 4(XY + XZ + YZ) = 0$$

$$H_{min} = (2g\beta)^{-1}[\delta^2 + 4(XY + XZ + YZ)]^{1/2} \qquad (75)$$

or

$$4(g\beta H_{\min})^2 - \delta^2 + \tfrac{4}{3}D^{*2} = 0$$

$$H_{\min} = (2g\beta)^{-1}[(\delta^2 - \tfrac{4}{3}D^{*2})]^{1/2} \tag{76}$$

$$= (2g\beta)^{-1}[\delta^2 - \tfrac{4}{3}(D^2 + 3E^2)]^{1/2}$$

The anisotropy is smallest for those molecules whose orientations are such that their resonant fields are in the neighborhood of $H_{\min}$, and, in solution, with the molecules randomly oriented, there will be a maximum in the signal strength at $H_{\min}$ (which does not lie along one of the canonical directions in the molecule). Frequently, this is the strongest and the only signal that is observable. The resonance at $H_{\min}$ may be observed with the microwave magnetic field either parallel or perpendicular to the static magnetic field.

The resonance fields when considered as functions of the orientation of the molecule in accordance with Eqs. (49) or (50) take on stationary values for the magnetic field along one of the three molecular axes x, y, z. These peaks, which under favorable conditions may be observed both in the $\Delta m = \pm 2$ and $\Delta m = \pm 1$ regions, are sufficient to define the zero-field splitting parameters. The analysis was carried out by Kottis and Lefebvre (1963) for the $\Delta m = \pm 2$ region and later extended to include the $\Delta m = \pm 1$ region (Kottis and Lefebvre, 1964). Another line-shape analysis was given by Wasserman et al. (1964). Both methods involve the summing of contributions from a large number of molecules with various orientations.

In the special case where $E = 0$, the H_x and H_y peaks coalesce both in the $\Delta m = \pm 2$ (low-field) and $\Delta m = \pm 1$ (high-field) region. In the $\Delta m = \pm 2$ region this gives rise to a particularly prominent resonance which, according to Table VII, requires parallel polarization. From Eqs. (73) it is seen that this resonance occurs at a field H_0, given by

$$H_0 = (2g\beta)^{-1}[\delta^2 - D^2]^{1/2}$$

For $H = H_0$, Eq. (72) gives $\cos\theta = 0$; thus this resonance is produced by those molecules oriented so that the magnetic field lies in the equatorial plane ($z = 0$).

It may happen that, at some particular value of magnetic field, the $m = \pm 1$ levels are separated by an energy 2δ, whereas each level is separated from the $m = 0$ level by an energy δ. A transition between the $m = +1$ and $m = -1$ levels becomes possible by a two-photon absorption process. The magnetic field H_d at which such resonances occur is obtained by setting the coefficient of the radical term in Eq. (50) equal to zero.

This gives

$$H_d = (2g\beta)^{-1}[\delta^2 - D^{*2}]^{1/2}$$

a result given by de Groot and van der Waals (1963c), who first observed and interpreted this resonance.

B. Calculations and Experiments

Investigations of the triplet state by electron spin resonance methods have been used in several ways: to determine zero-field splitting parameters, to obtain structural information, and to study environmental and dynamic effects.

Calculations of zero-field splitting have been performed by various authors including Chiu (1963), Hameka (1959), Boorstein and Gouterman (1963), Csavinszky (1962), and others. The general assumptions involved in such calculations are the following:

1. The controlling interaction is the spin-spin interaction in the configurations which contribute to the triplet state.
2. Only π electrons are considered in forming the triplet state.
3. Only the lowest triplet state is considered.
4. First-order perturbation is sufficient.
5. The spin-orbit interaction is negligible.
6. Solvent effects are ignored.

Two kinds of approximations are usually made. The first is in the construction of an electronic wave function in which it is generally necessary to include some configuration interaction; the second approximation occurs in the evaluation of integrals which appear in the computation of the coefficients D and E of the spin Hamiltonian. These are multicenter integrals (Geller and Griffith, 1964), and in most cases the three- and four-center integrals are ignored. We summarize the data on a few representative molecules.

a. Naphthalene. Hutchison and Mangum (1961) obtained the magnitude of D and E in an oriented system. Their measurements could not determine the sign; this was later supplied by a low-temperature measurement performed by Hornig and Hyde (1963). The values were $D = 0.1003 \pm 0.0006$ cm^{-1} and $E = -0.0137 \pm 0.0002$ cm^{-1}, which is equivalent to $X = 0.0197$, $Y = 0.0471$, $Z = -0.0669$ cm^{-1}. Several measurements of D^* have been made from solution spectra; these give $D^* = 0.1049 \pm 0.0015$ cm^{-1} (Smaller, 1962), 0.1063 ± 0.0004 cm^{-1} at 77°K in Lucite and $0.1020 \pm$

0.0004 cm^{-1} at 305°K in Lucite (Thomson, 1964). The decay times are given by de Groot and van der Waals (1963b) as 2.7 sec at 77°K and 2.8 sec at 20°K; those for deuteronaphthalene are 20.3 sec at 77°K and 20.5 sec at 20°K. In the $\Delta m = \pm 1$ region, the resonance peaks are considerably reduced in intensity; nevertheless, they were observed by Yager *et al.* (1962). In perdeuteronaphthalene, they deduced the values $D = 0.10046 \pm 0.00004$ cm^{-1}, $E = -0.01536 \pm 0.00004$. Boorstein and Gouterman (1963) obtained, by calculation, $D = 0.1003$, $E = -0.0133$ cm^{-1} or $D = 0.0958$, $E = -0.0211$ cm^{-1}, depending on the choice of orbitals.

b. Benzene. For benzene, $E = 0$. Some measured values of D (or D^*) are 0.1593 ± 0.0015 cm^{-1} (Smaller, 1962), 0.156 cm^{-1} (de Groot and van der Waals, 1963a). These values are obtained from H_{min}, which at x-band frequencies correspond to about 1350 gauss. Hameka (1959) computed $D = 0.15$ cm^{-1}, assuming that the triplet state was $^3B_{1u}$ and 0.09 cm^{-1} for the $^3B_{2u}$ state; Boorstein and Gouterman (1963) calculated $D = 0.1519$ cm^{-1}. Deuterobenzene (C_6D_6) produces a stronger signal; the measured value of D is 0.157 cm^{-1}, and the lifetime of the triplet state is 4.2 sec at 77°K and 11.7 sec at 20°K (de Groot and van der Waals, 1963a, b). The same authors concluded on the basis of a line-shape analysis that benzene in its lowest triplet state is not a regular hexagon and that the observed spectrum arises from tunnelling among equivalent conformations. The rate of tunnelling is estimated to be 10^9–10^{10} sec^{-1}.

c. Coronene. Coronene has trigonal symmetry and the spectra of de Groot and van der Waals (1963b) taken at 77°K and 20°K are consistent with that assumption. Smaller's (1962) value for D^* is 0.0971 ± 0.0015 cm^{-1}; Thomson (1964) gives $D^* = 0.0983 \pm 0.0004$ cm^{-1} at 77°K and 0.0943 ± 0.0004 cm^{-1} at 305°K, as measured in Lucite. De Groot and van der Waals (1960) obtained $D^* = 0.096$ cm^{-1} and a decay time at 77°K of 7.9 sec. The calculations of Boorstein and Gouterman (1963) give $D = 0.0522$ and 0.0608 cm^{-1}, depending on the orbitals.

d. Biomolecules. Shiga and Piette (1964a, b) observed triplet state resonances in flavins. Lifetimes varied from 15 to 24 msec under various environmental conditions, such as the pH of the solution, the presence of dissolved oxygen, and the formation of free radicals. Resonances were also observed in aromatic amino acids (also reported by Ptak and Douzou, 1963) and proteins with an indication that the protein resonances were due to tryptophan.

Electron spin resonance signals in L-tyrosine were investigated by Maling *et al.* (1964). The values of D^* were 0.161 cm^{-1} under conditions where the tyrosine was nonionized and 0.141 for ionized tyrosine. The ionization is on the hydroxyl group and was determined by comparison with optical absorption spectra. The lifetimes were approximately 3 sec.

REFERENCES

Boorstein, S. A., and Gouterman, M. (1963). *J. Chem. Phys.* **39**, 2443.

Chiu, Y. N. (1963). *J. Chem. Phys.* **39**, 2736.

Csavinszky, P. (1962). *In* "Luminescence of Organic and Inorganic Materials" (H. Kallman and G. Spruch, eds.), p. 263. Wiley, New York.

de Groot, M. S., and van der Waals, J. H. (1960). *Mol. Phys.* **3**, 190.

de Groot, M. S., and van der Waals, J. H. (1963a). *In* "Magnetic and Electric Resonance Relaxation" (J. Smidt, ed.), p. 379. Wiley, New York.

de Groot, M. S., and van der Waals, J. H. (1963b). *Mol. Phys.* **6**, 545.

de Groot, M. S., and van der Waals, J. H. (1963c). *Physica* **29**, 1128.

Geller, M., and Griffith, R. W. (1964). *J. Chem. Phys.* **40**, 2309.

Gouterman, M. (1962). *J. Chem. Phys.* **36**, 2846.

Hadley, S. G., Rast, H. E., Jr., and Keller, R. A. (1963). *J. Chem. Phys.* **39**, 705.

Hameka, H. F. (1959). *J. Chem. Phys.* **31**, 315.

Hameka, H. F., and Oosterhoff, L. J. (1958). *Mol. Phys.* **1**, 358.

Hammond, G. S., and Turro, N. J. (1963). *Science* **142**, 1541.

Horning, A. W., and Hyde, J. S. (1963). *Mol. Phys.* **6**, 33.

Hutchison, C. A., and Mangum, B. W. (1958). *J. Chem. Phys.* **29**, 952.

Hutchison, C. A., and Mangum, B. W. (1961). *J. Chem. Phys.* **34**, 908.

Jarrett, H. S. (1963). *In* "Solid State Physics" (E. Seitz and D. Turnbull, eds.), Vol. 14, p. 215. Academic Press, New York.

Kottis, P., and Lefebvre, R. (1963). *J. Chem. Phys.* **39**, 393.

Kottis, P., and Lefebvre, R. (1964). *J. Chem. Phys.* **41**, 379.

Lewis, G. N., and Kasha, M. (1944). *J. Am. Chem. Soc.* **66**, 2100.

Lewis, G. N., Calvin, M., and Kasha, M. J. (1949). *J. Chem. Phys.* **17**, 804.

Maling, J. E., Rosenheck, K., and Weissbluth, M. (1965). *Photochem. Photobiol.* **4**, 241.

McConnell, H. M. (1959). *Proc. Natl. Acad. Sci. U.S.* **45**, 172.

McLachlan, A. D. (1963). *Mol. Phys.* **6**, 441.

McWeeny, R. (1961). *J. Chem. Phys.* **34**, 399.

Ptak, M., and Douzou, P. (1963). *Nature* **199**, 1092.

Robinson, G. W., and Frosch, R. P. (1962). *J. Chem. Phys.* **37**, 1962.

Robinson, G. W., and Frosch, R. P. (1963). *J. Chem. Phys.* **38**, 1187.

Shiga, T., and Piette, L. H. (1964a). *Photochem. Photobiol.* **3**, 213.

Shiga, T., and Piette, L. H. (1964b). *Photochem. Photobiol.* **3**, 223.

Smaller, B. (1962). *J. Chem. Phys.* **37**, 1578.

Steele, R. H., and Szent-Györgyi, A. L. (1958). *Proc. Natl. Acad. Sci. U.S.* **44**, 540.

Thomson, C. (1964). *J. Chem. Phys.* **41**, 1.

Tinkham, M. (1964). "Group Theory and Quantum Mechanics." McGraw-Hill, New York.

van der Waals, J. H., and de Groot, M. S. (1959). *Mol. Phys.* **2**, 333.

Vladimirov, I. A., and Litvin, F. F. (1960). *Biofizika* **5**, 127 (in Russian); *Biophysics (USSR) (English Transl.)* **5**, 151.

Wasserman, E., Snyder, L. C., and Yager, W. A. (1964). *J. Chem. Phys.* **41**, 1763.

Yager, W. A., Wasserman, E., and Cramer, R. M. R. (1962). *J. Chem. Phys.* **37**, 1148.

The Study of Transient Molecular Configuration in Some Biophysical Problems

Laboratoire de Biophysique du
Muséum National d'Histoire Naturelle,
Paris, France

I. Introduction

Biological reactions involve organic molecules, and these molecules go through transient configurations in the course of their reactions. The transient configurations, often metastable, can be described in terms of quantum chemistry, according to physicochemical data. In that sense, "quantum biochemistry," developed in the book of Pullman and Pullman (1963), represents a pattern for future experiments on the dynamics of biological reactions.

Such experiments, concerning metastable molecular configurations, should be done by spectroscopic techniques (optical, Hertzian spectroscopies), by which we can detect the electronic and nuclear characteristics of the transient and often excited "states" of molecules. Molecular physics can study such molecular states, even if they are unstable, provided they possess specific spectroscopic properties. Through molecular physics we can also find the link between such states or configurations, and reconstitute the chain of events which led to the chemical evolution of molecules.

As we know, in molecular physics we work most often with electronically excited molecules and their excitation, which results from the absorption of optical quanta. The excited states thus obtained represent the excited "pictures" of the fundamental or normal configuration. As we shall see, their quantum (spectroscopic) properties are very useful to the knowledge and understanding of many molecular processes resulting from this optical excitation; these properties are specific for given molecules as a result of specific molecular interactions with its neighborhood. From this point of view, spectroscopic methods and, sometimes, their photochemical consequences are very useful and are continuously expanding. Since biological compounds have a specific "organization" at every stage (molecular complexes, macromolecules, molecular layers), molecular biophysics is a valuable means for testing the influence of such organization on the behavior of molecules, studied via the quantum (spectroscopic) responses of their transient excited states.

However, such molecules normally react according to bioenergetics, and the energy quanta involved in the exchanges which lead to the specific reactivity are not *a priori* able to create the preceding electronically excited states. A new methodology is necessary in molecular biophysics that will permit the study of transient low energetic configurations normally involved in biological reactions. Among different possible pathways, we may probably use classical optical excitation, by which we are sometimes able to determine not only the classical excited states (singlets, triplets); we may use photochemistry, as a consequence of this excitation; we may also examine some reversible photoproducts located in the thermal (vibrational) range that can be recognized by bioenergetics and that are mutually convertible to the normal configuration by moderate heating. Such experimental research, leading to low energetic transient configurations, raises many problems that we have to study through experimentation with models.

II. Possible Investigations of Excited States of Conjugated Polyatomic Molecules

A. The Lowest Excited States and Their Possible Exploitation in Biophysics

1. Optical Excitation and Relaxation

We know that the absorption of a photon determines an electronic transition from the fundamental state S_0 to the excited state S_1 or S_2, ..., S_n of the same symmetry. The deactivation is produced by relaxations, schematized in Fig. 1. We can distinguish among these different processes:

1. An internal conversion of energy from high vibrational levels to the lowest 0–0 vibrational level of every electronic state, and also between the adjacent states $S_n \rightarrow S_2 \rightarrow S_1$.

2. Some intercrossing system processes leading to singlet-triplet transitions (conversions), like $S_n \rightarrow T_n$, ..., $S_1 \rightarrow T_1$, and $T_n \rightarrow S_{n-1}$, ..., $T_1 \rightarrow S_0$.

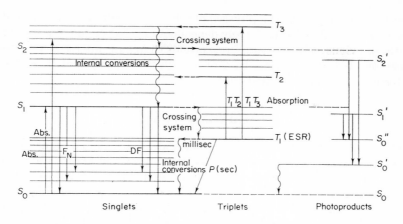

FIG. 1. Intercrossing system processes and corresponding phenomena.

3. The radiative deactivations, by the transitions $S_1 \rightarrow S_0$ and $T_1 \rightarrow S_0$, giving, respectively, the fluorescence and phosphorescence emissions.

Finally, in first approximation, we can simplify the preceding energetic scheme in order to point out that every optical excitation leads to two specific excited states (the lowest ones): singlet S_1 and triplet T_1 (see Fig. 2).

The lowest excited states S_1 and T_1 are remarkable in their electronic properties and lifetimes, which permit their recording and, through it, the study of their molecular dynamics. In the present paper we are concerned with the study of the lowest excited triplet state, which is the most impor-

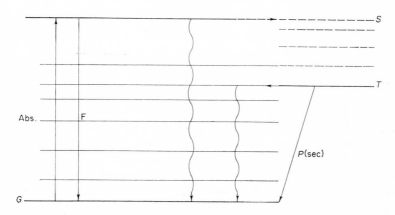

FIG. 2. The lowest excited singlet and triplet states.

tant for the study of any biophysical problem. Its electronic response and, in particular, its intensity are largely dependent on what happens in the course of the previous and "obscure" relaxations involving intercrossing system processes. We shall be concerned only with the recording of these results in terms of the lowest excited triplet states.

2. Lowest Excited Triplet State

One generally finds transitions from states with paired spins (excited singlet) to states with unpaired spins, that is, excited triplet states, as in Fig. 3. Among the other electronically excited states, the lowest triplet is the most interesting because it is characterized by a longer lifetime, an emission of phosphorescence, paramagnetic properties resulting from unpaired spins, its chemical behavior, and also its specific importance in biphotonic processes.

a. Lifetimes. The triplet-state lifetimes range from about 10^{-4} sec to several seconds, according to molecules, media, and temperature.

b. Electronic Properties. Phosphorescence and Optical Spectroscopy. The triplet-state lifetimes may be measured experimentally by using a rotating phosphoroscope. Phosphorescence is thus one of the most studied electronic properties of organic matter (Pringsheim, 1949). As we shall see in a moment and as stated in the other part of this volume, phosphorescence is a useful property which has contributed to the knowledge of many quantum processes involved in biological compounds.

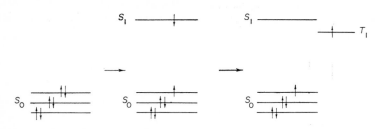

Fig. 3. Electronic transition and conversion of spin according to Pauli's principle.

Paramagnetism, Hertzian spectroscopy. The two unpaired electrons interact strongly with each other, giving a total spin of $S = 1$; this interaction can assume three orientations in a magnetic field (Androes and Calvin, 1962). The term triplet state then describes the state of these molecules.

However, electron spin resonance (ESR) signals of the triplet state can be detected only with special conditions, for example, single crystals of naphthalene in durene (solid solution) when irradiated by ultraviolet light at liquid nitrogen temperatures. The reasons for the broadening of the ESR signals beyond detection in these cases are two: 1. The three different levels resulting from $S = 1$ will be split even in the absence of an external magnetic field, owing to the asymmetric internal electrical field of the molecule. 2. In the presence of an external magnetic field, the zero-field energy levels will be split further into three states. The splitting will vary according to the angle between the external magnetic field axis and the electric field or molecular symmetry axis (anisotropy).

Consequently, in amorphous samples or solutions in which this angle varies from molecule to molecule, the splitting leads to an excessive broadening of the signal.

In the single crystal of a compound in which the molecular axes have a fixed orientation, it is theoretically possible that the overlapping ESR signals give rise to an observable signal. This is the case in the experiment with the crystal of naphthalene in durene (Hutchison and Mangum, (1961). (See Fig. 4.)

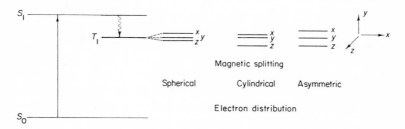

Fig. 4. Magnetic splitting and triplet state.

As explained by Weissbluth (1965), it is possible to induce a transition giving an ESR signal for $\Delta m = 2$. Such a transition often permits us to detect the triplet states of organic molecules in amorphous samples and solutions; an example of such a result is given below.

c. *Higher Triplet Levels: Triplet-Triplet Transition.* Once the triplet configuration is attained (by conversion, $S_1 \rightarrow T_1$), a whole series of higher excited states (triplet levels according to the selection rules) are accessible. These triplet-triplet transitions allow a molecule to accumulate an abnormal potential energy.

We know that Lewis *et al.* (1941) performed the pioneer work in this domain. Working with organic molecules, they found that their absorption in a boric acid glass changed completely if the measurements were made while the glass was illuminated by a high-intensity-light arc. The light source populated the lowest triplet state T_1 sufficiently for triplet-triplet absorption to occur.

Porter and Windsor (1953), using "flash" sources in which a high intensity spark is discharged very quickly through a circuit with large capacitance detected the triplet-triplet absorption spectrum for molecules with long-lived triplet states, in liquid solution at room temperature. Such a flash technique represents a decisive step toward the study of the kinetics or triplet-state decay time in varying environments and, in particular, as functions of the organization of the medium. Some observations have already been made on compounds of photobiological interest, like chlorophyll (Livingston, 1955; Livingston and Porter, 1954), demonstrating the existence of triplet levels in this "photoexcited" substance.

From another point of view, the possibility of a triplet-triplet transition during the course of an optical excitation might be of highest interest for biophysicists (Ptak and Douzou, 1963, 1964). It is generally admitted that the optical excitation of an organic molecule induces a [chain] of relaxation (deactivation) events until complete deactivation occurs.

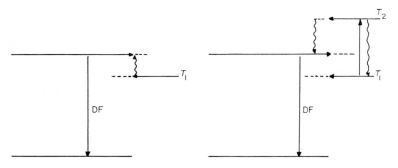

FIG. 5. Diagrams explaining the emission of delayed fluorescence (DF).

Triplet-triplet absorption, i.e., a "biphotonic process," increases the energy inside a molecule. This accumulation of energy might contribute to some specific chemical processes or modify the electronic behavior, the interpretation of which is of primary importance.

Since it is sometimes possible to determine the lowest triplet state by both its phosphorescence and its paramagnetism, it should be interesting to test an eventual triplet-triplet transition and some of its main consequences. When a triplet$_1$-triplet$_2$ transition occurs, there is a high probability of deactivation in the same way ($T_2 \rightarrow T_1$) and also a probability of some intercrossing system processes leading to delayed fluorescence. From Fig. 5 we see the development of the delayed fluorescence, where there is a $T_1 \rightarrow S_1$ conversion, and also a triplet-triplet ($T_1 \rightarrow T_2$) transition.

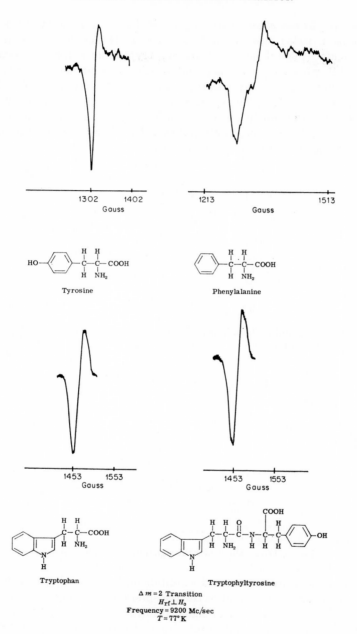

Fig. 6. Spectra of tyrosine, phenylalanine, tryptophan, and tryptophyltyrosine.

Triplet-triplet transition studied by ESR. In our laboratory, Ptak (Ptak and Douzou, 1963) was the first to record ESR signals for the aromatic amino acids (phenylalanine, tyrosine, tryptophan) for the transition $\Delta m = \pm 2$, working with ether-pentane-alcohol and alcoholic glasses at 77°K (liquid nitrogen temperature) in the optical cavity of a Varian spectrometer (100 Kc). The spectra are reproduced in Fig. 6. He was able to record simultaneously the decay of the signals and the decay of the classical phosphorescence, both induced by ultraviolet excitation. The apparatus shown in Fig. 7 was employed.

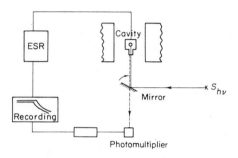

FIG. 7. Double recording of luminescence and paramagnetic signals of the triplet states. Apparatus built by Ptak.

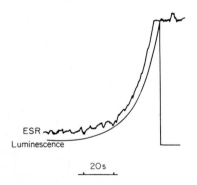

FIG. 8. Decay times of ESR signal and phosphorescence.

On the same graph paper, and simultaneously, Ptak obtained the decay curves of the ESR signal and of the phosphorescence (Fig. 8). For a value of $g = 2$, we recorded an ESR signal resulting from the radical formation from the alcoholic solvent, a result obtained several years ago by Smaller. The characteristic spectrum obtained in our experiment is the same (Fig. 9). In these experimental conditions, however, this spectrum is obtained

FIG. 9. ESR signal of an alcoholic radical.

only in the presence of the amino acid, and it results from the photosensitivity of the alcohol.

As pointed out by Ptak and Douzou (1964), several experimental facts demonstrate that there is a direct link between the formation of the triplet of the solute and the formation of the radical of the solvent. Moreover, it seems clear that such sensitivity is due to the energy transfer from the amino acid when it is involved in a triplet-triplet absorption, i.e., a biphotonic process. The same conclusions were made recently for aromatic amines by some Russian authors (Kholmogorev *et al.*, 1963; Bagdasarian, 1963). The procedure used by Ptak for study of the excited aromatic amino acids demonstrates how with these techniques we can get more and more information in order to study these properties in organized media or polymers; possibly other new techniques (like flash spectroscopy for the direct detection of the triplet-triplet transition) will also prove valuable.

d. The Triplet-Triplet Annihilation Interaction. The work done by Ptak on aromatic amino acids shows that the combined use of optical and Hertzian spectroscopy in both molecular physics and photochemistry might lead to the discovery of new electronic and physicochemical properties of these biological components. Such components (like the heterocyclic purine and pyrimidine bases of nucleic acids) are normally polymerized. Polymerization is a specific mode of aggregation for biological components. Often, these polyatomic molecules, being more or less conjugated, lie close together.

If, in an organic molecular crystal, triplet excitation occurs over some range of molecules and if there exists a probability of triplet-triplet annihilation with two colliding triplet excitons, such a process can be expressed by the following notation, using the common symbols:

$$T_1 + T_1 \rightarrow S_2 + S_0 \qquad \text{and} \qquad S_2 \rightarrow S_1 \rightarrow S_0$$

(delayed fluorescence)

$$T_1 + T_1 \rightarrow T_2 + S_0 \qquad \text{and} \qquad T_2 \rightarrow T_1 \rightarrow S_0$$

This process and its corresponding emission can be expressed in the scheme given in Fig. 10. From a spectroscopic point of view, the triplet-triplet

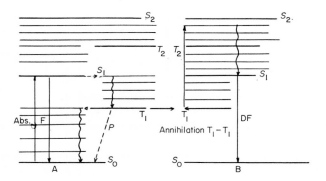

BIPHOTONIC PROCESSES

Fig. 10. Energetic scheme translating the annihilation T_1–T_1.

annihilation can be tested by recording delayed fluorescence (DF) and quenching of phosphorescence. Some recent papers discuss the mechanism and kinetics of this process (Sponer et al., 1958; Nieman and Robinson, 1962; Sternlicht et al., 1963).

In mixed molecular aggregates, the triplet states, being populated by optical excitation and located in the same energetic range may react by triplet-triplet annihilation, provided that the molecular components lie within a range less than 10 Å.

From a morphological point of view, certain macromolecular sequences can be considered "linear crystals." It should be interesting to experiment their possible energy transfer (exciton migration), and with the delayed fluorescence resulting from possible triplet-triplet annihilation. Such a process represents an "energy multiplication" inside molecules. Its existence could explain reactions in photobiological compounds. Similarly, the optical excitation of certain organic molecules in crystals or polymers might partially explain certain radiation damages and, in particular, their photochemical evolution.

e. Lowest Excited Triplet State and Biological Reactivity. The lowest excited triplet state seems to be the most reactive as well as the least energetic among the molecular excited states. But it lies in an energetic domain not frequently involved in chemistry and in biology. For this reason, the lowest excited triplet state remains responsible for photochemical and photobiological observations using ultraviolet or visible quanta, that is, photons of several electron volts (1 eV = 23 kcal/mole). Some exceptions are possible, according to a specific probability of transition $S_0 \rightarrow T_1$, involving thermal quanta (around 20–25 kcal/mole). The transition $S_0 \rightarrow T_1$ is known as "nonadiabatic" and can be studied in ethylenic compounds.

B. Molecular Transitions Induced by Adiabatic and Nonadiabatic Transitions

For several years, the ethylenic bond has been studied through investigation of the *cis-trans* isomerization and the chemical reactivity resulting from optical and thermal excitation of this bond. If we consider the aliphatic ethylenic compounds, the central double bond

can be dissociated to a single bond by two different energetic means (ultraviolet, thermal), which correspond to two different electronic mechanisms.

Adiabatic transitions involve the excitation via a singlet state (by ultraviolet absorption)

$$\diagdown \diagup\!\!\!\!\!\!C\!\!=\!\!C\diagup\diagdown \quad + \; h\nu \; \rightleftharpoons \quad \diagdown\!\!\!\!\downarrow \;\; \uparrow\!\!\!\diagup \; C\!=\!C \diagup\diagdown \qquad \text{(singlet)}$$

The spins of π electrons being opposite, the electrons can occupy the same orbital, and the molecule will have appreciable ionic character.

Nonadiabatic transitions move toward the lowest triplet state, obtained by thermal activation:

$$\diagdown \diagup\!\!\!\!\!\!C\!\!=\!\!C\diagup\diagdown \quad + \; kT \; \rightleftharpoons \quad \diagdown\!\!\!\!\downarrow \;\; \uparrow\!\!\!\diagup \; C\!-\!C \diagup\diagdown \qquad \text{(triplet)}$$

The spins of the electrons being the same, the electrons cannot occupy the same orbital on one carbon atom but occupy two orbitals, giving a weak ionic character.

These mechanisms are responsible for chemical reactions (substitution, addition) and also for *cis-trans* isomerizations around

when it is a single bond. Such phenomena were, in particular, studied by Magee, *et al.* (1941) and from a chemical point of view by Harman and Eyring (1942). In terms of *cis-trans* transitions (isomerizations), these phenomena are translated by the energy diagram of Fig. 11, and the two different transitions are described by the following equations:

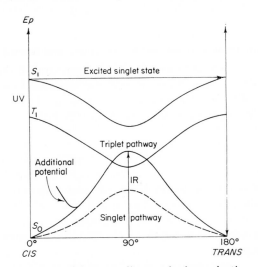

FIG. 11. Potential energy diagram for isomerization.

If C_1 and C_2 each represent a carbon atom, and the transition of electrons from π orbitals to an antibonding orbital is represented by

$$(2pC_1 + 2pC_2)^2 \rightarrow (2pC_1 + 2pC_2)^1(2pC_1 - 2pC_2)^1 \qquad (1)$$

and if

$$(2pC_1 + 2pC_2) = \phi_1 \qquad \text{and} \qquad (2pC_1 - 2pC_2 = \phi_2 \qquad (2)$$

then the corresponding excited states will be defined, for triplets, by

$$\phi_1^{(1)} \cdot \phi_2^{(2)} + \phi_1^{(2)} \cdot \phi_2^{(1)} \qquad (3)$$

and for the singlet by

$$\phi_1^{(1)} \cdot \phi_2^{(2)} - \phi_1^{(2)} \cdot \phi_2^{(1)} \tag{4}$$

The frequency factor of the thermal reactions via the triplet state is about 10^4. Such a *low probability* may be explained by the spin-conservation rule and by the fact that the potential surfaces representing the singlet and triplet states do not exactly match.

According to Harman and Eyring (1942), the probability of the transition $S_0 \rightarrow T_1$ is enhanced, on activation energy, without notable effect by the formation of activated complexes with paramagnetic substances (e.g., atoms, radicals). The heterogeneous magnetic field acts differently on each dipole of the π electrons of the

bond. H. McConnell (1952) pointed out that it was doubtful that the catalysis of isomerization was due to magnetic interactions. In general, for the saturated ethylenic compounds, the activation energy for the transition $S_0 \rightarrow T_1$ is about 20 kcal/mole, and often more. Thus, optical quanta are able to induce such transitions.

These transitions were observed many years ago, in particular, by Evans (1960) and, more recently, by Bylina and Grabowsky (1964) with dichloroethylenes under oxygen pressure. Even if the quanta normally involved in such $S_0 \rightarrow T_1$ transitions are higher than those involved in many biological reactions, the biophysicists should be interested in processes which are deeply influenced by paramagnetic substances acting on spin-orbit coupling.

If the substitutes in an ethylenic compound are aromatic rings more or less conjugated with the central double bond, the activation energy for isomerization is greatly lowered, but, at the same time, there is no transition toward the lowest triplet state. The partial-double-bond character of the central bond allows a quasi-free rotation with very low activation energy.

If such a molecule is not planar, rotations of 180° around the central bond are not possible. One must take account of "additional potentials," which lower the activation energy; this could be the case for many biological complexes. Before discussing these complexes, we must add that the coupling of electronic and steric processes occurring during isomerizations is not yet correctly interpreted [see the excellent review of Wyman (1955)].

Intersystem crossing processes between the lowest excited states of different configurations of the same molecular complex are difficult to investigate, especially in biological compounds.

C. Necessity of Investigating the Transient "Nonexcited" Configuration

The study of electronically excited states brought us some electronic data explaining quantum and physicochemical phenomena that occur with optically excited molecules. But, in fact, there are still few means of explaining the normal physicochemical behavior of molecules of biological interest by these electronic mechanisms. Besides the special case of some ethylenic compounds (in which the lowest excited triplet state plays a leading part in their physicochemical behavior), we saw that the way leading—at least apparently—to chemical evolution was photochemical, often via energy-accumulation processes inside molecules. So, from a biological point of view concerning the reactions occurring in the cellular darkness, according to the laws of bioenergetics, we must consider that the lowest excited states giving spectroscopic data (such as paramagnetic and luminescent processes) are not really involved in normal chemical evolution. We have to find another way to record the transient low energetic configurations involved in this evolution, and to establish their internal mechanism. This path leads to the study of other concepts and to experimentation with molecular models.

III. Investigations of Nonelectronically Excited States

A. Transient, Metastable Molecular Configurations; Investigation with Models

The configurations really involved in biology are located in the thermal (that is vibrational) range of the potential energy scheme, and we know very little about such transient, often metastable, molecular configurations. In fact, in this energetic range we know the tautomers, isomers, and stereoisomers of normal configuration. These molecular forms, classical or "rare" according to their stability, make possible a discussion of the problems raised by the existence of transient configurations, their mutual behavior, and their eventual experimentation.

As we have seen, apart from the specific cases (e.g., where isomerization is induced via a triplet mechanism), these molecular transitions do not involve an electronically excited state by thermal activation. They are due to a predissociation process, pictured by a Morse diagram in the case of a diatomic molecule. If we consider two possible configurations (tautomers, isomers) of the same molecule, we understand how the thermal activation of one produces a molecular transition, instead of the normal dissociation. A predissociation is located near the crossing of the curves in Fig. 12. The relative stability of each configuration is a function of the height of the energetic barrier Eb between A and B.

It is often difficult to experiment with such molecular transitions, because thermal activation induces the transition B $\rightarrow$ A. We are looking for transient configurations, and these are thermally unstable.

To investigate transient, metastable configurations we must adjust to a new methodology, noting that excited states of every molecular configuration can be obtained by optical excitation. If there is an intersection process between excited states, as there is an intersection between the unexcited

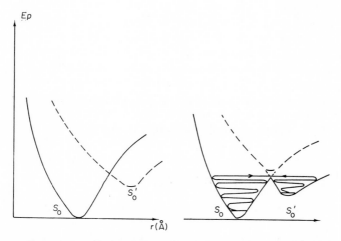

FIG. 12. Crossing of diatomic curves for the same molecule.

states, the equilibrium A $\rightleftharpoons$ B could be shifted by optical excitation of A, or B. Optical excitation occurs at the low temperatures at which a molecule is sterically or thermally "frozen," and then stabilized. Thus, by moderate and progressive heating, we can study the shifting of equilibrium of A $\rightleftharpoons$ B. For that purpose, we must use molecular models.

B. Experimentation with Models; Photochromic Compounds

We shall find and speculate upon the molecular transitions between two configurations A $\rightleftharpoons$ B of the same molecule, resulting from optical excitation of one of them, A, for instance, since it occurs most often. We have to induce a photochemical cycle, schematized in Fig. 13.

Many organic compounds, known as "photochromic," react in the following way; normally absorbing in the near ultraviolet, they change color

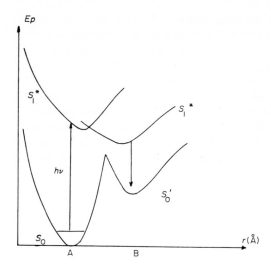

FIG. 13. Energetic scheme translating the photochromic process.

reversibly, by optical excitation, according to the cycle

$$S_0 \xrightarrow{h\nu} S_1^* \to S_1'^* \to S_0'$$

$$\uparrow \underline{\hspace{4cm}}_{kt}$$

in which a thermal effect (kT) permits the reverse transition $S_0' \to S_0$. In the excited state, each photochromic compound undergoes a structural transition (resulting from an atomic migration, or a dissociation, a breaking bond) and the deactivation occurs toward the nonelectronically excited state S_0' "homolog" of the $S_1'^*$ state.

In general, the quantum yield of such a reaction is very high (e.g., 0.9 for certain spiro-pyrane derivatives) and the complete reversibility, which is linked to the transition $S_0' \to S_0$, is a function of the temperature.

When such compounds are tested at very low temperature (liquid nitrogen or liquid oxygen temperatures), the S_0' configuration can be stabilized indefinitely. This is different from the other "metastable" states of the molecule, like the lowest excited triplet.

1. Principal Mechanisms of Photochromism

The photochromic molecule consists of two parts, A and B. Each part has π electrons which cannot migrate from one part to the other. So the

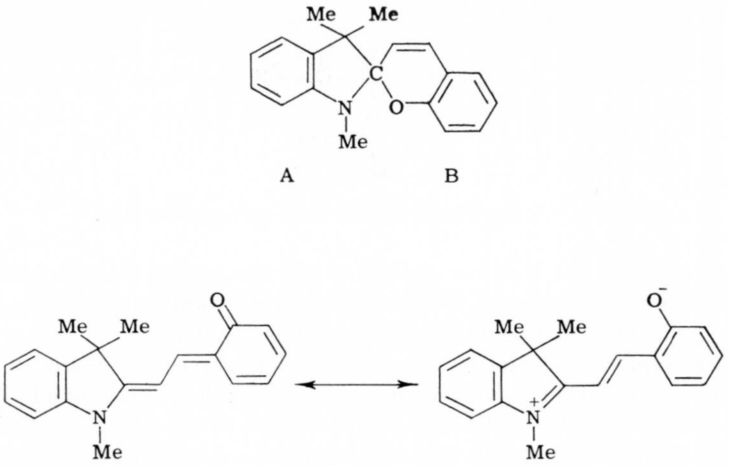

FIG. 14. *Top*: spiro-pyrane derivative; *bottom*: open quinone and zwitterion configurations.

absorption spectrum of the molecule will then result (as far as we may know) from the superposition of A and B spectra. If then, under the impact of radiation, the electrons migrate from one part to the other and if, consequently, the system of conjugate double bonds becomes sufficiently spread, the molecule absorbs in the visible.

This mechanism occurs relatively frequently and leads to important colorations. Let us take some examples: In the first one, the conjugation is realized by a simple break of a chemical bond, followed by an isomerization but without loss or transfer of atoms (Heligman-Rim *et al.*, 1962), if we consider Fig. 14, the formula of 1,3,3-trimethylindolino-2-spiro-2′-(b)-

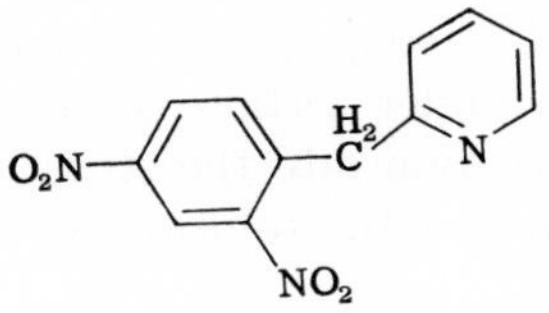

FIG. 15. Pyridine derivative.

benzopyran. Neither part of the molecule is conjugated; first for the obvious reason that there are not enough double bonds. Second, the planes holding the carbon atoms of part A and those of part B are perpendicular. But, by absorption of a photon, the C—O bond breaks and the molecule takes the resonating form (Fig. 14). Now, the A and B parts can exchange

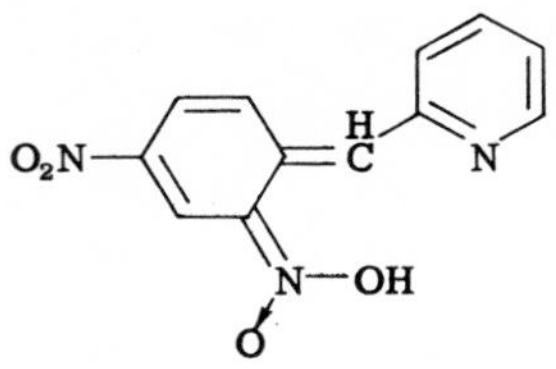

FIG. 16. Pyridine derivative after optical excitation.

their π electrons, for they are coplanar, and the conjugated double bonds exist in sufficient number. We see that the well-known structure of the coloring matter of merocyanine substances is obtained.

As a second example let us mention the derivatives of o-nitrotoluene in which the conjugation occurs by tautomerization: the shifting of a hydrogen atom (Margerum, 1962). To be more precise, let us consider 2-(2,4-dinitro-benzyl)pyridine, Fig. 15. In this molecule, the conjugation between the two parts of the molecule is hindered by the presence of the methylene group, which acts as a real "lock." But under irradiation, one of the hydro-

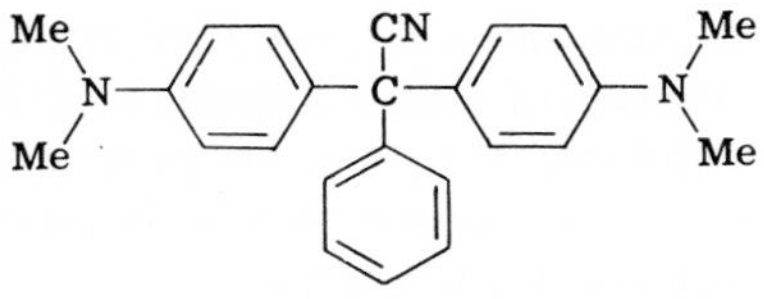

FIG. 17. Triphenyl methane derivative.

gen atoms of this group migrates toward the nitro group. The new formula is as given in Fig. 16. The molecule is open, it is colored.

In a final example, the conjugation is obtained by the expulsion of a sub-stituent (Sporer, 1961). The molecule in Fig. 17 is 4,4'-(dimethylamino)-triphenylmethanenitrile. No conjugation is possible between the three aromatic rings. However, under certain conditions, this molecule is dis-sociated by ultraviolet radiation into the structure of Fig. 18. The cation is that of malachite green and the solution, uncolored before irradiation, turns green.

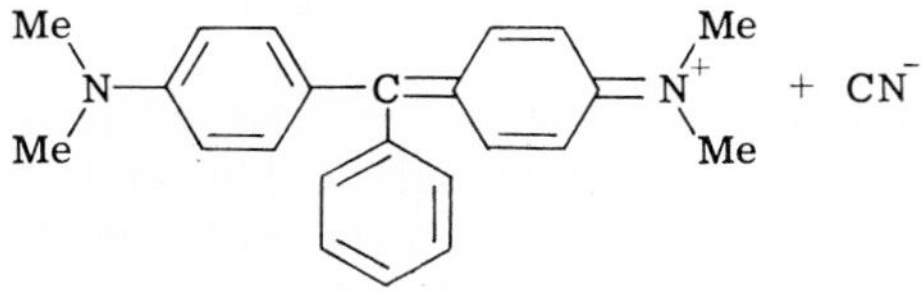

FIG. 18. Triphenyl methane after optical excitation.

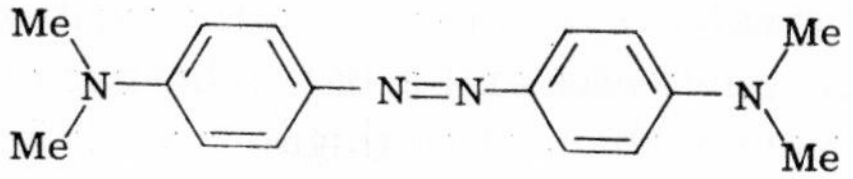

FIG. 19. N,N-Dimethyl-4,4'-aminoazobenzene.

The mechanisms of photochromism just described are the most important ones. There are many others. The changes in coloration by *cis-trans* photo-isomerization are relatively frequent. However, they are not usually spectacular, as for example the N,N-dimethyl-4,4'-aminoazobenzene (Fig. 19). Its solutions in dimethylformamide, which are yellow, become orange colored when lighted. Sometimes, the appearance of the color is due to the formation of a free radical, for instance, the 2,3,4,5-tetraphenyl-pyrryl radical which, in the dark, spontaneously dimerizes and gives a slightly colored compound, is dissociated again by irradiation (Wyman, 1955) (Fig. 20).

Finally we give an example of photochromism that is due to the triplet-triplet absorption. The coloring and bleaching reactions are, in that case, extremely fast, but Porter developed the technique of flash photolysis, which made the observation of these phenomena possible (Porter and Windsor, 1953).

If a solution of anthracene in cyclohexane is lighted with a flash, an absorption band with a maximum around 4.350 Å appears, a maximum that disappears a few fractions of a second later. This band is due to a transition from the first triplet state to a higher triplet state.

We may understand the bathochromic spectral shift if we consider, for instance, the canonical structures of a cyanine dye:

$$A^+ = [CH—CH=CH]_n — B$$

and

$$A — [CH=CH—CH]_n = B^+$$

The wave function Ψ of the mesomeric state is given by the equation

$$\Psi = \sum c_i \Psi_i \qquad \text{(all possible canonical forms)} \qquad (5)$$

where c_i is the coefficient corresponding to minimum energies and $E/c_i = 0$. The difference between the energy of mesomeric structures and the minimal energy of canonical structures is the resonance energy. The more mesomeric

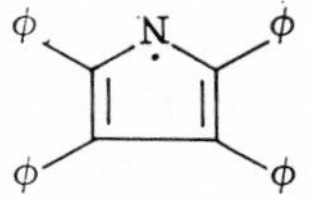

FIG. 20. 2,3,4,5-Tetraphenyl-pyrryl radical.

states there are, the greater is the energy. In the excited state, the number of canonical structures increases and a bathochromic effect is observed.

We may also consider a chain of conjugate double bonds of length

$$A - [C{=}C{-}C]_x = B$$

The π electrons are delocalized. The potential values are $V = 0$ on the whole chain and $V = \infty$ outside. The Schrödinger equation gives, for eigenenergies,

$$E_n = h^2 n^2 / 8mL^2 \tag{6}$$

If we consider $N\pi$ electrons, according to the Pauli principle, the highest occupied orbital possesses the value $E_{N/2}$ and the first empty level $E_{N/2+1}$. The maximum absorbed wavelength is

$$\lambda = 8mcN^2 l^2 / h(N + 1)$$

where $l = L/N$. Theory and experiment are in agreement, and the general behavior of the photochromic compounds can be roughly explained by the preceding considerations (Douzou and Wippler, 1963).

2. Thermal Effects and Photochromism

Temperature is the most important factor in the reactions (of molecular transition) initially induced by light and resulting from the corresponding deactivation. Progressive and moderate heating enhances the rate of the transition $S_0' \rightarrow S_0$. Heating may, in some cases, bring the sudden and reversible coloration of the configuration S_0, by the transition $S_0 \rightarrow S_0'$; this is thermochromism.

Thus, two types of energy act on the formation and the mutual conversion of transient low energetic configurations involved in the reactions of our models, (1) optically and (2) thermally. Both are pictured in Fig. 21.

In the optical method the transient configurations resulting from the electronic excitation and from the corresponding deactivation of the molecules are tested at very low temperatures and thus stabilized. But we know that such an optical excitation is artificial and damages the molecules. In the case of our model compounds, and as we shall see in the case of other compounds, it helps to draw an energetic scheme like that in Fig. 21.

Thermally, we have two alternate methods, classical experiments and infrared photoactivation. For the former, we can begin at room temperature or at a fixed temperature, like 4°C, and try by progressive heating to induce a thermal transition between two possible nonelectronically excited configurations. But in most cases, it is difficult or even impossible to accumulate the most unstable of them. For such a reason, following the pioneer theoretical works of Duchesne (1950), we tried to induce this molecular transition by infrared irradiation of our samples, at very low temperatures (77°K).

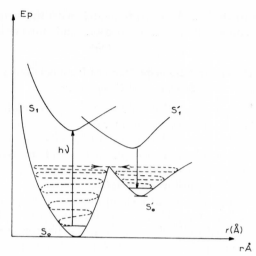

FIG. 21. Energetic scheme explaining both optical and thermal effects.

With infrared photoactivation, we proceed as follows: When our glassy transparent samples containing some photochromic compounds are irradiated at low, constant temperatures (77°K, controlled by thermocouples) by the total emission of a Nernst filament (the ultraviolet and visible emissions being filtered), a bathochromic effect is observed. It is similar to the effect induced under the same conditions by ultraviolet or visible excitation. The quantum yields of such "infrared activation" are very low if compared to the quantum yield of the ultraviolet or visible excitation. Several years ago, Duchesne (1950) pointed out that some structural changes might be induced in molecules by infrared excitation, leading to an isomerization, or chemical reactivity. More recently, Hall and Pimentel (1963) effected the *cis-trans* isomerization of nitrous acid by infrared excitation in nitrogen glasses at 20°K. Many difficult theoretical and practical problems are raised by the eventual infrared photoactivation of the molecules.

Our preliminary results, quite empirical, are difficult to explain, because we ignore how the vibrational excitation takes place and how it can be transferred (possibly in intervibrational transfer) to the molecular site, the evolution of which produces a transition. For the moment, we consider the action of the infrared radiation an empirical means of inducing and stabilizing some transient metastable configurations. And we think that these molecular transitions are due to a "thermal activation" in the neighborhood of every molecule that is hit. Nevertheless, infrared photoactivation may be a new and interesting way of working with the transition induced by the vibrational excitation of molecules. But, in such a case, we have necessarily to work with accurate models with the right methodology, including the monochromatized excitation and infrared spectrometric analysis.

3. Possible Applications in the Study of Transient Configurations of Biological Components

The Case of Nucleic Bases. Pyrimidine bases exist under different possible and unequally probable tautomeric configurations (Pullman and Pullman, 1963). Pyrimidine bases are photosensitive but, most often, their optical excitation produces photochemical transformations: the dimerization of thymine, 5,6-hydration of cytosine.

The percentage of phototautomerization seems to be low. Moreover, the tautomeric configurations absorb in the same range of wavelengths. Some of them are very unstable at room temperature, and thus it is difficult to find, by optical excitation, an eventual photoreversible process.

In 1963, working with cytosine, Hélène (Hélène and Douzou, 1964; Hélène *et al.*, 1964) found photoreversible reactions which may be due to specific tautomeric forms or to the combination of these with the solvent

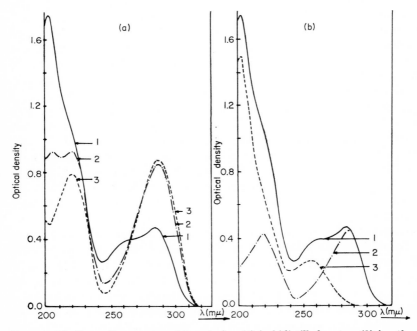

FIG. 22. (a) Absorption spectra of isocytosine (1) in bidistilled water, (2) in ethanol, and (3) in ethanol-ether (1:9, V/V). (b) Absorption spectra of isocytosine (1) in aqueous solution, (2) absorption due to the B form, and (3) absorption due to the A form.

(Fig. 22). More recently, Hélène (Hélène and Douzou, 1964a) worked with isocytosine; its tautomeric configurations A and B absorb, respectively, at 255 and 286 mμ. These configurations were found for the first time in crystals by McConnell *et al.* (1964). (See Fig. 23.)

Working in water, alcoholic and hydroalcoholic solutions as a function of temperature, Hélène played with the equilibrium A $\rightleftarrows$ B and determined approximately the activation energy of the transitions (Hélène and Douzou, 1964b). Moreover, at the liquid nitrogen temperature (77°K) and with EPA solutions which freeze without crystallizing, it was possible by selective optical excitation of the B configuration ($\lambda_{\max}$ absorption, 286 mμ) to induce the transition B $\rightarrow$ A, as in the case of our photochromic models.

A spectrophotometric study of aqueous and alcoholic solutions of cytosine and cytidine as a function of temperature demonstrated that the two

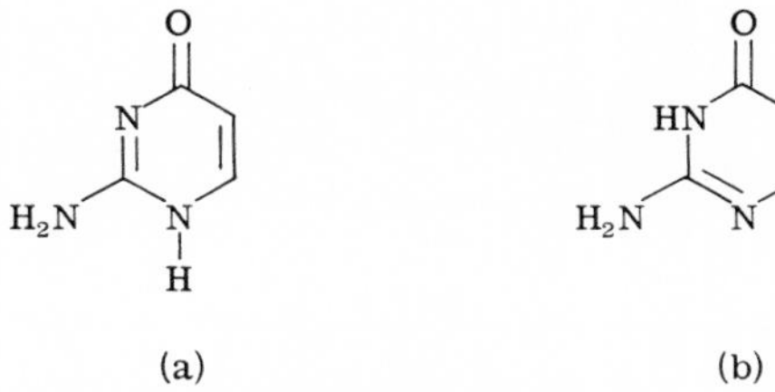

(a)   (b)

FIG. 23. Tautomeric configurations of cytosine.

"rare" tautomeric configurations already found (Hélène *et al.*, 1964) have an energy difference of a few kilocalories per mole, and that their relative stability is a function of the solvent. For instance, the tautomeric configuration absorbing at 240 mμ is more stable in ethanol than in water.

These different, preliminary results demonstrate the usefulness of the method of optical excitation, at various temperatures and in different solvents, for investigating the eventual transient (nonelectronically excited) configurations of a compound of biological interest.

4. Photochromic Compounds with Several Transient Configurations

a. Spiro-Pyranes. The spiro-pyrane derivatives tested as a function of the temperature above 77°K present several transient configurations:

$$S_0 \xrightarrow{h\nu} S_1{}^* \rightarrow S_1{}'^* \rightarrow S_0{}' \rightarrow S_0{}'' \rightarrow S_0{}'''$$

These transient configurations can be schematized in the potential energy diagram of Fig. 24. The transition $S_0 \rightarrow S_0{}'$ results from an optical excitation $(S_0 \rightarrow S_1{}^* \rightarrow S_1{}'^* \rightarrow S_0')$ at 77°K. By moderate and progressive heating, one gets the other configurations, S_0'', and S_0''', corresponding to thermal conversions through the mutual potential barriers. At room temperature, the optical excitation $S_0 \rightarrow S_1{}^*$ gives directly the configuration S_0'' or S_0''', according to conditions involved. By flash spectrophotometry it is possible to record some spectra of transient configurations.

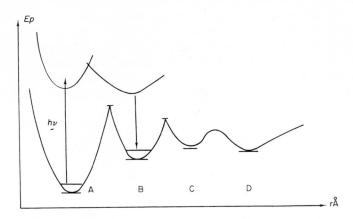

FIG. 24. Different configurations found in spiro-pyrane derivatives.

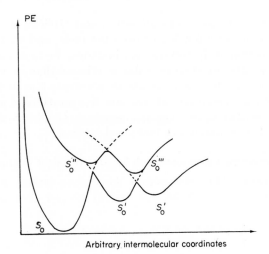

FIG. 25. Possible representations of crossing processes giving the transient configuration S_0'.

The problem of the identification of the transient configurations involved in the course of such photochromic processes is still to be solved. But the method of using optical excitation at low temperature, and the controlled thermal effect or infrared stimulation, appears to be promising when we have to find some transient low energetic molecular configurations. Schematizing these configurations by the Morse diagram discussed above, we may represent them as in Fig. 25. The possible existence of some other transient configurations (for instance, S_0'', S_0''') could show that optical and thermal activation lead to different configurations.

    b. Compounds and Reactions of Biological Interest. From the biophysicist's point of view, the most important result given by the photochromic

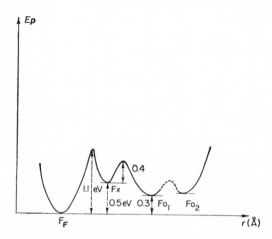

FIG. 26. Values obtained by experimentation on a spiro-pyrane derivative.

models is that, under certain conditions, some transient configurations of a molecular system might be studied during the course of its reaction. But, if in compounds of biological interest (e.g., coenzymes), the chemical evolution proceeds via a progressive extension of the electronic conjugation (delocalization), as did our photochromic models, then we see that the potential barriers leading to consecutive transient configurations become less and less.

    When the molecule, or the molecular complex, is raised to the first transition ($S_0 \rightarrow S_0'$), the necessary and sufficient energy absorbed should help us determine the other transition according to the scheme of Fig. 26. Thus, the detection of a transient configuration between the normal one and that corresponding to the whole chemical evolution seems questionable if we induce the transitions by heating, and by the optical excitation $S_0 \rightarrow S_1^*$. At very low temperatures, in glassy transparent solutions at 77°K, the first transient configuration S_0' is obtained. This may be due to the rigidity of the solvent matrix and thus to a steric hindrance.

But the question is: How can we experiment, even at low temperatures, on the molecular system in order to get one or more transient configurations? We have probably to experiment with reactive molecules involved in binary, or ternary, complexes or embedded in a molecular framework so that the transitional steps may be of the sort shown in Fig. 27. This could be the case for many enzymic (coenzyme, apoenzyme) systems, and also the case for photochromic models linked to certain molecules or

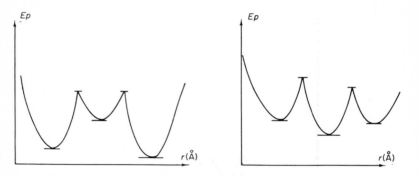

FIG. 27. Possible transitional steps during the internal conversion of complex molecules.

macromolecules in binary systems. We are presently working upon such compounds, in order to record eventually some transient (metastable) configurations in liquid media.

IV. Conclusions

1. The quantum and physicochemical behavior of conjugated polyatomic molecules are determined by some specific intersystem crossing processes between their possible transient (excited or not) configurations.

By optical excitation, the electronic transitions between stationary states of same multiplicity lead to two sorts of intersystem crossing processes, $S_n \rightarrow T_1$ (in fact, for us, $S_1 \rightarrow T_1$), the principal results of which were considered in Section II, and $S_n \rightarrow S_n'$, the consequences and characteristics of which are discussed in Section III.

By relaxation from S_n' (generally S_1'), we can obtain $S_n' \rightarrow S_0'$, and also $S_0' \rightarrow S_0$ or $S_0 \rightarrow S_0'$ by thermal activation (see Fig. 28). The $S_n \rightarrow T_n$ intersystem crossing process permits us to study several electronic properties, the specificity and the evolution of which are functions of intermolecular forces acting upon the studied molecule. Such a process could contribute to dynamic studies on organized organic compounds.

The $S_n \rightarrow S_n'$ and its nonexcited "homolog" $S_0 \rightarrow S_0'$ intersection processes permit us to get some transient, unexcited configurations which may be involved in biological processes according to the agreement between bioenergetics and the value of quanta involved in the transitions $S_0 \rightarrow S_0'$.

2. One of the most important problems remaining that we have to solve concerns the eventual choice between the different intersystem crossing processes which occur in the excited states of organic molecules and which finally give rise to the direct deactivation through S_1 and T_1 (electronically recordable) or to the deactivation via some transient nonexcited states S_0'', S_0', ...

In general, it seems that a given molecule shows only one of these two possible processes. But we must remember that such a molecule can be embedded in large molecular complexes and can then adopt a new collective behavior; for example, amino acids do not give transient unexcited configurations but their polypeptidic chains can adopt some isomeric and tautomeric configurations. Polymerization and other specific modes of aggregation of organic molecules of biological interest lead to new species and from there to new specific quantum mechanisms that we have to investigate, starting from observation of elementary components.

3. Moreover, when we consider the intersection processes between different transient nonexcited configurations (S_0', S_0'', ...), we have to solve the problem of their affiliation in order to establish their normal evolution.

These problems could be solved by infrared activation if we found a

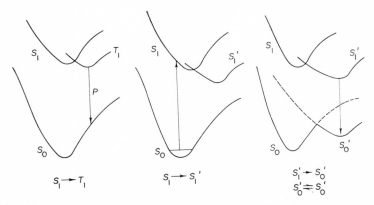

FIG. 28. Crossing processes of potential energy curves (for diatomic molecules) discussed in this chapter.

more accurate methodology than the present one. But these problems can be studied by optical excitations, because the same intersystem crossing processes should take place in the excited states. In that sense, experimentation with photochromic models could be useful, for it permits us to induce phenomena, like photoreversibility and the photoisomerization or tautomerization of a transient configuration, artificially "frozen."

Thus, the study of the intersystem crossing processes between different excited states, via the study of the mutual conversion of their unexcited states, represents a possible way for the solution of the remaining problems discussed here.

4. Indeed, we were obliged to schematize the mechanisms leading to molecular transitions in order to draw a clear network of the states involved in such transitions. The experimental study of every molecular model demonstrates how complicated the mechanism of the molecular transitions is. Moreover, such a study is made most often upon molecules isolated from their normal organized medium.

These restrictions give an idea of what biophysics has to do in the future. For the moment, our purpose was to survey the problems raised by molecular dynamics and by excited and nonexcited molecular configurations.

ACKNOWLEDGMENTS

This work was done under contract FR 112 of the DGRST with the full support of the CRSSA.

We are pleased to thank Prof. Charles Sadron, head of our laboratory, and Prof. Jules Duchesne of Liège (Belgium) for helpful discussions and advice. Last, we thank our friends and collaborators, Marius Ptak and Claude Hélène, who are responsible for many experiments discussed and described in this paper.

REFERENCES

Andros, G. M., and Calvin, M. (1962). *Biophys. J.* **2**, 217.
Bagdasarian, K. S., Muromtcev, V. I., and Sinitsyna, Z. A. (1963). *Dokl. Akad. Nauk SSSR.* **152**, 349, 374.
Blinder, S. M., Peller, M. L., Lord, N. W., Aamodt, L. C., and Ivanchukov, N. S. (1962). *J. Chem. Phys.* **36**, 4540.
Douzou, P., and Wippler, C. (1963). *J. Chim. Phys.* **60**, 1409
Duchesne, J. (1950). *J. Chem. Phys.* **18**, 1120.
Evans, D. F. (1960). *J. Chem. Soc.* p. 1735.
Grabowski, Z. R., and Bylina, A. (1964). *Trans. Faraday Soc.* **60**, 1131.
Hall, R. T., and Pimentel, G. C. (1963). *J. Chem. Phys.* **38**, 1889.
Harman, R. A., and Eyring, H. (1942). *J. Chem. Phys.* **10**, 557.
Heiligman-Rim, R., Hirshberg, Y., and Fischer, E. (1962). *J. Phys. Chem.* **66**, 2465.
Hélène, C., and Douzou, P. (1964). *Compt. Rend.* **258**, 196.
Hélène, C., and Douzou, P. (1964a). *Compt. Rend.* **259**, 4387.
Hélène, C., and Douzou, P. (1964b). *Compt. Rend.* **259**, 4853.

Hélène, C., Haug, A., Delbrück, M., and Douzou, P. (1964). *Compt. Rend.* **259**, 3385.
Hutchison, C. A., Jr., and Mangum, B. W. (1958). *J. Chem. Phys.* **29**, 952; *ibid.* (1961). *J. Chem. Phys.* **34**, 908.
J. Photochem. Photobiol. (1964). Wakulla Springs Confer. **3**, 269–580.

Kholmogorov, V. E., Baranov, E. V., and Terenin, A. N. (1963). *Dokl. Akad. Nauk SSSR* **149**, 142.
Lewis, G. N., Lipkin, D., and Magel, T. T. (1941). *J. Am. Chem. Soc.* **63**, 3005.
Livingston, R. (1955). *J. Am. Chem. Soc.* **77**, 2179.
Livingston, R., Porter, G., and Windsor, M. (1954). *Nature* **173**, 485.
McConnell, H. (1952). *J. Chem. Phys.* **20**, 1043.
McConnell, J. F., Sharma, B. D., and Marsh, R. E. (1964). *Nature* **203**, 399.
Magee, J. L., Shand, W. Jr., and Eyring, H. (1941). *J. Am. Chem. Soc.* **63**, 677.
Margerum, J. D., Miller, L. J., Saito, E., Brown, M. S., Mosher, H. S., and Hardwick, R. (1962). *J. Phys. Chem.* **66,,** 2434.
Nieman, G. C., and Robinson, G. W. (1962). *J. Chem. Phys.* **37**, 2150.
Porter, G., and Windsor, M. W. (1953). *J. Chem. Phys.* **21**, 2088.
Pringsheim, P. (1949). "Fluorescence and Phosphorescence." Wiley (Interscience), New York.
Ptak, M., and Douzou, P. (1963). *Nature* **199**, 1092.
Ptak, M., and Douzou, P. (1964). *J. Chim. Phys.* **61**, 1681.
Pullman, B., and Pullman, A. (1963). "Quantum Biochemistry." Wiley, New York.
Sponer, H., Kanda, Y., and Blackwell, L. A. (1958). *J. Chem. Phys.* **29**, 721
Sporer, A. H. (1961). *Trans. Faraday Soc.* **57**, 983.
Sternlicht, H., Nieman, G. C., and Robinson, G. W. (1963). *J. Chem. Phys.* **38**, 1326.
Weissbluth, M. (1965). *In* "Molecular Biophysics" (B. Pullman and M. Weissbluth, eds.). Academic Press, New York.
Wyman, G. M. (1955) *Chem. Rev.* **55**, 625.

Absorption and Rotation of Polarized Light by Polymers

IGNACIO TINOCO, JR.

Chemistry Department and Lawrence Radiation Laboratory,
University of California,
Berkeley, California

I. Observables

A. Absorption

A sample will absorb linearly polarized, monochromatic light, if the molecules in the sample have an absorption band which overlaps the wavelength of the light and which has a component of its polarization direction parallel to the plane of polarization of the light. If the molecules in the sample are not oriented, only the wavelength range of the absorption band is significant. If the incident light is not polarized, but the molecules are oriented, then the polarization of the absorption band is again significant. For example, a linear molecule with a parallel polarized absorption band will not absorb unpolarized light incident parallel to its axis.

For a given system, the absorption is measured by the absorbance A:

$$A = \log I_0/I \tag{1}$$

where I/I_0 is the fraction of light transmitted. A more useful measure is the molar extinction coefficient:

$$\epsilon = A/bc \tag{2}$$

where b is the path length of the light in centimeters and c is the concentration of the absorbers in moles per liter. The units of ϵ are then liters per mole-centimeter or square centimeters per millimole. Therefore ϵ can be thought of as a capture cross section for photons measured in square centimeters per millimole. Both A and ϵ will depend on wavelength and, for oriented samples, they will also depend on the direction of polarization of the light.

Useful measures of the total absorption of light by a band are given by the following integrals (Moffitt and Moscowitz, 1959). The integrals given here omit refractive index functions, which are supposed to correct for the difference between the internal field and the applied electromagnetic field (Weigang, 1964).

Dipole strength (units are esu² cm² or debye² $= 10^{-36}$ esu² cm²):

$$D = [3\hbar c(2303)/4\pi^2 N] \int (\epsilon/\nu) \, d\nu \qquad (3)$$

$$D = 9.180 \times 10^{-3} \int (\epsilon/\nu) \, d\nu \qquad \text{(units are debye²)} \qquad (3a)$$

$$D = 9.180 \times 10^{-3} \int (\epsilon/\lambda) \, d\lambda \qquad \text{(units are debye²)} \qquad (3b)$$

Oscillator strength (unitless):

$$f = [2303mc^2/\pi e^2 N] \int \epsilon \, d\nu \qquad (\nu \text{ in cm}^{-1}) \qquad (4)$$

$$f = 4.318 \times 10^{-9} \int \epsilon \, d\nu \qquad (4a)$$

$$f = 4.318 \times 10^{-9} \int (\epsilon/\lambda^2) \, d\lambda \qquad (\lambda \text{ in cm}) \qquad (4b)$$

Mean frequency (units are cm⁻¹):

$$\bar{\nu} = \int \epsilon \, d\nu \Big/ \int (\epsilon/\nu) \, d\nu \qquad (5)$$

$$\bar{\nu} = [3e^2\hbar/4\pi mc](f/D) \qquad (5a)$$

$$\bar{\nu} = 2.125 \times 10^6 (f/D) \qquad (D \text{ in debye²}) \qquad (5b)$$

Mean width (units are cm^{-1}):

$$\overline{\Delta \nu} = \left\{ \left[\int \epsilon \nu \, d\nu \bigg/ \int (\epsilon/\nu) \, d\nu \right] - \overline{\nu}^2 \right\}^{1/2} \tag{6}$$

These definitions give quantities which are most easily calculated theoretically. The integral in each equation is taken over the absorption band. Because most ultraviolet spectra are made up of overlapping bands, one must first resolve the spectrum into a sum of bands. Examples of the problems involved are shown in Fig. 1; there is no unique resolution. A major difficulty is that there is no theory for the shape of electronic absorption bands which can be used to guide the extrapolations.

Once the extrapolation is decided upon, numerical or graphical integration is used to obtain the observable parameters. However, for rough estimates, one can approximate the absorption band by a Gaussian, Lorentzian, etc., shape (Lowry, 1964) in either frequency or wavelength. Then the integrals can be determined analytically. The simplest practical shape is a rectangle with its width equal to the width of the band at half maximum. This approximates the area of a Gaussian to better than 10%.

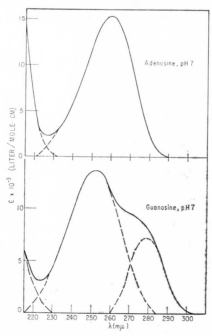

Fig. 1. The spectra of adenosine and guanosine at pH 7 (Pabst Circular, OR-10) and their arbitrary resolution into bands.

If the width at half maximum is called Γ_ν (cm^{-1}) or Γ_λ (cm) and the maximum extinction coefficient and corresponding frequency (or wavelength) are ϵ_m, ν_m (or λ_m):

Rectangular absorption bands:

$$D = 9.180 \times 10^{-3}\epsilon_m \ln\left[\frac{1 + \Gamma_\nu/2\nu_m}{1 - \Gamma_\nu/2\nu_m}\right] \tag{7}$$

$$D \cong 9.180 \times 10^{-3}\epsilon_m\Gamma_\nu/\nu_m \qquad (\Gamma_\nu \ll \nu_m) \tag{7a}$$

$$D \cong 9.180 \times 10^{-3}\epsilon_m\Gamma_\lambda/\lambda_m \qquad (\Gamma_\lambda \ll \lambda_m) \tag{7b}$$

$$f = 4.318 \times 10^{-9}\epsilon_m\Gamma_\nu \tag{8}$$

$$f \cong 4.318 \times 10^{-9}\epsilon_m\Gamma_\lambda/\lambda_m{}^2 \qquad (\Gamma_\lambda \ll \lambda_m) \tag{8a}$$

$$\bar{\nu} \cong \nu_m \tag{9}$$

$$\Delta\nu \cong \Gamma_\nu/(12)^{1/2} \qquad (\Gamma_\nu \ll \nu_m) \tag{10}$$

If a band is approximated by a Gaussian, either in frequency or wavelength,

$$\epsilon = \epsilon_m \exp\left[-(\nu - \nu_m)^2/\Theta_\nu{}^2\right] \qquad \text{or} \qquad \epsilon = \epsilon_m \exp\left[-(\lambda - \lambda_m)^2/\Theta_\lambda{}^2\right]$$

one finds:

Gaussian absorption bands:

$$D \cong 1.627 \times 10^{-2}\epsilon_m\Theta_\nu/\nu_m \qquad (\Theta_\nu \ll \nu_m) \tag{11}$$

$$D \cong 1.627 \times 10^{-2}\epsilon_m\Theta_\lambda/\lambda_m \qquad (\Theta_\lambda \ll \lambda_m) \tag{11a}$$

$$f = 7.654 \times 10^{-9}\epsilon_m\Theta_\nu \tag{12}$$

$$f \cong 7.654 \times 10^{-9}\epsilon_m\Theta_\lambda/\lambda_m{}^2 \qquad (\Theta_\lambda \ll \lambda_m) \tag{12a}$$

$$\bar{\nu} \cong \nu_m \tag{13}$$

$$\overline{\Delta\nu} \cong \Theta_\nu/\sqrt{2} \tag{14}$$

In these equations we have approximated

$$\int (1/\nu) \exp\left[-(\nu - \nu_m)^2/\Theta_\nu{}^2\right] d\nu \qquad \text{by} \qquad (1/\nu_m)\int \exp\left[-(\nu - \nu_m)^2/\Theta_\nu{}^2\right] d\nu$$

The values of these parameters for absorption bands in the ultraviolet and visible fall into two rough classes. Bands which have an ϵ_m of <1000, $D < 1$ debye^2, $f < 0.01$ can be called forbidden, whereas bands with values greater are allowed.

B. Circular Dichroism

If the incident light on a sample is circularly polarized, new parameters can be measured. The absorption of the light depends qualitatively on the same factors discussed under Section I, A. However, for an oriented sample, the circularly polarized light is analogous to unpolarized light in that the absorption depends only on the direction of propagation. The new quantitative factor is that for some molecules, the amount of absorption is dependent upon whether the light is right or left circularly polarized. The difference in extinction coefficients ($\epsilon_L - \epsilon_R$) is the circular dichroism. For all molecules which are identical to their mirror image, this difference is always zero. This requirement is both necessary and sufficient. A sufficient condition for the circular dichroism to be nonzero is that the molecule have no point or plane of symmetry; however, this is not a necessary condition.

Parameters analogous to those in Section I, A can be defined for the circular dichroism. As a factor of 4 was introduced in the original definition of the rotational strength (which is analogous to the dipole strength, Moffitt and Moscowitz, 1959), we shall also keep this factor in Eqs. (16), (16a), and (16b), analogous to the oscillator strength in absorption.

Rotational strength (units are esu-cgs):

$$R = [3\hbar c(2303)/16\pi^2 N] \int [(\epsilon_L - \epsilon_R)/\nu] \, d\nu \qquad (15)$$

$$R = 2.295 \times 10^{-39} \int [(\epsilon_L - \epsilon_R)/\nu] \, d\nu \qquad (15a)$$

$$R = 2.295 \times 10^{-39} \int [(\epsilon_L - \epsilon_R)/\lambda] \, d\lambda \qquad (15b)$$

Rotational oscillator strength (unitless):

$$C = [2303 mc^2/4\pi e^2 N] \int (\epsilon_L - \epsilon_R) \, d\nu \qquad (\nu \text{ in cm}^{-1}) \qquad (16)$$

$$C = 1.080 \times 10^{-9} \int (\epsilon_L - \epsilon_R) \, d\nu \qquad (16a)$$

$$C = 1.080 \times 10^{-9} \int [(\epsilon_L - \epsilon_R)/\lambda^2] \, d\lambda \qquad (\lambda \text{ in cm}) \qquad (16b)$$

Equations identical to Eqs. (5) and (6) define the mean frequency and mean width of the circular dichroism bands. The problem of separating an overlapping circular dichroism spectrum into bands is much more difficult than the analogous problem in absorption. Because the bands can

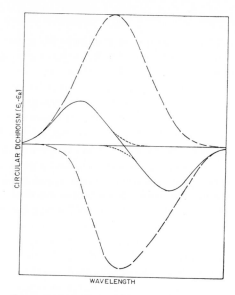

Fig. 2. A circular dichroism spectrum (solid line) and its arbitrary resolution into bands. The short dashes essentially follow the spectrum, whereas the long dashes give two large bands which nearly cancel.

be both positive and negative, two overlapping bands of opposite sign can be resolved in many quite different ways. This is illustrated in Fig. 2, where the experimental curve (solid line) is resolved into two quite different sums of positive and negative bands. One resolution (short dashes) essentially follows the experimental curve; the other (long dashes) shows two large bands which nearly cancel. Prior resolution of the absorption spectrum is a great help in solving the circular dichroism problem.

For an allowed absorption band the circular dichroism band will have the same position and shape as the absorption, whereas for a forbidden absorption band the circular dichroism curve will in general have the same shape, but will be shifted 100 to 1000 cm^{-1} toward the red (Moffitt and Moscowitz, 1959).

The values of the circular dichroic parameters are about $(\epsilon_L - \epsilon_R) \leq 100$, $R \leq 10 \times 10^{-38}$, $C \leq 0.001$.

A measurable quantity which is sometimes used instead of circular dichroism is the ellipticity θ. If plane-polarized light is passed through a circularly dichroic sample, it will emerge elliptically polarized. The tangent of θ is equal to the ratio of the minor to the major axis of this ellipse. This is illustrated in Fig. 3. The ellipticity is directly proportional to the circular dichroism.

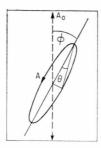

FIG. 3. The definitions of the rotation ϕ and the ellipticity θ of polarized light. The light is approaching the observer. The dashed line labeled A_0 represents the plane-polarized light incident on the sample. The transmitted light A is elliptically polarized. The rotation ϕ is positive for clockwise rotation, and the ellipticity θ is positive for right elliptically polarized light.

Ellipticity [units of (deg-liter/mole-cm) × 100]:

$$[\theta] = [9(2303)/2\pi](\epsilon_L - \epsilon_R) \tag{17}$$

$$[\theta] = 3298(\epsilon_L - \epsilon_R) \tag{17a}$$

C. Rotation

A sample which is circularly dichroic in some absorption bands will rotate the plane of incident, linearly polarized light. This rotation will depend on wavelength, but it will occur at all wavelengths. For an absorbing sample, the emergent light is elliptically polarized, and the rotation is measured relative to the major axis of the ellipse (as shown in Fig. 3). The units of rotation are very confusing, because the present researchers still use those defined by Biot in 1836 (Lowry, 1964, p. 22). The specific rotation $[\alpha]$ is

$$[\alpha] = \alpha/bc \tag{18}$$

where α is the rotation in degrees, b is the path length in decimeters, and c is the concentration in grams per cubic centimeter. One can think of it as having units of (deg-cm²/gm) × 0.1. The molar rotation $[\phi]$ is defined as

$$[\phi] = M[\alpha]/100 \tag{19}$$

where M is the molecular weight. This leads to units for $[\phi]$ of (deg-liter/mole-cm) × 100.

Each circular dichroism band makes a contribution to the rotation at all wavelengths which can be calculated from the Kronig–Kramers equations (MacDonald and Brachman, 1956). In the following equations we shall use ϕ or θ without brackets to specify rotations or ellipticities in arbitrary units (Moscowitz, 1957, 1960).

$$\phi(\nu) = \frac{2\nu^2}{\pi} \int \frac{\theta(\nu')\,d\nu'}{\nu'(\nu'^2 - \nu^2)} \qquad (20)$$

$$\phi(\lambda) = \frac{2}{\pi} \int \frac{\lambda'\theta(\lambda')\,d\lambda'}{(\lambda^2 - \lambda'^2)} \qquad (20a)$$

The bar through the integral means that one must take the principal value of this integral. The shape of the curves for rotation vs. ν or λ (the optical rotatory dispersion curves or ORD curves) will thus depend on the circular dichroism curves and therefore on the absorption curves. However, at wavelengths removed from the absorption bands, the ORD curves will all have the same general shape. We can see this by choosing a delta function at ν_0 or λ_0 for θ. Using Eqs. (20) and (20a), one finds

$$\phi(\nu) = a_\nu \left(\frac{\nu^2}{\nu_0{}^2 - \nu^2} \right) \qquad (\nu \gg \nu_0, \nu \ll \nu_0) \qquad (21)$$

$$\phi(\lambda) = a_\lambda \left(\frac{1}{\lambda^2 - \lambda_0{}^2} \right) \qquad (\lambda \gg \lambda_0, \lambda \ll \lambda_0) \qquad (21a)$$

where a_ν, a_λ represent the constant terms in each equation. These equations are the Drude equations. Near an absorption band, one can use either damped Drude equations

$$\phi(\nu) = a_\nu \left[\frac{\nu^2}{\nu_0{}^2 - \nu^2 + \nu^2\Gamma_\nu{}^2/(\nu_0{}^2 - \nu^2)} \right] \qquad (22)$$

$$\phi(\lambda) = a_\lambda \left[\frac{1}{\lambda^2 - \lambda_0{}^2 + \lambda^2\Gamma_\lambda{}^2/(\lambda^2 - \lambda_0{}^2)} \right] \qquad (22a)$$

or the Kronig–Kramers transforms of a Gaussian circular dichroism curve $\theta = \theta_m \exp\left[-(\nu - \nu_m)^2/\Theta_\nu{}^2\right]$ or $\theta = \theta_m \exp\left[-(\lambda - \lambda_m)^2/\Theta_\lambda{}^2\right]$ (Moscowitz, 1957, 1960):

$$\phi(\nu) = \frac{2}{\sqrt{\pi}}\,\theta_m \left[e^{-c^2} \int_0^c e^{x^2}\,dx + \frac{\Theta_\nu}{2(\nu_m + \nu)} - \frac{\Theta_\nu}{\nu_m} \right] \qquad (23)$$

where $c = (\nu_m - \nu)/\Theta_\nu$, and

$$\phi(\lambda) = \frac{2}{\sqrt{\pi}}\,\theta_m \left[e^{-c^2} \int_0^c e^{x^2}\,dx - \frac{\Theta_\lambda}{2(\lambda + \lambda_m)} \right] \qquad (23a)$$

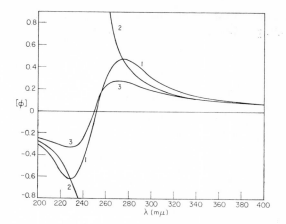

FIG. 4. Optical rotatory dispersion curves for a circular dichroism curve Gaussian in frequency. Curve 1 is Eq. (23), curve 2 is Eq. (21), and curve 3 is Eq. (22).

where $c = (\lambda - \lambda_m)/\Theta_\lambda$. Tabulated values of

$$e^{-c^2} \int_0^e e^{x^2}\, dx$$

are available (Lohmander and Rittsten, 1958). The wavelength dependence of $\phi(\nu)$ is plotted in Fig. 4, curve 1, for a Gaussian (in ν) circular dichroism band, using Eq. (23). The constant $2\,_m/\sqrt{\pi}$ was set equal to 1, $\nu_m = 40{,}000$, and $\Theta: = 4000$. The approximate results for this shape band obtained from Eqs. (21) and (22) are also shown. Curve 2 is Eq. (21) with $a_\nu = \Theta/\nu_m$, and curve 3 is Eq. (22) with $\Gamma = 2(\ln 2)^{1/2}\Theta_\nu$.

As the contribution to $\phi(\lambda)$ from each circular dichroism band extends over all wavelengths, it is very difficult to separate an experimental ORD curve into unique components from individual bands. One can write

$$\phi = \sum_i c_i \phi_i \qquad (24)$$

with each ϕ_i having the form of one of Eqs. (21–23a). For λ not close to any circular dichroism bands, the most used forms have been

$$\phi = \sum_i [c_i/(\lambda^2 - \lambda_i^2)] \qquad (25)$$

$$\phi = \sum_{n=1} [b_n/(\lambda^2 - \lambda_0^2)^n] \qquad (25a)$$

where Eq. (25a) is seen to be a Taylor expansion of Eq. (25) around λ_0. If an experimental ORD curve has somehow been resolved into components (the partial rotations of Moffitt, 1956), one can obtain values of the corresponding rotational strengths. For Eqs. (21–22a),

$$R = (\hbar c/48N)a_\nu \tag{26}$$

$$R = 1.093 \times 10^{-42}a_\nu \tag{26a}$$

$$R = (\hbar c/48N)(a_\lambda/\lambda_0^2) \tag{27}$$

$$R = 1.093 \times 10^{-42}(a_\lambda/\lambda_0^2) \tag{27a}$$

For the damped Drude equations and the Gaussian transforms, the maximum (peak) and minimum (trough) in each curve can be used to calculate a rotational strength.

Damped Drude:

$$\nu_{\text{peak}}, \nu_{\text{trough}} \cong \nu_0 \pm \Gamma_\nu/2 \tag{28}$$

$$R \cong (\hbar c\Gamma_\nu/48N\nu_0)([\phi]_{\text{peak}} - [\phi]_{\text{trough}}) \tag{28a}$$

$$R \cong 1.093 \times 10^{-42}(\Gamma_\nu/\nu_0)([\phi]_{\text{peak}} - [\phi]_{\text{trough}}) \tag{28b}$$

$$\lambda_{\text{peak}}, \lambda_{\text{trough}} \cong \lambda_0 \pm \Gamma_\lambda/2 \tag{29}$$

$$R = (\hbar c\Gamma_\lambda/48N_0\lambda_0)([\phi]_{\text{peak}} - [\phi]_{\text{trough}}) \tag{29a}$$

$$R = 1.093 \times 10^{-42}(\Gamma_\lambda/\lambda_0)([\phi]_{\text{peak}} - [\phi]_{\text{trough}}) \tag{29b}$$

Gaussian:

$$\nu_{\text{peak}}, \nu_{\text{trough}} \cong \nu_m \pm \Theta_\nu/\sqrt{2} \tag{30}$$

$$R \cong (\hbar c\Theta_\nu/48N\nu_m)([\phi]_{\text{peak}} - [\phi]_{\text{trough}}) \tag{30a}$$

$$R \cong 1.093 \times 10^{-42}(\Theta_\nu/\nu_m)([\phi]_{\text{peak}} - [\phi]_{\text{trough}}) \tag{30b}$$

$$\lambda_{\text{peak}}, \lambda_{\text{trough}} \cong \lambda_m \pm \Theta_\lambda/\sqrt{2} \tag{31}$$

$$R \cong (\hbar c\Theta_\lambda/48N\lambda_m)([\phi]_{\text{peak}} - [\phi]_{\text{trough}}) \tag{31a}$$

$$R \cong 1.093 \times 10^{-42}(\Theta_\lambda/\lambda_m)([\phi]_{\text{peak}} - [\phi]_{\text{trough}}) \tag{31b}$$

Of course, one could use the Kronig–Kramers transforms to obtain a circular dichroism curve from the rotation curve and then integrate the dichroism curve to obtain rotational strengths (Moscowitz, 1957, 1960):

$$\theta(\nu) = -\frac{2\nu^2}{\pi}\int_0^\infty \frac{\phi(\nu')\,d\nu'}{\nu'^2(\nu'^2 - \nu^2)} \tag{32}$$

$$\theta(\lambda) = -\frac{2}{\pi\lambda}\int_0^\infty \frac{\phi(\lambda')\lambda'^2}{\lambda^2 - \lambda'^2}d\lambda \tag{32a}$$

The trouble is that ϕ must be known or approximated over all ν or λ from 0 to ∞.

Values of $[\phi]$ expected are from 10 to 100 outside an absorption band and approaching 10^5 within a band.

II. Structure Correlations

A. Composition

Measurement of the absorbance or the circular dichroism or the optical rotation of a mixture at M wavelengths can give the concentrations of N components with $N \leq M$. These methods have been applied to analysis of RNA hydrolyzates with four major components (Reid and Pratt, 1960), sRNA hydrolyzates with up to nine components (Lee *et al.*, 1964), and native and denatured DNA with two independent components (Samejima and Yang, 1965). The general procedure can be illustrated by using absorption of light. One must solve the simultaneous linear equations

$$A(\lambda_i) = \sum_{j=1}^{N} \epsilon_j(\lambda_i) c_j \qquad (i = 1, 2, \ldots, M) \qquad (33)$$

for the unknown concentrations c_j. Because there are usually more equations (M) than unknowns (N), the values of c_j which give the best least-squares fit to all the equations are obtained. This is easily done using matrix methods. Equation (33) is rewritten as

$$\mathbf{A} = \boldsymbol{\varepsilon}\mathbf{c} \qquad (34)$$

where $\mathbf{A}$ is a row vector with M components, $\boldsymbol{\varepsilon}$ is an $N \times M$ matrix, and $\mathbf{c}$ is a column vector with N components. One multiplies by the transpose of $\boldsymbol{\varepsilon} = \tilde{\boldsymbol{\varepsilon}}$,

$$\tilde{\boldsymbol{\varepsilon}}\mathbf{A} = \tilde{\boldsymbol{\varepsilon}}\boldsymbol{\varepsilon}\mathbf{c} \qquad (35)$$

to form the square matrix $\tilde{\boldsymbol{\varepsilon}}\boldsymbol{\varepsilon}$ which has an inverse $(\tilde{\boldsymbol{\varepsilon}}\boldsymbol{\varepsilon})^{-1}$. Therefore the required solution is

$$\mathbf{c} = (\tilde{\boldsymbol{\varepsilon}}\boldsymbol{\varepsilon})^{-1}\tilde{\boldsymbol{\varepsilon}}\mathbf{A} \qquad (36)$$

This means that, for a given system in which a fixed number of absorbances are measured at set wavelengths, the coefficients of the absorbances need be calculated only once. Then the concentration of each component can be easily obtained as a sum of weighted absorbances:

$$c_j = \sum_{i} w_{ij} A(\lambda_i) \qquad (37)$$

If only ratios of components are desired, the number of unknowns is decreased by one. For DNA the value of the rotation at one wavelength has been calibrated to give the $(A + T)/(G + C)$ ratio (Samejima and Yang, 1965).

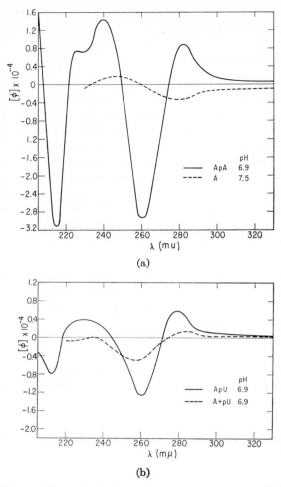

FIG. 5. (a) The optical rotatory dispersion of adenylyl-(3′−5′)adenosine (ApA) is compared with that of adenosine; (b) the ORD of adenylyl-(3′−5′)uridine (ApU) is compared with the sum of adenosine and uridylic acid.

B. Sequence

The optical properties can be used to give information about the sequence of units in oligomers. Michelson (1963) has presented characteristic difference spectra for the dinucleoside phosphates adenylyl-(3′–5′)cytidine (ApC) and cytidylyl-(3′–5′)adenosine (CpA) relative to their monomers. The optical rotatory dispersion of dinucleoside phosphates show greater differences from the sum of the monomers. Examples are given in Fig. 5, where the ORD of adenylyl-(3′–5′)adenosine (ApA) and adenylyl-

$(3'-5')$ uridine (ApU) are compared with their monomers (Warshaw and Tinoco, 1965). These data can be used to identify nearest-neighbor frequencies in polymers. For oligomers this may be sufficient to determine the sequence.

The simplest possible example is, of course, a trimer. Two chromatographic peaks (the fifth and sixth peaks) from the trimer fraction of a ribonuclease hydrolyzate of RNA correspond to the sequence isomers ApGpU and GpApU (Rushizky and Sober, 1964). If the main contribution to the rotation of the trimer comes from the nearest-neighbor inter-

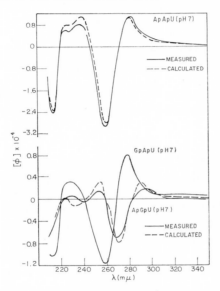

FIG. 6. The optical rotatory dispersion for ApApU, GpApU, and ApGpU. Calculated curves from Eq. (38) (dashed lines) are also given for ApApU and ApGpU.

actions between bases, their rotations should be predictable from the following equation:

$$3\,[\phi](\text{ABC}) = 2\,[\phi](\text{AB}) + 2\,[\phi](\text{BC}) - [\phi](\text{B}) \qquad (38)$$

where $[\phi](\text{AB})$ represents the rotation per monomer of the appropriate dimer. Figure 6 shows the measured and calculated rotation for the known isomer ApApU. The good agreement gives confidence in Eq. (38); therefore the comparison in Fig. 6 of measured and calculated rotations for ApGpU and GpApU leads to the identification of the fifth chromatographic peak as GpApU and the sixth peak as ApGpU (Cantor and Tinoco, 1965).

The pH and temperature dependence of the ORD of dinucleoside phosphates can be used as a further tool in identifying sequences. The temperature dependence of the absorption of DNA has been used to obtain in-

TABLE I

MEASURED AND CALCULATED HYPOCHROMISM [EQ. (39)] FOR POLYMERS OF
ADENYLIC ACID[a]

Polymer	Measured (%)	Nearest-neighbor-only interaction (%)	Inverse cube of distance interaction (%)
A_2	9	(9)	(9)
A_3	12	12	12.75
A_4	15	13.6	14.8
A_∞	26	18	21.6

[a] Measured at pH 5.7 and room temperature by S. L. Davis in this laboratory.

formation about regions in the double-strand helix which are rich in AT
or GC base pairs (Felsenfeld and Sandeen, 1962; Fresco et al., 1963).

C. Chain Length

For a rigid oligomer of strongly interacting chromophores, there should
be a significant dependence of the position of the absorption maximum on
the number of chromophores (Tinoco et al., 1963). However, biopolymers
do not usually fit the theoretical criteria for significant frequency shifts,
and large shifts have not been found experimentally. The intensity of
absorption for these polymers does depend both theoretically and experimentally on the chain length. A convenient measure of the decrease in
absorption of a polymer relative to its monomers is the hypochromism:

$$H = (1 - f_P/f_M)100 \tag{39}$$

The oscillator strength of the polymer and monomer, respectively, are
f_P and f_M. Table I compares some measured hypochromisms, at pH 5.7
and room temperature, for oligomers and adenylic acid with those calculated from the measured dimer hypochromism. If one assumes the polymers
are linear arrays of stacked bases which interact only with their nearest
neighbors (column 2), or by an interaction which depends on the inverse
cube of the distance (column 3), one can get satisfactory agreement with
experiment. Although these data are useful for empirical chain-length
determination, in order to make a fair choice between the two models, all
the oligomers must have the same conformation. This is not true at room
temperature for these polymers; therefore we should make the comparison
among extrapolated, low-temperature hypochromisms, which are not yet
available.

D. Helices

Most measurements of optical properties of polymers have been used to determine the presence or absence of helices. As shown in Fig. 7, the absorption of both polypeptides and polynucleotides decreases when they form single- or double-strand helices. This has been used qualitatively to study the conformation of polymers (see Section III). It can be used quantitatively to determine the amount of helix present in the system if either (1) each polymer molecule is present either as a helix or not, but is

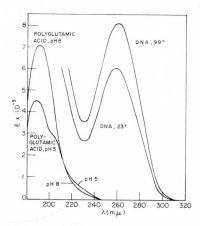

FIG. 7. The spectra of polyglutamic acid (Tinoco *et al.*, 1962) at pH 5 (single-strand helix) and pH 8 (disordered) and calf thymus DNA (E. Barrett, personal communication) at 23°C (double-strand helix) and at 99°C (disordered).

not partially helical, or (2) the molecule is partially helical, but the statistics of distribution of helix lengths is known. For condition (1) the amount of helix is just

$$\% \text{ helix } = 100 \left(\frac{A - A_0}{A_{100} - A_0} \right) \tag{40}$$

where A is measured absorbance, A_0 is absorbance for no helix, and A_{100} is absorbance for 100% helix. For condition (2), the absorbance of the helix must be known as a function of chain length. In general this leads to a complicated function of % helix vs. measured absorbance (Applequist, 1961).

The same discussion applies to circular dichroism or optical rotatory dispersion. If the values at 100% and 0% helix content are the same for a given class of polymers, then of course the method becomes more useful.

284   TINOCO

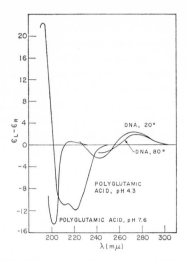

FIG. 8. The circular dichroism of polyglutamic acid (Holzwarth and Doty, 1965) at pH 4.3 (single-strand helix) and pH 7.6 (disordered) and calf thymus DNA (Brahms and Mommaerts, 1964) at 20°C (double-strand helix) and at 80°C (disordered).

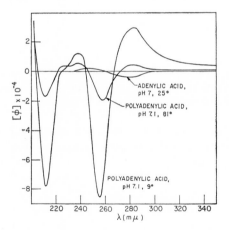

FIG. 9. The optical rotatory dispersion of polyadenylic acid, pH 7.1 (Holcomb and Tinoco, 1965) at 9°C (partially disordered, single-strand helix) and at 81°C (very disordered, single-strand helix). The ORD of adenylic acid is shown for comparison.

The Moffitt–Yang equation (Moffitt and Yang, 1956) for ORD at wavelengths far removed from an absorption band,

$$[\phi] = \frac{a_0\lambda_0^2}{\lambda^2 - \lambda_0^2} + \frac{b_0\lambda_0^4}{(\lambda^2 - \lambda_0^2)^2} \tag{41}$$

was proposed for this purpose. The value of b_0 was suggested to be a direct measure of helix content. This has been used extensively for polypeptides and proteins (Urnes and Doty, 1961). However, now that ORD and circular dichroism measurements can be made at the amide absorption band (Holzwarth and Doty, 1965), a more direct and more sensitive measure of the conformation of the polypeptide chain can probably be made. Similar studies in the absorption band of polynucleotides have recently been made. Because these studies are just beginning, we shall content ourselves at this time by giving a few illustrations of recent results in Figs. 8 and 9. It is clear that an understanding of these results will lead to new information about biopolymers in solution.

E. Folding of Helices

One would like to know, for a protein, not only the amount and type of helix, but also how these helices are folded. Evidence for conformation changes when enzymes interact with substrates or inhibitors should be obtainable from the optical properties. This work is barely started, but it shows promise. Possible evidence for effects of folding in polynucleotides is shown in Fig. 10, where the ORD of several DNA-containing bacteriophages is presented. The ORD curve for phage α is very similar in shape to that

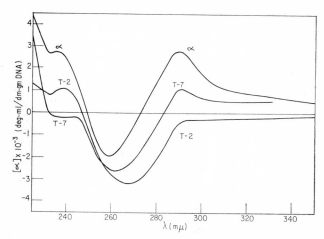

FIG. 10. The optical rotatory dispersion of three DNA-containing bacteriophage (Maestre and Tinoco, 1965). The specific rotation per gram per milliliter of DNA is plotted vs. wavelength.

of native DNA in solution (Samejima and Yang, 1964). However, the curves for the other phages are significantly different. Whether this does reflect the amount of folding of the DNA inside the phage head or is caused by a different effect remains to be seen.

III. Annotated Bibliography

Because it is impossible in a single chapter to make a significant survey of the pertinent work in this area, a bibliography of reviews and recent papers should help the interested reader find detailed discussions of specific topics.

A. General Books

"Theory and Applications of Ultraviolet Spectroscopy," H. H. Jaffé and M. Orchin. Wiley, New York, 1962.

"Optical Rotatory Power," T. M. Lowry, Dover, New York, 1964.

B. Absorption

1. Theory

(a) Optical rotatory dispersion of helical polymers. W. Moffitt, *J. Chem. Phys.* **25**, 467 (1956). Selection rules and polarization directions for absorption of light by single-strand helices.

(b) Hypochromism in polynucleotides. I. Tinoco, Jr., *J. Am. Chem. Soc.* **82**, 4785 (1960). Errata in *J. Am. Chem. Soc.* **84**, 5047 (1961).

(c) Optical and other electronic properties of polymers. I. Tinoco, Jr., *J. Chem. Phys.* **33**, 1332 (1960). Errata in *J. Chem. Phys.* **34**, 1067 (1961). Static electric field contribution to optical properties.

(d) Hypochromism and other spectral properties of helical polynucleotides. W. Rhodes, *J. Am. Chem. Soc.* **83**, 3609 (1961). Selection rules and polarization directions for absorption of light by double-strand helices.

(e) Hypochromism in the ultraviolet absorption of nucleic acids and related structures. H. C. Bolton and J. H. Weiss, *Nature* **195**, 666 (1962). See, however, Ref. B, 1(h).

(f) Symmetry of helical polymers. Electronic states of double-stranded polynucleotides. W. Rhodes, *J. Chem. Phys.* **37**, 2433 (1962).

(g) The symmetry and spectral properties of helical polynucleotides. W. Rhodes, *Radiation Res.* **20**, 120 (1963).

(h) Polarizability theories of polynucleotide hypochromism. H. DeVoe, *Nature* **197**, 1295 (1963). Shows that model in Ref. B, 1(e) leads to no hypochromism.

(i) Absorption and rotation of light by helical oligomers: The nearest neighbor approximation. D. F. Bradley, I. Tinoco, Jr., and R. W. Woody, *Biopolymers* **1**, 239 (1963).

(j) Theory of hypochromism. R. K. Nesbet, *Mol. Phys.* **7**, 211 (1964). Quantum mechanical treatment of model in Ref. B, 1(e).

(k) Some remarks on the hypochromicity of polynucleotides. T. A. Hoffman and J. Ladik, *J. Theoret. Biol.* **6**, 26 (1964). Use simple Hückel MO theory to calculate oscillator strengths of 16 possible dinucleotides.

(l) Optical properties of molecular aggregates. I. Classical model of electronic absorption and refraction. H. DeVoe, *J. Chem. Phys.* **41**, 393 (1964). Hypochromism, band shifts, and band shapes with no first-order perturbation approximation.

(m) On the theory of hypochromism. G. N. Fowler, *Mol. Phys.* **8**, 383 (1964). Discusses Refs. B, 1(e) and (j).

(n) Theory of the optical and other properties of biopolymers: applicability and elimination of the first-neighbor and dipole-dipole approximations. D. F. Bradley, S. Lifson, and B. Honig, *in* "Electronic Aspects of Biochemistry" (B. Pullman, ed.), p. 77. Academic Press, New York, 1964.

2. Experiments

(a) Ultraviolet spectra of proteins and amino acids. D. B. Wetlaufer, *Advan. Protein Chem.* **17**, 303 (1962). Review includes absorption of synthetic polypeptides.

(b) The dispersion of the hyperchromic effect in thermally induced transitions of nucleic acids. G. Felsenfeld and G. Sandeen, *J. Mol. Biol.* **5**, 587 (1962).

(c) Secondary structures of nucleic acids in organic solvents, III. Relationship of optical properties to conformation. G. K. Helmkamp and P. O. P. Ts'O, *Biochem. Biophys. Acta.* **55**, 601 (1962).

(d) Properties of helic polycytidylic acid. E. O. Akinrimisi, C. Sander, and P. O. P. Ts'O, *Biochemistry* **2**, 340 (1963).

(e) A new spectroscopic approach to the determination of helical secondary structure in ribonucleic acids. J. R. Fresco, L. C. Klotz, and E. G. Richards, *Cold Spring Harbor Symp. Quant. Biol.* **28**, 83 (1963). Dispersion of hypochromism.

(f) Absorption spectra of nucleotides, polynucleotides, and nucleic acids in the far ultraviolet. D. Voet, W. B. Gratzer, R. A. Cox, and P. Doty, *Biopolymers* **1**, 193 (1963).

(g) Physical chemistry of nucleic acids, A. M. Michelson, "The Chemistry of Nucleosides and Nucleotides," Chap. 8. Academic Press, New York, 1963. Good review of optical properties.

(h) Polynucleotides. VI. Molecular properties and conformation of polyribouridylic acid. E. G. Richards, C. P. Flessel, and J. R. Fresco, *Biopolymers* **1**, 431 (1963).

(i) Optical properties of the poly-L-proline and collagen helices. W. B. Gratzer, W. Rhodes, and G. D. Fasman, *Biopolymers* **1**, 319 (1963).

(j) Conformational aspects of polypeptides. VII. Helical assignments via far ultraviolet absorption spectra and optical activity. M. Goodman, J. Listowsky, Y. Masuda, and F. Boardman, *Biopolymers* **1**, 33 (1963). Methyl-L-aspartate and methyl-L-glutamate as a function of chain length.

(k) Polarized absorption spectra of single crystals of 1-methylthymine, 9-methyladenine, and their hydrogen-bonded complex. R. F. Stewart and N. Davidson, *Biopolymers Symp.* **1**, 465 (1964).

(l) Solvent-induced ultraviolet hypochromism in nucleosides. E. Charney and M. Gellert, *Biopolymers Symp.* **1**, 469 (1964).

(m) Helix–random coil transitions in DNA homopolymer pairs. R. B. Inman and R. L. Baldwin, *J. Mol. Biol.* **8**, 452 (1964). Absorption data for synthetic DNA's.

(n) The ultraviolet spectra of native and denatured deoxyribonucleic acid. M. Falk, *J. Am. Chem. Soc.* **86**, 1226 (1964).

(o) Transitions of DNA homopolymers. R. B. Inman, *J. Mol. Biol.* **9**, 624 (1964). Absorption data for synthetic DNA's.

(p) Some observations on the hypochromism of DNA. H. R. Mahler, B. Kline, and B. D. Mehrotra, *J. Mol. Biol.* **9**, 801 (1964). The composition dependence of hypochromism.

(q) The structure of the three-stranded helix, poly (A + 2U). H. T. Miles, *Proc. Natl. Acad. Sci. U.S.* **51**, 1104 (1964). Infrared absorption data.

(r) Infrared demonstration of two- and three-strand helix formation between poly C and guanosine mononucleotides and oligonucleotides. F. B. Howard, J. Frazier, M. N. Lipsett, and H. T. Miles, *Biochem. Biophys. Res. Commun.* **17**, 93 (1964).

(s) Polynucleotides. Propriétés physiques de dinucleotides. J. Massoulie and A. Michael Michelson, *Compt. Rend. Acad. Sci.* **259**, 2923 (1964).

(t) Une méthod spectrophotometrique permettant d'étudier séparément les complexes en double et triple hélice formés par les acides polyriboadénylique et polyribouridylique. J. Massoulie, R. Blake, L. Klotz, and J. Fresco, *Compt. Rend. Acad. Sci.* **259**, 3104 (1964).

(u) The structure and properties of biomolecules and biological systems. *Advan. Chem. Phys.* **7**, (1964). Contains articles on the spectra and other electronic properties of biological polymers.

3. Calculations

(a) The effect of chain length upon hypochromism in nucleic acids and polynucleotides. A. Rich and I. Tinoco, Jr., *J. Am. Chem. Soc.* **82**, 6409 (1960).

(b) The hypochromism of helical polynucleotides. H. DeVoe and I. Tinoco, Jr., *J. Mol. Biol.* **4**, 518 (1962).

(c) Interaction of two ethylene molecules. R. K. Nesbet, *Mol. Phys.* **5,** 63 (1962).

(d) The relation between conformation and light absorption in polypeptides and proteins. I. Tinoco, Jr., A. Halpern, and W. T. Simpson, *in* "Polyamino Acids, Polypeptides and Proteins" (M. A. Stachmann, ed.), p. 147. Univ. of Wisconsin Press, Madison, 1962. Hypochromism in α-helix.

(e) Solvent effects and a test of the theory of hypochromism. M. T. Vala, Jr. and S. A. Rice, *J. Chem. Phys.* **39,** 2348 (1963). Isotactic polystyrene.

(f) Spectral characterization of oligonucleotides by computational methods. A. W. Pratt, J. N. Toal, G. W. Rushizky, and H. A. Sober, *Biochemistry* **3,** 1831 (1964).

C. Rotation and Circular Dichroism

1. Theory

(a) Theories of optical rotatory power. E. U. Condon, *Rev. Mod. Phys.* **9,** 432 (1937). A review.

(b) Theoretical aspects of optical activity. Part one: Small molecules. A. Moscowitz, *Advan. Chem. Phys.* **4,** 67 (1962); Part two: Polymers. I. Tinoco, Jr., *Advan. Chem. Phys.* **4,** 113 (1962). A review which includes theoretical papers up to 1961.

(c) Origin of the Cotton effect of helical polypeptides. J. A. Schellman and P. Oriel, *J. Chem. Phys.* **37,** 2114 (1962). Rotational strength of an electric dipole forbidden transition in a helix.

(d) Optical rotatory power. S. F. Mason, *Quart. Rev. (London)* **17,** 20 (1963). A review.

(e) Optical rotation. D. J. Caldwell and H. Eyring, *Rev. Mod. Phys.* **35,** 577 (1963). Discusses magnitude of different contributions to rotational strength.

(f) The optical rotation of oriented helices. IV. A free electron on a helix. I. Tinoco, Jr. and R. W. Woody, *J. Chem. Phys.* **40,** 160 (1964).

(g) Optical rotation. D. J. Caldwell and H. Eyring, *Ann. Rev. Phys. Chem.* **15,** 281 (1964). A review.

(h) Theory of optical rotatory power. W. J. A. Maaskant and L. J. Oosterhoff, *Mol. Phys.* **8,** 319 (1964).

2. Experiment

(a) Optical rotation and the conformation of polypeptides and proteins. P. Urnes and P. Doty, *Advan. Protein Chem.* **16,** 401 (1961). A review.

(b) Polarimetry analysis of protein structure. D. Ridgeway, *Advan. Biol. Med. Phys.* **9,** 271 (1963). A review.

(c) Some optical properties of poly-1-benzyl-L-histidine and poly-L-histidine. K. G. Norland, G. D. Fasman, E. Katchalski, and E. R. Blout, *Biopolymers* **1**, 277 (1963).

(d) Optical rotatory dispersion of deoxyribonucleotides. J. T. Yang and T. Samejima, *J. Am. Chem. Soc.* **85**, 4039 (1963).

(e) Optical activity and the conformation of polynucleotides. J. Brahms, *J. Am. Chem. Soc.* **85**, 3298 (1963).

(f) Optical rotatory dispersion of DNA and RNA. T. Samejima and J. T. Yang, *Biochemistry* **3**, 613 (1964).

(g) Absorption spectra and optical activity of α-helical polypeptides. G. Holzwarth, W. B. Gratzer, and P. Doty; *Biopolymers Symp.* **1**, 389 (1964).

(h) Extrinsic and intrinsic cotton effects in polypeptides and proteins. E. R. Blout, *Biopolymers Symp.* **1**, 397 (1964).

(i) A study of the conformation of nucleic acids in solution by means of circular dichroism. J. Brahms and W. F. H. M. Mommaerts, *J. Mol. Biol.* **10**, 73 (1964).

(j) Circular dichroism investigations of the two conformations of poly-riboadenylic acid. J. Brahms, *Nature* **202**, 4934 (1964).

(k) The helical conformation of polycytidylic acid: Studies on the forces involved. G. D. Fasman, C. Lindblow, and L. Grossman, *Biochemistry* **3**, 1015 (1964).

(l) Study of the optical rotatory dispersion of proteins with improved spectropolarimetric techniques. B. Jirgensons, *Makromol. Chem.* **72**, 119 (1964).

(m) Optical rotatory dispersion of sperm-whale myoglobin and its derivatives. T. Samejima and J. T. Yang, *J. Mol. Biol.* **8**, 863 (1964).

(n) Etude comparative de la dispersion rotatoire optique et du dichroisme circulaire en chimie organique. P. Crabbé, *Tetrahedron* **20**, 1211 (1964).

3. Calculations

(a) See Refs. C, 1(a), (b) and C, 2(a) for calculations before 1961.

(b) Absorption and rotation of light by helical polymers: The effect of chain length. I. Tinoco, Jr., R. W. Woody, and D. F. Bradley, *J. Chem. Phys.* **38**, 1317 (1963). Poly A.

(c) The exciton contribution to the optical rotation of polymers. I. Tinoco, Jr., *Radiation Res.* **20**, 133 (1963). Dimers.

(d) Circular dichroism and rotatory dispersion curves for helices. I. Tinoco, Jr., *J. Am. Chem. Soc.* **86**, 297 (1964).

(e) An analysis of the optical rotatory dispersion of polypeptides and proteins. I. E. Schechter and E. R. Blout, *Proc. Natl. Acad. Sci. U.S.* **51**,

695 (1964). II. *Proc. Natl. Acad. Sci. U.S.* **51**, 794 (1964). III. E. Schechter, J. P. Carver and E. R. Blout, *Proc. Natl. Acad. Sci. U.S.* **51**, 1029 (1964).

(f) Estimation of parameters of rotatory dispersion curves of proteins. D. Ridgway, *Biophys. J.* **3**, 167 (1963). The Moffitt–Yang equation.

REFERENCES

Applequist, J. (1961). *J. Am. Chem. Soc.* **83**, 3158.

Brahms, J., and Mommaerts, W. F. H. M. (1964). *J. Mol. Biol.* **10**, 73.

Cantor, C., and Tinoco, I., Jr. (1965). *J. Mol. Biol.* (in press).

Felsenfeld, G., and Sandeen, G. (1962). *J. Mol. Biol.* **5**, 587

Fresco, J. R., Klotz, L. C., and Richards, E. G. (1963). *Cold Spring Harbor Symp. Quant. Biol.* **28**, 83.

Holcomb, D., and Tinoco, I., Jr. (1965). *Biopolymers* (in press).

Holzworth, G. and Doty, P. (1965). *J. Am. Chem. Soc.* **87**, 218.

Lee, S., McMullen, D., Brown, G. L., and Stokes, A. R. (1964). *Biochem. J.* **94**, 314.

Lohmander, B., and Rittsten, S. (1958). *Lunds Univ. Arsskr.* **28**, 45; see also *J. Phys. Chem.* **35**, 2878 (1931).

Lowry, T. M. (1964). "Optical Rotatory Power." Dover, New York.

MacDonald, J. R., and Brachman, M. K. (1956). *Rev. Mod. Phys.* **28**, 393.

Maestre, M. F., and Tinoco, I., Jr. (1965). *J. Mol. Biol.* (in press).

Michelson, A. M. (1963). "The Chemistry of Nucleosides and Nucleotides," p. 541 Academic Press, New York.

Moffitt, W. J. (1956). *J. Chem. Phys.* **25**, 467.

Moffitt, W., and Moscowitz, A. (1959). *J. Chem Phys.* **30**, 3.

Moffitt, W., and Yang, J. T. (1956). *Proc. Natl. Acad. Sci. U.S.* **42**, 596.

Moscowitz, A. (1957). Ph.D. Thesis, Harvard, Univ., Cambridge, Massachusetts.

Moscowitz, A. (1960). *In* "Optical Rotatory Dispersion" (C. Djerassi, ed.), Chap. 12. McGraw-Hill, New York.

Reid, J. C., and Pratt, A. W. (1960). *Biochem. Biophys. Res. Commun.* **3**, 337.

Rushizky, G. W., and Sober, H. A. (1964). *Biochem. Biophys. Res. Commun.* **14**, 276.

Samejima, T., and Yang, J. T. (1964). *Biochemistry* **3**, 613.

Samejima, T., and Yang, J. T. (1965). *J. Biol. Chem.* (in press).

Tinoco, I., Jr., Halpern, A., and Simpson, W. T. (1962). *In* "Polyamino Acids, Polypeptides, and Proteins" (M. A. Stahman, ed.), Univ. of Wisconsin Press, Madison, Wisconsin.

Tinoco, I., Jr., Woody, R. W., and Bradley, D. F. (1963). *J. Chem. Phys.* **38**, 1317.

Urnes, P., and Doty, P. (1961). *Advan. Protein Chem.* **16**, 401.

Warshaw, M. M., and Tinoco, I., Jr. (1965). *J. Mol. Biol.* (in press).

Weigang, O. E., Jr. (1964). *J. Chem. Phys.* **41**, 1435.

Electronic Distribution in Molecules by NQR Spectroscopy

EOLO SCROCCO

Institute of Chemical Physics,
University of Pisa,
Pisa, Italy

I. Introduction

The three new fields of spectroscopy—nuclear magnetic resonance, electron spin resonance, and nuclear quadrupole resonance—are being increasingly used in chemistry. Nuclear magnetic resonance is already yielding good results in structural determinations, whereas electron spin resonance is particularly useful in the study of free radicals.

On the other hand, nuclear quadrupole resonance has been, thus far, little used in biology, even though the interpretation of its experimental results is rather intuitive and very closely related to the electronic structure of the bonds between an atom (having a quadrupolar nucleus) and its neighboring atoms. However, this kind of spectroscopy will reasonably give, in the near future, some useful information about molecules containing chlorine, bromine, iodine, and particularly nitrogen. It must be admitted that the problem of experimental detection of resonance frequencies has been adequately solved for the halogens, but for nitrogen things are much more difficult, and this nucleus has been, thus far, less studied.

Let us recall that the quadrupolar nucleus is used as a local probe to investigate the electronic charge distribution, and therefore there is no need to explain how important the experimental results of nuclear quadrupole resonance would be in the case of nitrogen contained in molecules of biological interest.

The efforts now directed to the development of highly sophisticated techniques for increasing instrument sensitivity at nitrogen resonance frequencies are therefore very important.

II. Interpretation of NQR Data

A. General Considerations

It is well known that nuclei with spin greater than $\frac{1}{2}$, besides possessing a mechanical moment and a magnetic moment, also have a quadrupole moment eQ, owing to lack of spherical symmetry in the distribution of their electric charge.

Different quantum levels arise from the interaction of the nuclear quadrupole moment and the electric field gradient at the nucleus, which is caused by the surrounding electrons and nuclei. Each quantum level corresponds to a certain orientation of the nuclear quadrupole moment, with respect to the field gradient.

It is possible to cause transitions, between two of these quantum levels, by interaction with the magnetic component of an electromagnetic field of suitable frequency, produced on the sample by means of a coil. Absorption of energy will take place when the electromagnetic field has the frequency $\nu = (E_2 - E_1)/h$, according to the Einstein equation.

The theory of this phenomenon has been extensively developed by Pound (1950) for solid substances, and also by Townes and Dailey (1949, 1955) for free molecules; therefore it is now possible to interpret the experimental data in terms of the following quantities:

1. The quadrupole coupling constant e^2Qq, where $eq = \partial^2 V/\partial z^2$ is the z component of the field gradient, and eQ is the nuclear quadrupole moment

2. The so-called asymmetry parameter η defined as

$$\eta = \frac{(\partial^2 V/\partial x^2) - (\partial^2 V/\partial y^2)}{\partial^2 V/\partial z^2} \tag{1}$$

This quantity is a measure of the lack of cylindrical symmetry of the field gradient about the z axis. Therefore, eq and η are directly related to the potential V, caused by the charge distribution in the particular molecule at the quadrupolar nucleus.

The dependence of the experimental frequencies on the quantities reported above is a function of the value of the nuclear spin I. As an example, the level schemes and the equations for $I = 1, \frac{3}{2},$ and $\frac{5}{2}$ are reported in Fig. 1. Nitrogen, for instance, has nuclear spin 1; hence, if η is different from zero, it has three levels and three frequencies.

Any theory for the interpretation of the data of NQR spectroscopy must be able to draw information about the electronic distribution in the molecules from the measured values of eq and η. The Townes and Dailey theory does this, and we shall summarize its basic features later.

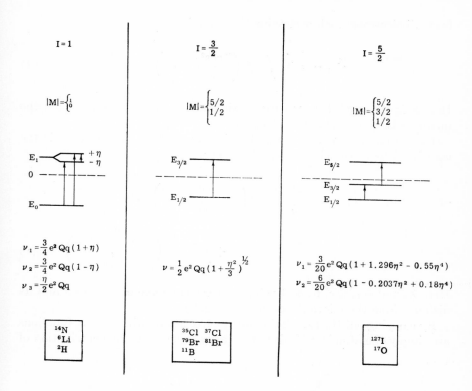

FIG. 1. Energy levels and frequencies for nuclei with spin $I = 1$, $\frac{3}{2}$, and $\frac{5}{2}$.

We shall first make some introductory considerations, assuming the knowledge of a wave function, though approximate, for the molecule.

The wave function commonly used for an atomic or molecular system with n electrons is an antisymmetrized product (Slater determinant) of one-electron functions (or spin orbitals) ϕ_i:

$$\Psi(1, 2, \cdots, n) = (n!)^{-1/2} \det \{\phi_1(1), \phi_2(2), \cdots, \phi_n(n)\} \qquad (2)$$

Each spin orbital is a function of the position and spin coordinates.

Neglecting the spin-spin and spin-orbit interaction terms in the Hamiltonian operator, the spin orbitals ϕ_i may be factorized into a position factor φ_i and a spin factor (α or β).

In this approximation, it is easy to show that the z component of the electric field gradient that is produced by the electrons in the position occupied by the quadrupolar nucleus is a sum of the contributions resulting from all electrons, each occupying the orbital φ_i:

$$(eq)_{\text{el}} = e \sum_i^n \int \varphi_i{}^* \left(\frac{3 \cos^2 \theta_i - 1}{r_i^3} \right) \varphi_i \, d\tau \tag{3}$$

Here θ_i is the angle between the z axis and the radius vector r_i from the quadrupolar nucleus to the i electron.

The actual z component of the electric field gradient will also contain the contributions of the charges of all nuclei in the molecule:

$$eq = (eq)_{\text{el}} + (eq)_n = e \sum_i \int \varphi_i{}^* \left(\frac{3 \cos^2 \theta_{iA} - 1}{r_{iA}^3} \right) \varphi_i \, d\tau$$

$$+ e \sum_\alpha Z_\alpha \left(\frac{3 \cos^2 \theta_{A\alpha} - 1}{R_{A\alpha}^3} \right) \tag{4}$$

Here Z_α and $R_{A\alpha}$ are, respectively, the electric charge of nucleus α and its distance from the relevant nucleus A (Fig. 2).

By carrying out the calculation for the free atom (where the φ_i functions are simply the atomic orbitals), it is easily found that the contribution of

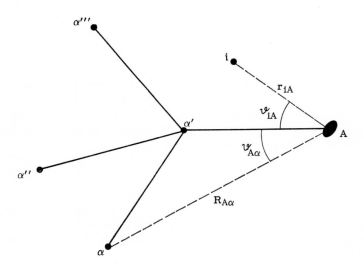

FIG. 2. Scheme of notations used in Eq. (4) (for a molecule with C_{3v} symmetry). A, quadrupolar nucleus; α, other nucleus in the molecule; i, generic electron.

the s electrons is zero, because of their spherical distribution, whereas the contribution of any completely filled shell is also zero.

In general, for an electron described by a hydrogenoid-type function with quantum numbers n, l, m $(l \neq 0)$, one finds:

$$(eq)_{n,l,m=0} = \frac{4eZ^3}{n^3 a_0^3 (2l-1)(2l+1)(2l+3)}$$

$$(eq)_{n,l,m=\pm l} = -\frac{2l-1}{l+1} (eq)_{n,l,m=0} \tag{5}$$

Equations (5) show that the contribution to the field gradient is inversely proportional to the third power of both the quantum numbers n and l, so that the contribution is small when $l > 1$. We shall confine ourselves to considering only the contributions from the p-type electrons. For such an electron $(l = 1)$, we find from Eq. (5),

$$(eq)_{p_x} = (eq)_{p_y} = -\tfrac{1}{2}(eq)_{p_z} \tag{6}$$

We also see that, for any incomplete p shell in the free atom containing n_x electrons of p_x type, n_y of the p_y type, and n_z of the p_z type:

$$eq = n_x(eq)_{p_x} + n_y(eq)_{p_y} + n_z(eq)_{p_z} = [-\tfrac{1}{2}(n_x + n_y) + n_z](eq)_{p_z} \tag{7}$$

The quantity in the brackets is called the *number of unbalanced electrons* of the shell.

For instance, in the case of the Cl atom, where the configuration is $n_x = 2$, $n_y = 2$, $n_z = 1$, this number is equal to -1, and therefore

$$(eq)_{at} = -(eq)_{pz} \tag{8}$$

Thus, the electric field gradient generated by five electrons p equals, apart from the sign, that generated by a single p_z electron; that is, it equals that of a "hole" in a full p shell. In the case of a chlorine ion, where $n_x = n_y = n_z = 2$, the number in brackets is zero.

For a molecular system, the one-electron functions correspond to molecular orbitals occupied by two electrons with antiparallel spin, which are approximated by linear combinations of the atomic orbitals of the various atoms contained in the molecule:

$$\varphi_i = \sum_r c_{r_i} \chi_r \qquad (i = 1, 2, \cdots, n/2) \tag{9}$$

Therefore, the electronic contribution to the field gradient can be written:

$$(eq)_{el} = 2e \sum_{i}^{n/2} \int \left(\sum_{r} c^*_{ri}\chi_r^* \right) \left(\frac{3 \cos^2 \theta_{iA} - 1}{r_{iA}^3} \right) \left(\sum_{s} c_{si}\chi_s \right) d\tau$$

$$= 2e \sum_{r} \sum_{s} \left[\sum_{i} c^*_{ri}c_{si} \right] \int \chi_r^* \left(\frac{3 \cos^2 \theta_{1A} - 1}{r_{1A}^3} \right) \chi_s \, d\tau \qquad (10)$$

$$= 2e \sum_{r} \sum_{s} R_{rs}q_{rs}$$

Here q_{rs} denotes the integrals involving the basic atomic functions χ, and R_{rs} stands for the sum contained in the brackets.

The quantity R_{rs} is known to be simply related to the "electronic population" associated with the function $\chi_r\chi_s$ in the space of the basic functions χ. Therefore, the electronic contribution to the electric field gradient q may be regarded as a mosaic of terms, the relative importance of which depends on two factors: the electronic population and the magnitude of the integrals q_{rs}.

The electric field gradient can then be obtained, using the basic set of electronic functions χ, by computing the coefficients c_{ri}, which define the molecular orbitals as a function of the basic atomic orbitals.

Equation (10) is the basis of any *ab initio* calculation of the quadrupole coupling constant in the Hartree–Fock molecular orbital approximation.

A complete utilization of Eq. (10) is, at present, possible only for a limited number of diatomic molecules for which sufficiently correct wave functions are available. We shall see later some results concerning the hydrochloric acid and nitrogen molecules.

In the case of more complex molecules, we are forced to apply an approximate method. Rather appealing in its simplicity is the method proposed by Townes and Dailey, which is the procedure generally adopted at the present time (Das and Hahn, 1958; Gordy, et al., 1953).

B. Townes and Dailey Theory

In the Townes and Dailey method (1949, 1955), all terms in Eq. (10) which are small or even partially compensated for by analogous terms, owing to the nuclear charges of the other atoms in the molecule, are neglected.

Let us consider, for simplicity, the expression for the electric field gradient acting on the nucleus of the atom A, in a diatomic molecule AB, and let us collect the terms of eq in groups in the following way:

$$(eq)_{\mathrm{mol}} = (eq)_{\mathrm{el}} + (eq)_n = (2e \sum_r \sum_s R_{rs}q_{rs})_{\mathrm{atom\ A}}$$

$$+ \left[(2e \sum_r \sum_s R_{rs}q_{rs})_{\mathrm{atom\ B}} + (2e \sum_r \sum_s R_{rs}q_{rs})_{\mathrm{overlap\ AB}} - (2eZ_{\mathrm{B}}/R_{AB}^3) \right]$$

$$(11)$$

It is easy to see that, because of the factor $1/r_{1A}^3$ in the expression for q_{rs}, the second and third sums are rather small and are furthermore approximately compensated for the last term, which arises from the nuclear charge of atom B.

Moreover, if the hypothesis is made that the internal shells maintain their spherical symmetry in the molecules, the first sum (relative to the quadrupolar atom A) can be reduced so as to contain only the contributions of the valence shell electrons. Of these contributions, only those due to the p orbitals will be of appreciable magnitude.

The expression of q for the molecule is thus greatly simplified:

$$(eq)_{\mathrm{mol}} = (eq)_{\mathrm{atom\ A}}^{\mathrm{el}} = (n_x(eq)_{p_x} + n_y(eq)_{p_y} + n_z(eq)_{p_z})_{\mathrm{atom\ A}} \qquad (12)$$

Townes and Dailey also make the further assumption that all the q's in this equation are equal to the corresponding quantities in the free atom. They therefore obtain the following, very simple equation:

$$e^2Qq_{\mathrm{mol}} = eQ\{[n_z - \tfrac{1}{2}(n_x + n_y)](eq)_{p_z}\}_{\mathrm{atom\ A}} \qquad (13)$$

Later we shall see to what extent these assumptions are verified in an example on hydrochloric acid. But let us first illustrate the Townes and Dailey theory by application to the pyridine molecule and to other N-heteroaromatics.

C. Applications to Pyridine and Other N-Heteroaromatics

In the pyridine molecule the nitrogen quadrupole coupling constant is $(e^2Qq)_{\mathrm{mol}} = 4.6$ Mc and the asymmetry parameter $\eta = 0.4$. The experimental data have been obtained by L. Guibé (1962), and the interpretation on the basis of the Townes and Dailey theory has been made by Lücken (1961).

According to Eqs. (13) and (1), it is possible to obtain information concerning the electronic population of the nitrogen nucleus by knowing: (1) the experimental value of the coupling constant in the molecule, (2) the coupling constant in the atom, and (3) the value of the asymmetry parameter.

First, it must be recalled that the value of $(eq)_{p_z}$ in the nitrogen atom is not known. Therefore, we shall be content with an approximate value -2.04 au calculated on the basis of the Hartree–Fock function, and we shall use the value $Q = 0.02 \times 10^{-24}$ cm^2 given by Townes and Schawlow (1955). With these values the atomic constant is

$$e^2 Q q_{p_z} = 9.5 \text{ Mc} \tag{14}$$

The valence shell of nitrogen in the pyridine molecule, may be described by three hybrid trigonal orbitals and by one p_x orbital, as shown in Table I.

TABLE I

Orbitals and Occupation Numbers for N in the Pyridine Molecule

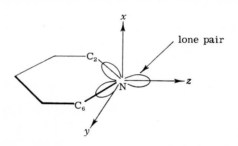

Orbitals	Type	Occupation number
$\varphi_\pi = p_x$	π bond	a
$\varphi_{\sigma_1} = \frac{1}{\sqrt{3}} s + \sqrt{\frac{2}{3}} p_z$	Lone pair	2
$\varphi_{\sigma_2} = \frac{1}{\sqrt{3}} s - \frac{1}{\sqrt{6}} p_z - \frac{1}{\sqrt{2}} p_y$	N—C$_2$ bond	b
$\varphi_{\sigma_3} = \frac{1}{\sqrt{3}} s - \frac{1}{\sqrt{6}} p_z + \frac{1}{\sqrt{2}} p_y$	N—C$_6$ bond	b

It is easily seen that, if a is the occupation number of the π orbital, and b that of the σ bonding orbitals, then

$$n_x = a$$
$$n_y = b \tag{15}$$
$$n_z = 2 \cdot \tfrac{2}{3} + \tfrac{1}{3} b$$

For instance, the value $n_y = b$ results, for one-half, from the φ_{σ_2} orbital, and for the other half from the φ_{σ_3} orbital. Therefore, for the electric field gradient along the z axis, we have

$$(eq)_z = \partial^2 V/\partial z^2 = [n_z - \tfrac{1}{2}(n_x + n_y)](eq_{p_z})_{at}$$

$$= \left(-\frac{a}{2} - \frac{1}{6}b + \frac{4}{3}\right)(eq_{p_z})_{at} \qquad (16)$$

By rotating the indices, we easily obtain the electric field gradient along the x and y axes, respectively, which depends explicitly from the occupation numbers a and b:

$$(eq)_x = \partial^2 V/\partial x^2 = \left(n_x - \frac{n_y + n_z}{2}\right)(eq_{p_z})_{at} = (a - \tfrac{2}{3}b - \tfrac{2}{3})(eq_{p_z})_{at}$$

$$(eq)_y = \partial^2 V/\partial y^2 = [n_y - \tfrac{1}{2}(n_x + n_z)](eq_{p_z})_{at}$$

$$= \left(-\frac{a}{2} + \frac{5}{6}b - \frac{2}{3}\right)(eq_{pz})_{at} \qquad (17)$$

Thus, the coupling constant and the asymmetry parameter have the values

$$(e^2Qq)_{mol} = (-\tfrac{1}{2}a - \tfrac{1}{6}b + \tfrac{4}{3})(e^2Qq_{p_z})_{at} = 4.6 \text{ Mc} \qquad (18)$$

$$\eta = \frac{(\partial^2 V/\partial x^2) - (\partial^2 V/\partial y^2)}{\partial^2 V/\partial z^2} = \frac{-3(a-b)}{a + (b/3) - \tfrac{8}{3}} = \pm 0.4 \qquad (19)$$

Equations (18) and (19) allow us to calculate the values of a and b. However, there are two possibilities: $a > b$ or $a < b$. Lücken was able to show that the actual case was $a > b$, and under this condition the two equations give, for the occupation numbers,

$$a_\pi = 1.24; \qquad b_\sigma = 1.37$$

Guibé (private communication, 1964) also recently obtained experimental data on pyrazine, phenazine, and *sym*-triazine. The results of the calculation of the occupation numbers, still carried out by Lücken's method, are summarized in Fig. 3.

For all compounds a π charge excess on nitrogen is obtained (0.24 electron in pyridine), which agrees with the existence of ionic resonant structures (I)–(III).

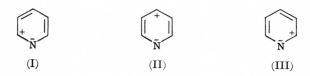

(I)   (II)   (III)

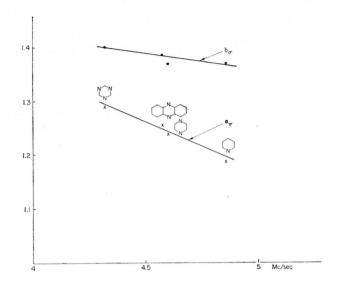

FIG. 3. Occupation numbers a_π and b_σ vs. experimental e^2Qq for some N-heteroaromatics.

In the series of compounds examined, the changes in the occupation number from one molecule to the other are, as expected, smaller in the σ than in the π orbitals. On the other hand, the charge excess on the two trigonal hybrids which form the two N—C bonds (0.37 electron in pyridine) seems to be a little too high. However, it must be remembered that, up to now, we do not have completely reliable occupation numbers for these molecules; only the π electrons have been extensively studied and the results obtained by many authors, using the molecular orbital method (McWeeny and Peacock, 1957; Nakajima and Pullman, 1958; Peacock 1960; Miller *et al.*, 1962; etc.), show fair agreement with the above reported values. Thus the basic reliability of the Townes and Dailey theory seems also to be confirmed for these relatively complex molecules.

It is nonetheless worthwhile to remember that these results depend on several assumptions which are not free from criticism:

1. The value of $(e^2Qq)_{at}$ for nitrogen in the true valency state may be different from the adopted value, which is an approximate value for the isolated atom.

2. The population of the nitrogen lone pair has been assumed equal to two. The actual value may instead be slightly less, owing to partial delocalization of the corresponding orbital.

3. In Eq. (13) all contributions of the charges of neighboring atoms and of the overlap charges are neglected.

4. The values of $(eq)_{p_x}$, $(eq)_{p_y}$, and $\frac{1}{2}(eq)_{p_z}$ of the quadrupolar atom have still been considered all equal in the molecule.

The objection to the first assumption is completely reasonable. It would certainly be more correct to calculate a more accurate value of $(e^2Qq)_{at}$; however one would obtain only a parallel shift of all the corresponding occupation numbers but no substantial change in the correlation among the various molecules.

The objection to the second assumption is also reasonable: unfortunately we do not have reliable information about the magnitude of the lone pair delocalization. More accurate quantum-mechanical calculations, which will be made in the near future, will probably answer this question, which is also of chemical interest, being directly related to the interpretation of the basic strength of these compounds.

The criticisms of assumptions 3 and 4 are less evident; they more directly concern the simplified theory exposed above. This theory has been shown to be valid at least in a first approximation. Only more precise calculations can or cannot therefore support the opportunity of introducing some corrections in the sense of objections 3 and 4 in order to make possible a closer interpretation of the experimental data. This will be the subject of the next section.

III. A Refinement of the Townes and Dailey Interpretation: The HCl Molecule

To further refine the Townes and Dailey theory, we need to consider some simpler molecular systems for which it is currently possible to determine enough accurate wave functions. We shall make use of the results of an SCF-MO-LCAO *ab initio* calculation of the ground state of the HCl molecule (Scrocco and Tomasi, 1964a, b).[1]

For such a calculation, we chose a set of basic atomic orbitals χ, more extended than the necessary minimum, and composed of 19 Slater-type functions with orbital exponents, as shown in Table II. Each atomic orbital (except the 1s of the chlorine atom) is described by means of two Slater functions with different orbital exponents for better flexibility.

---

[1] Nesbet (1964) has also recently obtained a good SCF wave function for HCl. The quadrupole coupling constant which may be calculated by using this function is 72.3 Mc. Considerations exactly similar to those reported in the following pages can also be deduced from this paper.

TABLE II

SLATER FUNCTIONS AND ORBITAL EXPONENTS FOR HCl

Atom	Function	ζ	Function	ζ
H	$1s_H = h$	1.27		
	$2p_{\sigma H} = p$	2.20		
Cl	$1s_{Cl} = 1s$	16.7	$2p_{xCl} = 2x$	8.35
	$2s_{Cl} = 2s$	8.35	$2p'_{xCl} = 2\xi$	4.50
	$2s'_{Cl} = 2\sigma$	4.50	$3p_{xCl} = 3x$	2.64
	$3s_{Cl} = 3s$	2.64	$3p'_{xCl} = 3\xi$	1.42
	$3s'_{Cl} = 3\sigma$	1.42	$2p_{yCl} = 2y$	8.35
	$2p_{zCl} = 2z$	8.35	$2p'_{yCl} = 2\eta$	4.50
	$2p'_{zCl} = 2\zeta$	4.50	$3p_{yCl} = 3y$	2.64
	$3p_{zCl} = 3z$	2.64	$3p'_{yCl} = 3\eta$	1.42
	$3p'_{zCl} = 3\zeta$	1.42		

On this basis, the molecular orbitals have been calculated for the 18 electrons of the molecule for which the matrix of the coefficients is shown in Table III, where the analogous coefficients for the Cl⁻ ion are also reported, in italics, for comparison. Note that $\varphi_{1\sigma}$, $\varphi_{2\sigma}$, $\varphi_{3\sigma}$, and $\varphi_{1\pi}$ are essential atomic core orbitals belonging to the shells with $n = 1$ and $n = 2$ for the chlorine atom; in fact, $\varphi_{1\sigma}$ is approximately the $1s$ orbital, whereas $\varphi_{2\sigma}$ and $\varphi_{3\sigma}$ almost coincide with the $2s$ and $2p_z$ orbitals, respectively. (In the $\varphi_{2\sigma}$ orbital the notable contribution of the $1s$ and $3s$ orbitals comes from the orthogonalization with $\varphi_{1\sigma}$ and $\varphi_{2\sigma}$ orbitals.)

The remaining two orbitals belong to the valence shell of chlorine and hydrogen. The former is a bonding orbital, whereas the latter is practically an orbital occupied by the nonbonding electron **pair** of chlorine.

On the basis of these molecular orbitals, a value of 72.9 Mc is obtained, in fair agreement with the experimental datum 67.3 Mc for deuterium chloride (Cowan and Gordy, 1958).

The value of the contribution of each molecular orbital to the quadrupole

TABLE III

MOLECULAR ORBITALS FOR HCl AND Cl⁻

	$\varphi_{1\sigma}$	$\varphi_{2\sigma}$	$\varphi_{3\sigma}$	φ^b	φ^{nb}	$\varphi_{1\pi}, \varphi_{1\bar{\pi}}$	$\varphi_{2\pi}, \varphi_{2\bar{\pi}}$
h	0.00011	−0.00430	−0.00273	−0.52557	0.00065	—	—
p	0.00031	−0.01744	−0.00696	−0.04993	−0.00684	—	—
1s	−0.98923 *0.98923*	0.32065 *0.32083*	−0.00470	−0.01254	−0.09150	—	—
2s	−0.02604 *0.02599*	−0.26299 *0.26475*	0.00512	0.00825	0.04627	—	—
2σ	0.00996 *0.00987*	−0.91454 *0.91161*	0.01101	0.07009	0.40699	—	—
3s	−0.00361 *0.00345*	0.22769 *0.21967*	−0.00088	−0.09986	−0.98661	—	—
3σ	0.00131 *0.00132*	−0.08721 *0.08767*	0.00213	0.08842	−0.17552	—	—
2z	−0.00024	−0.00261	−0.50080 *−0.50302*	0.09804	−0.03102	—	—
2ζ	0.00025	−0.01502	−0.58176 *−0.57901*	0.15235	−0.03588	—	—
3z	−0.00026	0.01142	0.07092 *0.06832*	−0.49223	0.12745	—	—
3ζ	0.00004	−0.00158	−0.02434 *−0.02510*	−0.24368	0.14082	—	—
2x				—	—	0.50349	−0.12807
2ξ				—	—	0.57855	−0.17719
3x				—	—	−0.06830	0.60161
3ξ				—	—	0.02495	0.53581

coupling constant is shown in Table IV. As one can see, an interesting
result is that the group of atomic core orbitals of the chlorine atom gives a
contribution of 11.9 Mc, which is fairly different from zero, being 17% of
the over-all value. This fact shows that, in the process of formation of the
molecule, the electrons of the atomic core of chlorine undergo a nonnegligible polarization by the hydrogen atom, losing their spherical symmetry.

Let us now analyze more closely the valence shell orbitals of the molecule.
We shall see that the good flexibility of these orbitals, owing to the fairly

TABLE IV

ORBITAL CONTRIBUTIONS TO THE QUADRUPOLE COUPLING CONSTANT IN HCl

HCl	Core orbitals (e^2Qq, Mc)	Valence shell (e^2Qq, Mc)	H nucleus (e^2Qq, Mc)
Core orbitals			
$\varphi_{1\sigma}$	0	—	—
$\varphi_{2\sigma}$	-0.463	—	—
$\varphi_{3\sigma}$	-2939.687	—	—
$\varphi_{1\pi}$	2952.050	—	—
Valence-shell orbitals			
φ^b	—	-38.203	—
φ^{nb}	—	-94.036	—
$\varphi_{2\pi}$	—	190.572	—
	11.900	58.33	2.651

Total $(e^2Qq)_{\text{calc.}} = 72.9$ (Mc)

$(e^2Qq)_{\text{exp.}} = 67.3$ (Mc)

high number of basic atomic functions, leads to a more detailed interpretation of the various contributions to the electric field gradient.

For this purpose, let us write the bonding and the antibonding orbitals
in a more compact way:

$$\varphi^b = 0.0708 S^b + 0.6397 P_z^b + 0.52794 H^b$$

$$\varphi^{nb} = 0.9697 S^{nb} - 0.2381 P_z^{nb} - 0.0069 H^{nb} \qquad (20)$$

$$\varphi_{2\pi} = P_\pi$$

In each expression, the contribution of all the basic type-s and type-p
functions of chlorine have been collected in two terms, respectively, and

the contribution of the atomic functions of hydrogen have been collected in a third term. And so, the two bonding and nonbonding orbitals assume the usual form representing an s–p hybrid of a chlorine atom combined with a hydrogen orbital.

Usually the nonbonding function is considered a pure s–p hybrid; in fact, it can be seen that the coefficient of H in φ^{nb} is very small.

The new atomic functions contained in these orbitals are given explicitly in Eq. (21). They are normalized and still have the angular properties of the original basis functions.

$$S^b = 0.1779\,(1s) - 0.1164\,(2s) - 0.9894\,(2\sigma) + 1.4097\,(3s)$$
$$- 1.2482\,(3\sigma)$$

$$P_z^{\,b} = -0.1533\,(2z) - 0.2382\,(2\zeta) + 0.7695\,(3z) + 0.3810\,(3\zeta)$$

$$H^b = 0.9955\,(h) + 0.0946\,(p)$$

$$S^{nb} = 0.0944\,(1s) - 0.0477\,(2s) - 0.4197\,(2\sigma) + 1.0174\,(3s)$$
$$+ 0.1810\,(3\sigma) \qquad (21)$$

$$P_z^{\,nb} = -0.1303\,(2z) - 0.1507\,(2\zeta) + 0.5353\,(3z) + 0.5915\,(3\zeta)$$

$$H^{nb} = 0.0947\,(h) - 0.9986\,(p)$$

$$P_\pi = -0.1281\,(2x) - 0.1772\,(2\xi) + 0.6016\,(3x) + 0.5358\,(3\xi)$$

Let us turn our attention now to the differences existing among the functions $P_z^{\,b}$, $P_z^{\,nb}$, and P_π. These differences are to be intuitively attributed to the different perturbations that the hydrogen atom induces in the orbitals of the chlorine atom in the molecule, and are very important in the calculation of the coupling constant. They are seen more clearly in Fig. 4, where the radial parts of the functions P^b and P^{nb} are reported; the P_π function is intermediate between the other two and is not shown.

These differences cause the three values of $(eq)_P$ of σ and π type to be unequal, as assumed by the simplified formula of Townes and Dailey; in fact they have these rather different values:

$$(eq)^b_{P_z} = -7.89; \qquad (eq)^{nb}_{P_z} = -4.80; \qquad 2\,(eq)_P{}^\pi = 5.14 \text{ au}$$

Therefore, instead of the simplified formula

$$(eq)_{mol} = \left[n_z - \tfrac{1}{2}(n_x + n_y) \right] (eq_{p_z})_{at} \qquad (22)$$

it seems more correct to use the more general expression

$$(eq)_{mol} = n_x (eq)_{p_x} + n_y (eq)_{p_y} + n_z (eq)_{p_z} \qquad (23)$$

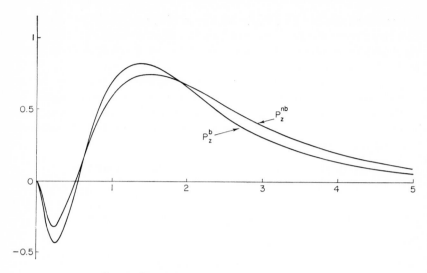

FIG. 4. $P_z{}^b$ and $P_z{}^{nb}$ for HCl $[P = rR(r)]$.

Concerning assumption 3 in Section II, C, we can say that, at least for this molecule, it is completely valid. In fact, a detailed analysis of the results (Scrocco and Tomasi, 1964b) shows that the contribution of the overlap charges and that of the charges localized on the hydrogen atom are small and almost completely compensated for by the contribution of the charge of the proton. (The sum of these three terms amounts to 0.007 au, which corresponds to 0.2% of the over-all value.)

The results obtained for HCl confirms what Richardson (1960) already found in an analysis of some wave functions of the nitrogen molecule; in fact he showed that there is a fairly large difference between the contributions of the σ and the π orbitals to the field gradient. However it must be noted that, in the nitrogen atom, the contribution that is due to the polarization of the inner shell is very small, and this fact simplifies the treatment.

In conclusion, we may say that the measurements of the quadrupole coupling constants can bring a notable contribution to the knowledge of electronic distribution in the molecules. Furthermore, the Townes and Dailey method is a valid, easily applicable tool for the interpretation of the results of nuclear quadrupole resonance spectroscopy, and also for molecules of biological interest. A test with well-known molecular systems suggests that this method might be improved with minor modifications, the most important of which is the adoption of different $(eq)_P$ values for the different orbitals.

Finally, a feature which makes this method particularly acceptable to the chemist is that it is built on the classical concept of the orbital, that is, on a formalism on which present chemical thought is largely based.

ACKNOWLEDGMENTS

The author thanks Dr. Tomasi for most helpful discussion and is indebted to him for kind assistance in the preparation of the manuscript.

REFERENCES

Cowan, M., and Gordy, W. (1958). *Phys. Rev.* **111**, 209.
Das, T. P., and Hahn, E. L. (1958). "Nuclear Quadrupole Resonance Spectroscopy." Academic Press, New York.
Gordy, W., Smith, W. V., and Trambarulo, R. F. (1953). "Microwave Spectroscopy." Wiley, New York.
Guibé, L. (1964). Private communication.
Guibé, L. (1962). *Ann. Phys.* **7**, 177.
Lücken, E. A. C. (1961). *Trans. Faraday Soc.* **57**, 729.
McWeeny, R., and Peacock, T. E. (1957). *Proc. Phys. Soc. (London)* **A70**, 41.
Miller, R. L., Lykos, P. G., and Schmeising, H. V. (1962). *J. Am. Chem. Soc.* **84**, 4623.
Nakajima, T. M., and Pullman, A. (1958). *Compt. Rend.* **41**, 1047.
Nesbet, R. K. (1964). *J. Chem. Phys.* **41**, 100.
Peacock, T. E. (1960). *J. Chem. Soc.* 1946.
Pound, R. V. (1950). *Phys. Rev.* **79**, 685.
Richardson, J. W. (1960). *Rev. Mod. Phys.* **32**, 461.
Scrocco, E., and Tomasi, J. (1964a). *In* "Molecular Orbitals in Chemistry, Physics and Biology" (B. Pullman and P. O. Löwdin, eds.), pp. 263–280. Academic Press, New York.
Scrocco, E., and Tomasi, J. (1964b). *Theoret. Chim. Acta* **2**, 386.
Townes, C. H., and Dailey, B. P. (1949). *J. Chem. Phys.* **17**, 782.
Townes, C. H., and Dailey, B. P. (1955). *J. Chem. Phys.* **23**, 118.
Townes, C. H., and Schawlow, A. L. (1955). "Microwave Spectroscopy." McGraw-Hill, New York.

Magnetic Excitations in Molecular Crystals[1]

HARDEN M. McCONNELL

Department of Chemistry,
Stanford University,
Stanford, California

I. Introduction

Evidence for excitons and energy transfer is well known in photosynthetic systems (Robinson, 1964), and has even been found recently in DNA (Isenberg *et al.*, 1964). In investigating the possible role of collective excitations in biological systems, it is sometimes convenient to consider pure molecular crystals, where the elementary electronic excitations are amenable to direct experimental and theoretical study. The magnetic excitations of certain molecular crystals are especially interesting in this regard, since they can be studied in exhaustive detail using paramagnetic resonance. To this end, we summarize some of the recent work on paramagnetic excitations in molecular crystals. We feel, however, that the importance of the present work for biology is not restricted to problems of energy transfer. This work illustrates the enormous detailed molecular structural information that can be inferred from paramagnetic resonance studies. It is a reasonable hope that biologically significant molecules may some day be "tagged" with paramagnetic species, whose magnetic resonance spectra will provide detailed information on molecular conformation and reactions.

II. Triplet Excitons

A. Elementary Considerations

Let us first consider the paramagnetic resonance of a single electron, with no orbital angular momentum. The Hamiltonian for this problem is

$$\mathcal{3C} = g \mid \beta \mid H_0 s_\lambda \tag{1}$$

[1] This work has been supported primarily by the National Science Foundation under Grant No. GP 3430.

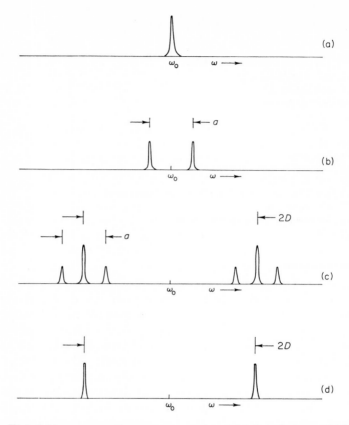

Fig. 1. High-field paramagnetic resonance spectra of (a) free electrons, (b) hydrogen atoms, (c) oriented hydrogen molecules in their triplet states, and (d) triplet excitons moving along an infinite alternating linear chain of hydrogen atoms.

where H_0 is the strength of the applied magnetic field, $|\beta|$ is the absolute value of the Bohr magneton, and $g = 2.0023$. The component of electron spin angular momentum in the applied field direction (λ) is s_λ, and $s_\lambda = \pm\frac{1}{2}$. The paramagnetic resonance then occurs at angular frequency ω, where

$$\hbar\omega = g\,|\beta|\,H_0 \qquad (2)$$

This paramagnetic resonance is illustrated in Fig. 1(a).

Next, consider the paramagnetic resonance of a hydrogen atom, for which the Hamiltonian is

$$\mathcal{3C} = \hbar\omega s_\lambda + \hbar a \mathbf{I}\cdot\mathbf{s} \qquad (3)$$

Here a is the isotropic nuclear hyperfine interaction, and $\mathbf{I}$ is the nuclear spin angular momentum. In strong applied fields, where $\hbar\omega \gg \hbar a$, the paramagnetic resonance of a hydrogen atom is a simple doublet, as illustrated in Fig. 1(b).

For our purposes, the Hamiltonian for two hydrogen atoms can be represented as follows:

$$\mathcal{3C} = \hbar\omega(s_{1\lambda} + s_{2\lambda}) + \hbar\mathbf{s}_1\cdot\mathbf{T}\cdot\mathbf{s}_2 + J\mathbf{s}_1\cdot\mathbf{s}_2 + \hbar a(\mathbf{s}_1\cdot\mathbf{I}_1 + \mathbf{s}_2\cdot\mathbf{I}_2) \qquad (4)$$

In this expression J is the electron-electron exchange interaction and can be assumed to be much larger than all other terms in Eq. (4). The Zeeman energy $\hbar\omega(s_{1\lambda} + s_{2\lambda})$ and hyperfine energy $\hbar a(\mathbf{s}_1\cdot\mathbf{I}_1 + \mathbf{s}_2\cdot\mathbf{I}_2)$ are simple extensions of Eqs. (1) and (3) to the two-electron two-nucleus problem. The magnetic spin dipole-dipole fine-structure interaction is given by the symmetric dyadic $\mathbf{T}$. In the paramagnetic electronic triplet state, where the total electronic spin $S = 1$, the paramagnetic resonance spectrum can be described by the spin Hamiltonian,

$$\mathcal{3C}_s = \hbar\omega S_\lambda + D S_z^2 + E(S_x^2 - S_y^2) + \hbar a \mathbf{S}\cdot\mathbf{F} \qquad (5)$$

The axes x, y, z are the principal axes of the fine-structure interaction; when z is taken parallel to the internuclear axis, $E = 0$, because of the axial symmetry of H_2. The total spin momenta $\mathbf{S}$ and $\mathbf{F}$ are

$$\mathbf{S} = \mathbf{s}_1 + \mathbf{s}_2 \qquad (6)$$

$$\mathbf{F} = \mathbf{I}_1 + \mathbf{I}_2 \qquad (7)$$

In the strong field case, $\hbar\omega \gg |D|, |E|$, and when $|D| > |\hbar a|$, we obtain the spectrum sketched in Fig. 1(c) for, say, the applied field parallel to the internuclear axis.

Finally, let us consider the paramagnetic resonance of the linear alternating array of hydrogen atoms sketched in Fig. 2. The Hamiltonian for this problem is

$$\mathcal{3C} = J \sum_{i=1,3\,5,\cdots} \mathbf{s}_i\cdot\mathbf{s}_{i+1} + J' \sum_{j=2,4,6,\cdots} \mathbf{s}_j\cdot\mathbf{s}_{j+1} + \hbar\omega \sum_{k=1,2\,3,\cdots} s_{k\lambda}$$

$$+ \sum_{i=1,3,5,\cdots} \mathbf{s}_i\cdot\mathbf{T}\cdot\mathbf{s}_{i+1} + \sum_{j=2,4,6,\cdots} \mathbf{s}_j\cdot\mathbf{T}'\cdot\mathbf{s}_{j+1} + \hbar a \sum_{k=1,2,3,\cdots} \mathbf{s}_k\cdot\mathbf{I}_k \qquad (8)$$

J and J' give the exchange integrals between hydrogen atoms, separated by internuclear distances l and l'. Similarly, $\mathbf{T}$ and $\mathbf{T}'$ give the magnetic spin-spin fine-structure interaction between spins on neighboring hydrogen

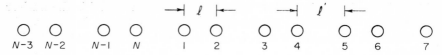

FIG. 2. Alternating linear array of hydrogen atoms.

atoms separated by internuclear distances l and l'. Only nearest-neighbor interactions are included in the calculation.

In the case of strong alternation ($J \gg J' > 0$), the ground state energy of the linear chain has total spin $S = 0$ and total energy $-\frac{1}{4}J$, to first order. When $J' = 0$, the first excited state of the linear chain is a triplet state, with energy J above the ground state. This state obviously has an $(N/2)$-fold space degeneracy, since the triplet excitation of energy J can be located on any one of the $N/2$ possible molecular pairs. The exchange interaction proportional to J' produces a first-order splitting of this degeneracy to yield a triplet exciton band of width J'. The dispersion relation for the case of strong alternation is illustrated in Fig. 3. We focus our attention on the expected paramagnetic resonance of a single excitation of spin $S = 1$ on an infinite chain ($N \to \infty$) with strong alternation $J \gg J'$.

The triplet exciton state will show no nuclear hyperfine structure since the excitation is distributed over many nuclear sites (Sternlicht and McConnell, 1961; McConnell and Lynden-Bell, 1961). In general, the fine-structure splitting depends on the pseudo-momentum k of the exciton wave (Lynden-Bell and McConnell, 1962):

$$D = d + d' \cos k \qquad (9)$$

Here d is the fine-structure splitting due to spins separated by the distance l, and d' is the fine-structure splitting due to spins separated by the distance

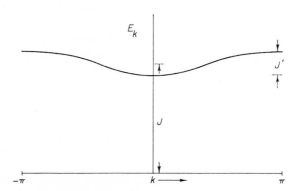

FIG. 3. Dispersion relation for triplet excitons moving along a linear array of hydrogen atoms $J > > J' > 0$. The exciton band width is J', and the gap from the ground state to the center of the band is J.

l'. When the rate of exciton scattering from one k state to another is large compared to d', then the observed fine-structure splitting in a paramagnetic resonance experiment will be $d + d' \langle \cos k \rangle$, where $\langle \cos k \rangle$ is the thermal average of $\cos k$ over the exciton band. For $J' \ll kT$, we have $\langle \cos k \rangle = 0$, and the observed fine-structure splitting corresponds simply to that due to the spin dipolar interaction between electrons separated by the shorter interatomic distance l. The paramagnetic resonance spectrum of a triplet exciton on a linear alternating chain of hydrogen atoms is sketched in Fig. 1(d).

The foregoing discussion provides a brief theoretical introduction to the paramagnetic resonance of a triplet exciton. We next consider real molecular crystals, where such paramagnetic resonance spectra can be observed. It may be noted at this point, however, that as yet one does not have the answer to the following important question: What happens to the paramagnetic resonance spectrum of an elementary magnetic excitation when $J' \to J$? This problem is considered briefly in Section III.

B. Free Radical Salts

The crystal structures of a number of solid ionic aromatic free radicals are known, and in most cases the structures can be described as being built up from linear chains of aromatic radical ions stacked face-to-face (Turner and Albrecht, 1954; Chesnut and Arthur, 1962). If there is, for example, a simple strong alternation in the intermolecular stacking distances corresponding to that illustrated in Fig. 2 for the hydrogen atom chain, then we may anticipate an exciton paramagnetic resonance spectrum similar to that illustrated in Fig. 1(d). Indeed, the paramagnetic resonance spectra of a number of solid ionic free radicals are of just this type (Chesnut and Phillips, 1961; Chesnut and Arthur, 1962; Thomas *et al.*, 1963). Figure 4 illustrates the paramagnetic resonance spectrum of a single crystal of Wurster's blue perchlorate at various temperatures, and it will be noted that the lower temperature spectra do indeed have the appearance of spectrum sketched in Fig. 1(d). An isolated Wurster's blue cation (I), in

(I)

liquid solution, exhibits a nuclear hyperfine structure that extends over more than 300 Mc. This hyperfine structure is evidently completely removed by the exciton "motion" in the low-temperature spectra in Fig. 4.

There is X-ray evidence that at low temperatures the Wurster's blue cations do form an alternating linear face-to-face array, as sketched in Fig. 5 for a single chain of the positive ions. (Kamb *et al.*, 1963). Chesnut and Phillips (1961) and Chesnut and Arthur (1962) have resolved similar exciton paramagnetic resonance spectra in a number of solid ionic free radicals based on the negative ion (II) of the acceptor TCNQ. As an

$$\left[\begin{array}{c}\underset{NC}{\overset{NC}{\diagdown}}C-\langle\!\!\!\bigcirc\!\!\!\rangle-C\overset{\diagup CN}{\diagdown_{CN}}\end{array}\right]^{-}$$

(II)

example, the paramagnetic resonance of the crystal (morpholinium)$^+$-(TCNQ)$^-$ is similar to that sketched in Fig. 1(d). Here again the crystal structure of this salt is almost certainly based on alternating linear chains

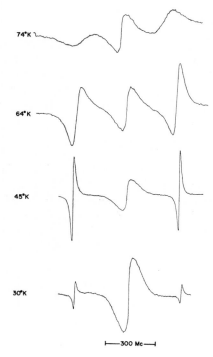

74°K

64°K

45°K

30°K

$\longmapsto$300 Mc$\longmapsto$

Fig. 4. Paramagnetic resonance spectra of a single crystal of Wurster's blue perchlorate at several temperatures. The central resonance at low temperatures is due to an impurity.

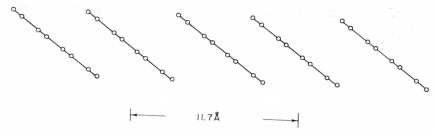

FIG. 5. Schematic representation of alternating linear array of Wurster's blue cations in the low-temperature crystal structure of Wurster's blue perchlorate.

of the TCNQ anions stacked in a face-to-face (or tilted face-to-face) arrangement similar to that in Fig. 5. Chesnut and Phillips (1961) and Chesnut and Arthur (1962) have also studied a number of other salts which show exciton paramagnetic resonance spectra, but which, at least formally, involve both TCNQ negative ions and TCNQ neutral molecules in the linear chains. In this case the "neutral" molecules appear merely to accentuate the alternation of the ion pairs. (Of course, the spin must, in fact, be distributed over *all* the TCNQ molecules to some extent.) To simplify our discussion, we restrict ourselves to the simply alternating linear chain analogous to that in Fig. 2, although many of our remarks do apply equally well to the TCNQ salts with the more complex stoichiometry. Furthermore, unless indicated otherwise, we always assume strong alternation, $J \gg J'$.

The energy gap J to the triplet exciton band can be determined from the temperature dependence of the paramagnetic resonance intensity. The observed J values are in the range 0.02–0.4 eV. There is evidence that the J values themselves may be somewhat temperature dependent (Jones and Chesnut, 1963; Chesnut, 1964). The origin of the energy gap J is presumably the following.

Consider, for example, two Wurster's blue cations, each of which is designated D^+. Let $| D^+D^+; 0 \rangle$ be a wave function for the ion pair where the spins are coupled, so that the total spin $S = 0$. Now consider the two $S = 0$ excited states $| DD^{++}; 0 \rangle$ and $| D^{++}D; 0 \rangle$. Second-order mixing of these two (virtual) excited states with the $S = 0$ state $| D^+D^+; 0 \rangle$ will lower the energy of this state by $2\gamma^2/\Delta E$, where γ is the Mulliken charge-transfer integral,

$$\gamma = \langle D^+D^+; 0 \,|\, \mathcal{K} \,|\, DD^{++}; 0 \rangle \qquad (10)$$

On the other hand, if we make the reasonable assumption that the *triplet* charge-transfer states $| DD^{++}; 1 \rangle$ and $| D^{++}D; 1 \rangle$ have energies very much higher than the singlet charge-transfer states $| DD^{++}; 0 \rangle$ and

$| D^+ {}^+D; 0 \rangle$, then we shall be able to neglect the second-order correction to energy of the triplet ion pair state, $| D^+D^+; 1 \rangle$. Thus, the *effective* exchange interaction between the unpaired spins on two D^+ ions is simply,

$$J = (2\gamma^2/\Delta E) \tag{11}$$

This discussion can be immediately extended to the linear chain problem, leading to the exchange spin Hamiltonian of Eq. (8), with appropriate equations for J and J', similar to Eq. (11). Preliminary and very crude theoretical estimates of J for two Wurster's blue ion radicals do lead to values that are of the same order as the observed value ($J = 246$ cm^{-1}).

At the present time it appears that rather accurate *a priori* theoretical calculations of the parameters D, E, and the (x, y, z) principal axis orientations [cf. Eq. (5)] can be made when the appropriate crystal structure is known, and when the spin distribution in the ion radical is known, or can be estimated. For example, in the Wurster's blue perchlorate crystal, the experimentally observed $| D |$ and $| E |$ are 0 and 216 Mc, respectively, and the theoretically estimated D and E are ~ -19 and 186 Mc, respectively (Thomas *et al.*, 1963). There is also good agreement between the theoretical and experimental axis orientations. Similar good agreement is currently being obtained in an *a priori* calculation in these laboratories of the fine-structure splitting parameters in (morpholinium)$^+$(TCNQ)$^-$ by N. Maréchal. The success of such calculations, of course, depends on the accuracy of the relative molecular orientations, the spin distributions, and, most interestingly, on *the absence of intermolecular charge transfer in the triplet state*. That is, small contributions of $S = 1$ electronic states of the charge-transfer type (e.g., $DD^{+\,+}$, or $AA^=$) would destroy the good agreement between the observed and calculated D and E values.

C. Exciton-Phonon and Exciton-Exciton Interaction

There are several reasons to believe that exciton-phonon coupling in ionic free radicals is large. First, there is an obvious theoretical mechanism. Intermolecular charge-transfer integrals γ are expected to be strongly dependent on intermolecular distance R. Thus, from Eq. (11), J is expected to also be strongly dependent on R. If we include the distance dependence of J, $j = \partial J/\partial R$, but neglect as much smaller $j' = \partial J'/\partial R$, then the dominant part of the exciton-phonon coupling can be expressed in the form (McConnell and Soos, 1964),

$$\mathcal{K}_c = \sum_{n=1,3,5} \mathcal{K}_c(n) \tag{12}$$

$$\mathcal{K}_c(n) = jN^{-1/2}\hat{\eta}_n \sum_k (2\hbar/m\omega_k)^{1/2} \sin \tfrac{1}{2}k \exp\left[-ik(n + \tfrac{1}{2})\right](b_k^+ - b_{-k}) \tag{13}$$

Here N is the number of molecules in the chain (cf. Fig. 2), ω_k is the angular vibrational frequency of the kth vibrational mode, m is the molecular mass, $b_k{}^+$ and b_{-k} are phonon creation and annihilation operators, and $\hat{\eta}_n$ is the exciton occupation number operator for the molecule pair $(n, n + 1)$. For simplicity, the phonon spectrum is taken to be that corresponding to the simple mechanical arrangement of balls and springs sketched in Fig. 6. Near neighbors are coupled by a spring of force constant g, far neighbors coupled by the same force constant g, and all molecules are "tied down" to a rigid framework (representing the rest of the three-dimensional lattice) by a spring with force constant G.

This expected coupling between excitons and phonons has many consequences, all of which appear to be in accord with various observed experimental effects.

Unpublished order-of-magnitude estimates by Soos and McConnell indicate that the exciton-phonon interaction coupling is so large that it is best described by an "inverse Born–Oppenheimer limit." That is, as an

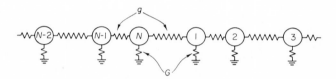

FIG. 6. Mechanical ball-and-spring model for estimating the effective phonon spectrum of an alternating linear chain of ionic free radicals.

exciton moves down a linear chain, a rather large nuclear deformation follows the electronic excitation almost perfectly. This means that, when we use a Hamiltonian such as that given in Eq. (8) to fit experimental data, the various parameters really refer to an electronic excitation plus nuclear distortion. For example, J is then not simply the energy required to unpair two electrons on adjacent molecules, but it is actually this energy minus the distortion energy gained when the lattice relaxes to its new equilibrium conformation. For the model in Fig. 6, this "self-energy" resulting from exciton-phonon coupling is (McConnell and Soos, 1964):

$$V(0) = \frac{-j^2}{2g}\left\{1 - \left[\frac{\lambda - 2}{\lambda + 2}\right]^{1/2}\right\} \tag{14}$$

Here $\lambda = 2 + G/g$. Rough estimates indicate that the self energy $V(0)$ is of the order of magnitude of J itself. This large exciton-phonon coupling immediately suggests that the *effective mass* of the triplet exciton is large. (That is, a large self energy implies large nuclear distortions, a narrowing of the exciton band width, and an increase of effective mass.) A large effective mass suggests a "classical" or diffusional motion of the triplet exciton. That is, the triplet exciton hops from molecular pair to molecular pair in a random, Brownian-motion fashion. This motion is thus consistent with the absence of the otherwise expected k dependence of the exciton fine-structure splitting [cf. Eq. (9)]. In the "moderate temperature" region, $\hbar\omega_{max} < kT < \frac{1}{2}J$, where J is the observed value of J, the jumping frequency can be calculated theoretically, and is found to be (Soos, 1964):

$$\tau^{-1} = \hbar^{-2}(\hbar/kTA)^{1/2}$$
$$\times \exp\left(-\hbar A/4kT\right)\left\{\left(\frac{J'}{4}\right)^2 + \frac{kT(j')^2}{64g}\left[1 - \left(\frac{\lambda - 2}{\lambda + 2}\right)^{1/2}\right]\right\} \quad (15)$$

where

$$A = \hbar^{-1}(2V(0) + V(2)) \quad (16)$$

Here ω_{max} is the upper frequency limit of the phonon spectrum.

In this temperature region, the jumping frequency is exponentially dependent on the temperature, with an "activation energy" $\Delta E^{\ddagger}$:

$$\Delta E^{\ddagger} = \frac{1}{2}[V(0)] + \frac{1}{4}[V(2)] \quad (17)$$

The broadening of the exciton paramagnetic resonance seen at the higher temperature in Fig. 4 for Wurster's blue perchlorate is due to exciton-exciton spin exchange interaction. This leads to exchange narrowing at still higher temperatures. Similar effects have been observed in numerous TCNQ free radical salts. Theoretical considerations lead to the expectation that the initial low-temperature spin exchange broadening ν is of the form (Thomas et al., 1964)

$$\nu \sim f\tau^{-1} c \exp\left(-V(2)/kT\right) \quad (18)$$

Here f is the fraction of the exciton-exciton collisions that produce a line-broadening effect. In the likely event that $J'\tau \gtrsim 1$, then f is of the order of magnitude of one. The quantity $V(2)$ is the phonon-coupled repulsion between triplet excitons localized on adjacent molecular pairs. $V(2)$ has been calculated by several methods, all of which yield

$$V(2) = \epsilon_1 e^{-\theta} \quad (19)$$

Here

$$\epsilon_1 = \frac{j^2 G(G + 2g)}{g\alpha_1(1 - \alpha_2{}^2)^{1/2}}$$

$$\theta = \ln\left\{\alpha_2^{-1}[1 + (1 - \alpha_2{}^2)^{1/2}]\right\}$$

$$\alpha_1 = G^2 + 4gG + 2g^2$$

$$\alpha_2 = 2g^2/\alpha_1$$

(Strictly speaking, the phonon-coupled repulsion decays exponentially with distance, $\epsilon_1 \exp - \theta n$, where n is the number of pairs separating the localized excitons. For brevity, we only consider in the present discussion the repulsion between the nearest-neighbor excitons.) A convenient derivation of the above formulas is given by Krugler (1965). Chesnut (1964a, b) has proposed that phonon-coupled interactions between triplet excitons are "probably attractive."

Since $c \sim \exp - J/kT$ when $kT \ll J$, the "activation energy" for spin exchange line broadening is

$$\Delta\mathcal{E}^{\ddagger} = \Delta E^{\ddagger} + J + V(2) \tag{20}$$

$$= J + \tfrac{1}{2}V(0) + \tfrac{5}{4}V(2) \tag{21}$$

in the temperature region where Eq. (15) is valid. Thus, in this temperature region both a self-energy term $V(0)$ and a phonon-coupled repulsion $V(2)$ contribute to the activation energy for line broadening. It has been shown theoretically by Soos (1964) that at low temperatures, where Eq. (15) is no longer valid, *the diffusional probability becomes temperature independent* but remains large enough to wipe out the nuclear hyperfine structure, even at $0°K$. Unfortunately the phonon spectra of ionic molecular crystals are not known with any accuracy, so the precise range of validity of Eq. (15) in any particular case is not known. The foregoing considerations are qualitatively compatible with the important observation, first made by Jones and Chesnut (1963) for TCNQ salts, but also seen later in Wurster's blue perchlorate, that in general the activation energy for exchange broadening always exceeds J by a variable, but usually substantial, amount. According to the present theoretical discussion, the "excess" activation energy must always involve the phonon-coupled repulsion $V(2)$, but may also involve the exciton self energy $V(0)$ through the role that this quantity can play in thermally activated diffusion.

The jumping rate τ^{-1} has been estimated in one material, $(\phi_3\text{AsCH}_3)^+$ $(\text{TCNQ})_2{}^-$, to be of the order of 10^{12} sec^{-1} from both exchange-broadening data and nuclear hyperfine broadening (Thomas *et al.*, 1964). In this case, the evidence is that there is no activation energy for exciton diffusion at $\sim 77°K$.

D. Phase Transitions

Two solid ionic free radicals that show exciton paramagnetic resonance spectra also show phase transitions in which the magnetic susceptibility changes discontinuously. These ionic radicals are $(\phi_3\text{PCH}_3)^+(\text{TCNQ})_2{}^-$ (Chesnut and Phillips, 1961) and Wurster's blue perchlorate (Chu *et al.*, 1953). In both cases, the phase transition is first order. In Wurster's blue

perchlorate the phase transition is at $180°K$, and in $(\phi_3PCH_3)^+(TCNQ)_2^-$
the transition is at $315°K$. More recently, a similar phase transition in
$(\phi_3AsCH_3)^+(TCNQ)_2^-$ has been discovered at room temperature and 2000
atm pressure in these laboratories.

Current interest in these phase transitions stems from the question of
how they may be related to the presence of triplet excitons. Chesnut
(1964a) has proposed an interesting phenomenological theory of these
phase transition based on an effective attractive long-range interaction.
Here we present a simple alternative explanation. In contrast to the theory
of Chesnut, we assume a rigid lattice, except for a change in structure
associated with a phase transition.

We consider two crystal structures, I and II. We assume that the alter-
nations are such that $J_I > J_{II}$. Thus, we have two spin Hamiltonians $\mathcal{H}_I$
and $\mathcal{H}_{II}$, corresponding to the Hamiltonian in Eq. (8). *For simplicity*, we
assume a strong alternation in both I and II, so that $J_1 \gg J_1'$, and $J_{II} \gg$
J_{II}'. In this case the thermodynamic quantities are dominated by :the
large exchange terms J, and the J' terms may be neglected. The spin exchange free energy A_I^s, A_{II}^s per molecular pair is

$$A^s = -\tfrac{1}{2}J - kT \ln \left[1 + 3 \exp \left(-J/kT\right)\right] \tag{22}$$

In deriving expression (22) for the spin exchange free energy, it must be
noted that the spin exchange Hamiltonian in Eq. (8) uses a zero of energy
equal to $-\tfrac{1}{2}J$. This energy must be included in Eq. (22), since we wish to
compare the free energies A_I^s and A_{II}^s for different J values, J_I and J_{II}.

To begin with, assume the lattice free energies of structures I and II to
be the same, $A_I^l = A_{II}^l$. Then we expect a phase transition at a temperature T^* for which,

$$A_I^s = A_{II}^s \tag{23}$$

When $J_I = J_{II} + \delta$, where $\delta/J_I \ll 1$, the condition Eq. (23) for a phase
transition occurs at the temperature

$$kT^* = J/\ln 3$$

$$= J/1.0986 \tag{24}$$

Obviously the temperature T^* will be shifted if δ/J_I is not small, or if
$A_I^l \neq A_{II}^l$. Indeed, if the difference between A_I^l and A_{II}^l is large enough,
there will, of course, be no phase transition at any temperature. The above
discussion provides the basis for a simple explanation for the occurrence of
phase transitions in dense exciton systems.

III. Charge Transfer in Molecular Crystals

There exist a large number of $1:1$ crystal complexes DA between aromatic donor molecules D and aromatic acceptor molecules A. Recently, the Hartree–Fock molecular field approximation has been used to show that the ground electronic state of a $1:1$ *crystal* complex between D and A molecules should contain molecules that are very nearly nonionic, or very nearly ionic. (McConnell et al., 1964). This conclusion is particularly applicable to donor molecules D and acceptor molecules A that contain single aromatic rings, and substituents that permit a close packing of the molecules in the crystal lattice in the well-known —DADADA— linear chains, where the intermolecular distances are ca. 3.4–3.5 Å. The crystals with the nonionic ground states are expected to be diamagnetic or, at most, feebly paramagnetic. The DA crystals with ionic ground states then have a free spin on each molecule. X-ray diffraction data show many of these linear chains, —D$^+$A$^-$D$^+$A$^-$—, to be regular; i.e., there is no alternation in the intermolecular distance. A particular example of this regular array where there is no detectable alternation of intermolecular distances in the ionic lattice (at least at room temperature) is the $1:1$ complex between the anion of TCNQ and Wurster's blue cation (Hoffman and McConnell, 1964). The spin exchange Hamiltonian for these linear arrays (where spin exchange between different chains can be neglected) is,

$$\mathcal{H} = J \sum_{i=1,2,3,\cdots} \mathbf{s}_i \cdot \mathbf{s}_{i+1} \tag{25}$$

The eigenstates of this simple spin exchange Hamiltonian are not known, although they have been the subject of extensive investigation. We are thus confronted with a problem far more difficult than that considered in Section II, where there is an alternating array of $s = \frac{1}{2}$ molecules. At the present time both preliminary theoretical calculations and the experimental magnetic resonance spectra appear to be in accord on the following qualitative points.

The susceptibility vs. temperature data for the ionic DA crystals are at least qualitatively similar to those for the triplet exciton crystals. At low temperatures there is a detectable fine-structure broadening of the magnetic resonance lines of D$^+$A$^-$ crystals, which has its origin in the same interaction which gives rise to the sharp fine-structure doublets seen in the triplet exciton spectra. The exchange integrals J in Eq. (25) for the ionic D$^+$A$^-$ crystal problem are estimated from the spin susceptibility data to be more or less in the same range as the exchange integrals J observed in the triplet exciton systems. The origin of this effective exchange interaction is the same as that discussed earlier for the triplet exciton systems. Here there is a "back-charge-transfer" Mulliken resonance integral,

$$\gamma = \langle D^+A^- \mid \mathfrak{K} \mid DA \rangle \tag{26}$$

and this in second order gives an effective exchange interaction J,

$$J = \gamma^2/\Delta E \tag{27}$$

where ΔE is the energy required to create a neutral pair DA in an ionic D^+A^- lattice.

The D^+A^- ionic crystals obviously present many new and challenging experimental and theoretical problems.

REFERENCES

Chesnut, D. B. (1964a). *J. Chem. Phys.* **40**, 405.
Chesnut, D. B. (1964b). *J. Chem. Phys.* **41**, 472.
Chesnut, D. B., and Arthur, P., Jr. (1962). *J. Chem. Phys.* **36**, 2969.
Chesnut, D. B., and Phillips, W. D. (1961). *J. Chem. Phys.* **35**, 1002.
Chu, T. L., Pake, G. E., Paul, D. E., Townsend, J., and Weissman, S. I. (1953). *J. Phys. Chem.* **57**, 504.
Hofiman, B. M., and McConnell, H. M. (1964). Unpublished X-ray diffraction studies.
Isenberg, I., Leslie, R. B., Baird, S. L., Jr., Rosenbluth, R., and Bersohn, R. (1964). *Proc. Natl. Acad. Sci. U.S.* **52**, 379.
Jones, M. T., and Chesnut, D. B. (1963). *J. Chem. Phys.* **38**, 1311.
Kamb, B., Hughes, E., and McConnell, H. M. (1963). Unpublished experiments on the low-temperature crystal structure of Wurster's blue perchlorate.
Krugler, J. I. (1965). "Spin Absorption in Triplet Exciton Systems," Ph.D. Thesis, California Institute of Technology, Pasadena, California.
Lynden-Bell, R., and McConnell, H. M. (1962). *J. Chem. Phys.* **37**, 794.
McConnell, H. M., and Lyndel-Bell, R. (1961). *J. Chem. Phys.* **36**, 2393.
McConnell, H. M., and Soos, Z. (1964). *J. Chem. Phys.* **40**, 586.
McConnell, H. M., Hoffman, B. M., and Metzger, R. M. (1965). *Proc. Natl. Acad. Sci. U.S.*, **53**, 46.
Robinson, G. W. (1964), *Ann. Rev. Phys. Chem.* **15**, 311.
Soos, Z. (1964). Unpublished calculations.
Sternlicht, H., and McConnell, H. M., (1961). *J. Chem. Phys.* **35**, 1793.
Thomas, D. D., Keller, H., and McConnell, H. M. (1963). *J. Chem. Phys.* **39**, 2321.
Thomas, D. D., Merkl, A. W., Hildebrandt, A. F., and McConnell, H. M. (1964). *J. Chem. Phys.* **40**, 2588.
Turner, J. D., and Albrecht, A. C. (1954). Unpublished determination of the crystal structure of Wurster's blue perchlorate.

Intermolecular Forces[1]

JOSEPH O. HIRSCHFELDER
Theoretical Chemistry Institute,
University of Wisconsin,
Madison, Wisconsin

Intermolecular force is the glue which binds together the biologically active molecules. There are many varieties of intermolecular forces which occur. A quantitative explanation of these forces is difficult, because biologically active molecules are large and complex and the field of biological action is an aqueous solution. However, a semiquantitative treatment is possible and may serve as a guide to the interpretation of experimental data.

First, let us sketch the various types of intermolecular forces which occur between a pair of isolated molecules. Then we shall discuss the effects of solvation. Further details are available in MTGL.[2]

Although it is convenient to speak about intermolecular forces, all our serious thinking is in terms of the energy of interaction. The force on a particular molecule is minus the gradient of the interaction energy with respect to the coordinates of this molecule. Table I gives the types of intermolecular energies which we shall consider.

Excluding the magnetic and relativistic interactions, Hellmann (1937) and Feynman (1939) have proved (see MTGL, p. 932) that the quantum mechanical forces are just exactly what one would expect on the basis of classical electrostatics for a given configuration of the nuclei and a known electron probability density. In other words, once the distribution of the

[1] This investigation was supported by Public Health Service Research Grant No. GM 11315-01, from the National Institute of General Medical Services.

[2] Hirschfelder, Curtiss, and Bird (1964) *Molecular Theory of Gases and Liquids* will henceforth be referred to as MTGL. Chapters 12 and 13 are especially pertinent.

TABLE I

INTERMOLECULAR INTERACTIONS

Type	Range	
I. Direct electrostatic	Long	
II. Polarized or induced	Long	
III. Dispersion or fluctuation	Long	Electrostatic
IV. Resonance	Long	
V. Charge exchange	Intermediate	
VI. Valence or chemical	Short	
VII. Magnetic and relativistic	All	

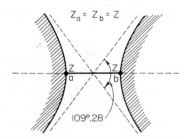

FIG. 1. Bonding and antibonding regions for a homonuclear diatomic molecule.

electron cloud has been determined by solving the Schrödinger equation, the forces on the nuclei are coulombic.

Berlin (1951) dramatized this result (see MTGL, p. 935) by making a diagram showing the region in which an increment of the electron cloud helps to draw the nuclei together, in contrast to other regions in which it would tend to pull the nuclei apart. In Figs. 1 and 2 the antibonding regions are hatched. It is antibonding if the increment of electron cloud produces a larger z component of force on the closer nucleus than on the farther nucleus (where z is the internuclear axis).

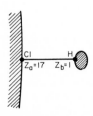

FIG. 2. Bonding and antibonding regions for hydrogen chloride.

As Table I shows, there are six different types of electrostatic interactions. Let us consider them individually.

I. Direct Electrostatic Interactions

Direct electrostatic interactions are long ranged. At a separation of 562 Å, the energy of interaction between two ions, H^+ and H^+, is 600 cal/mole (or RT at room temperature). The same energy occurs when a polar molecule (H_2O) approaches an ion (H^+) at a separation of 14.6 Å; or the H_2O approaches another polar molecule (H_2O) at a distance of 5.5 Å.

It is customary to express the charge distribution of a molecule in terms of a multipole expansion: charge, dipole, quadrupole, octupole, etc. Then the direct electrostatic interaction between two molecules is the sum of the interactions of their respective multipole moments. However, in order that the multipole-multipole interactions be applicable, it is necessary (see MTGL, p. 844) that the separation R between the two molecules A and B be larger than the sum of the greatest radii of the two molecules.

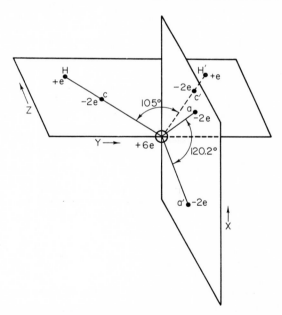

Fig. 3. Monopole electrostatic model of the water molecule as suggested by Duncan and Pople (1953) (see also MTGL, p. 103). Here the water molecule is represented by seven monopoles, one at each of the hydrogen and oxygen atoms, one along each of the OH bonds, and two "lone pair" electron monopoles in the plane perpendicular to the H_2O.

If r_{max} is the greatest distance to the center of the molecule of any element of charge in the molecule, then the requirement for the validity of a multipole-multipole interaction between two molecules is that

$$R > (r_{max})_A + (r_{max})_B \qquad (1)$$

For the interaction of two large biologically active molecules, separations sufficiently large for condition (1) to apply are seldom of interest.

Thus, I recommend that the electrical charge distribution of a molecule A be idealized by a set of monopoles i with charge $\epsilon(A)_i$ located at positions $\mathbf{r}(A)_i$. Figure 3 shows such a monopole electrostatic model for the water molecule. The Pullmans (1963) and others very frequently use monopoles to idealize the charge distribution of biologically active molecules. The direct electrostatic interaction energy between two molecules is then given as the sum of a set of coulombic energy terms:

$$E_{AB}^{(\text{direct}-\text{elect})} = \sum_{i,j} \frac{\epsilon(A)_i\,\epsilon(B)_i}{|\,\mathbf{r}(A)_i - \mathbf{r}(B)_j\,|} \qquad (2)$$

Two monopoles of opposite charges form a "real" dipole. In real dipoles, there is a finite separation l between the positive and negative charges ϵ. The dipole moment is $\mu = \epsilon l$. Consider the interaction between two such polar molecules with their dipoles pointed in the same direction along the line of nuclei:

$$|\leftarrow l \rightarrow| \qquad\qquad |\leftarrow l \rightarrow|$$

$$-\epsilon \qquad +\epsilon \qquad\qquad -\epsilon \qquad +\epsilon$$

$$|\longleftarrow R \longrightarrow|$$

Here, according to Eq. (2),

$$E_{AB}^{(\text{direct}-\text{elect})} = \epsilon^2 \left[\frac{2}{R} - \frac{1}{R-l} - \frac{1}{R+l} \right]$$

$$= -\frac{2\epsilon^2 l^2}{R(R^2 - l^2)} = -\frac{2\mu^2}{R(R^2 - l^2)} \qquad (3)$$

The energy of interaction of two "ideal" dipoles in the same configuration is $-2\mu^2/R^3$. If the separations R and l are comparable, the energy of interaction of the real dipoles can be much larger than for ideal dipoles.

The very large binding energy of hydrogen bonds can be explained in terms of a monopole representation. As shown in Fig. 4, the partially unshielded proton of one molecule comes very close to the lone pair electrons of the oxygen atom of another molecule.

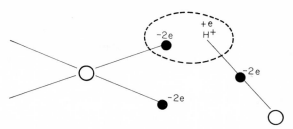

FIG. 4. Monopole electrostatic model of hydrogen bonding. Here the proton of one molecule comes close to the lone pair electrons of an oxygen atom of a second molecule.

Direct electrostatic interactions are generally dependent on the orientations of the two molecules, as well as on their separations. If the system is at thermal equilibrium, the average energy of interaction of two molecules separated by a distance R is given by the Boltzmann average:

$$\bar{E}_{AB} = \frac{\iint E_{AB} \exp\left(-E_{AB}/kT\right) d\omega_A \, d\omega_B}{\iint \exp\left(-E_{AB}/kT\right) d\omega_A \, d\omega_B} \tag{4}$$

Here the integrations are taken over all the orientations of A and B, corresponding to the solid angles ω_A and ω_B. This Boltzmann averaging has a profound effect on the experimentally observable interaction energies. For example, at very low temperatures where $|E_{AB}| > kT$, two dipoles tend to align, so as to give the lowest energy of interaction and $\bar{E}_{AB} = -2\mu^2/R^3$. But at high temperatures, the Boltzmann average only slightly favors the energetically favorable configurations, so that the average energy of interaction between two dipoles is $\bar{E}_{AB} = -(2/3kT)\mu^4/R^6$. The Boltzmann-averaged direct electrostatic energy of interaction is always negative, corresponding to a net attraction between the molecules.[2] In the remainder of this paper, we shall not consider the Boltzmann averaging. However, statistical averaging over a thermal distribution of energy states is frequently required in connection with experimental problems.

II. Polarization or Induced Electrostatic Interactions

Polarization or induced electrostatic forces are usually very small and unimportant. However, in large biologically active molecules there is the

[2] The direct orientational average [Eq. (4) without the Boltzmann factor] of any multipole-multipole interaction energy is zero (MTGL, p. 846). Since the Boltzmann factor favors orientations with negative interaction energy, the Boltzmann-averaged multipole-multipole energy is negative. The only exception is the charge-charge coulombic energy in the interaction of two positive or two negative ions.

FIG. 5. Dipole induced in molecule B by a charge C_A^+ on molecule A.

possibility of inducing zwitterions with very large induced dipole moments. Thus, polarization forces should be carefully considered (see MTGL, pp. 29, 984).

If molecule A has the charge C_A, it produces an electric field $\mathcal{E}_A = +C_A/R^2$ at the position of molecule B. This induces a dipole moment $\mu^{(\text{ind})} = \alpha_B \mathcal{E}_A$; see Fig. 5. The energy of interaction of the induced dipole with the electric field is then

$$E_{AB}^{(\text{polar})} = -\int_0^{\mathcal{E}_A} \mu^{(\text{ind})} d\mathcal{E}_A = -\tfrac{1}{2}\alpha_B \mathcal{E}_A^2 = -\frac{C_A^2 \alpha_B}{2R^4} \tag{5}$$

Similarly, if molecule A possesses a dipole moment μ_A in a direction θ_A with respect to the internuclear axis, this dipole can induce a dipole moment in molecule B which interacts with the original dipole moment to produce the energy

$$E_{AB}^{(\text{polar})} = \frac{-\mu_A^2 \alpha_B (3 \cos^2 \theta_A + 1)}{2R^6} \tag{6}$$

This induction energy was first obtained by Debye (1920) and Falkenhagen (1922).

III. Dispersion or Fluctuation Interaction

From quantum mechanical considerations, there are rapid fluctuations in the electronic charge distributions. Thus even a nonpolar molecule A has an instantaneous dipole moment $\mu_A^{(\text{instant})}$, which induces a dipole moment in molecule B, which interacts with the instantaneous dipole to produce the instantaneous energy, according to Eq. (6),

$$E_{AB}^{(\text{instant})} = \frac{-[\mu_{AB}^{(\text{instant})}]^2 \alpha_B [3 \cos^2 \theta_A + 1]}{2R^6} \tag{7}$$

The London dispersion energy (see MTGL, p. 960) results from time-averaging $E_{AB}^{(\text{instant})}$:

$$E_{AB}^{(\text{dispers})}$$

$$= -\frac{1}{R^6} \sum_{i,j}' \frac{[\mu_x(A)_{0i}\mu_x(B)_{0j} + \mu_y(A)_{0i}\mu_y(B)_{0j} - 2\mu_z(A)_{0i}\mu_z(B)_{0j}]^2}{E(A)_{i0} + E(B)_{j0}}$$

$$+ O(1/R^8) + \cdots \tag{8}$$

Here, as in most of the remainder of this paper, all distances are given in Bohr radii (a_0) and all energies are in atomic units (e^2/a_0); the term $E(A)_{i0} = E(A)_i - E(A)_0$ is an excitation energy of molecule A; the $\mu_x(A)_{0i}$, $\mu_y(A)_{0i}$, and $\mu_z(A)_{0i}$ are the x, y, and z components of the transition dipole moment of molecule A going from 0 to i; the z axis is the line joining the centers of A and B and has the same direction for B as for A. The prime on the summation excludes transitions for which $E(A)_{i0}$ or $E(B)_{j0} = 0$. In addition, those high-energy transitions must be excluded for which[3] $E(A)_{i0} > hc/R$ or $E(B)_{j0} > hc/R$.

For many biologically active molecules, there is either one or only a few important electronic transition bands for which the values of the transition dipole moments are appreciable. In such cases, Eq. (8) may be useful for calculating the dispersion energy from the experimentally observed molecular absorption spectra.

The dispersion energy can also be written in the form

$$E_{AB}^{(dispers)} = -\sum_{i,j}' \frac{N_A{}^2 N_B{}^2 \mid \langle 0, 0 \mid r_{ab}^{-1} \mid i, j \rangle \mid^2}{E(A)_{i0} + E(B)_{j0}} \qquad (9)$$

Here N_A and N_B are the number of electrons in molecules A and B, respectively; r_{ab} is the distance between electron a in molecule A and electron b in molecule B; and the matrix component is

$$\iint \Psi_0(A)^* \Psi_0(B)^* r_{ab}^{-1} \Psi_i(A) \Psi_j(B) d\tau_A \, d\tau_B$$

where the integrations are to be made over the spin and coordinate space of all the electrons in the two molecules. Equation (9) has the advantage over Eq. (8) that it is applicable to intermediate as well as to very large separations.

Now let us define the transition charge density of A to be

$$\rho_{0i}(a) = N_A \int \Psi_0(A)^* \Psi_i(A) \, d\tau_{N_A - 1} \qquad (10)$$

where the integration is over the spin-configuration space of all the electrons in A except a and over the spin space of a; and $\rho_{0j}(b)$ is similarly defined as the transition charge density of B. Thus

$$N_A N_B \langle 0, 0 \mid r_{ab}^{-1} \mid i, j \rangle = \iint \rho_{0i}(a) r_{ab}^{-1} \rho_{0j}(b) \, d\tau_a \, d\tau_b \qquad (11)$$

[3] Stephen (1964a) points out that these high-energy transitions should be excluded because time changes in the phases of their transition charge density make the induced dipole moment out of phase with the instantaneous dipole. This is a retardation effect.

London (1942) and Haugh and Hirschfelder (1955) suggested that the transition charge densities might conveniently be approximated by sets of monopoles (see MTGL, p. 971). Thus $\rho_{0i}(a)$ is approximated by the set of charges $\epsilon_{0i}^{(k)}(A)$ at the positions $\mathbf{r}_{0i}^{(k)}(A)$. Similarly, $\rho_{0j}(b)$ is approximated by the set of changes $\epsilon_{0j}^{(l)}(B)$ at the positions $\mathbf{r}_{0j}^{(l)}(B)$. Thus,

$$\iint \rho_{0i}(a) r_{ab}^{-1} \rho_{0j}(b) \, d\tau_a \, d\tau_b = \sum_{k,l} \frac{\epsilon_{0i}^{(k)}(A) \epsilon_{0j}^{(l)}(B)}{|\mathbf{r}_{0i}^{(k)}(A) - \mathbf{r}_{0j}^{(l)}(B)|} \tag{12}$$

and

$$E_{AB}^{(\text{dispers})} = -\sum_{i,j}' \frac{\{\sum_{k,l} [\epsilon_{0i}^{(k)}(A) \epsilon_{0j}^{(l)}(B)]/[|\mathbf{r}_{0i}^{(k)}(A) - \mathbf{r}_{0j}^{(l)}(B)|]\}^2}{E(A)_{i0} + E(B)_{j0}} \tag{13}$$

Equation (13) is particularly useful for calculating the dispersion energy between asymmetric molecules at intermediate separations.

Coulson and Davies (1952), Haugh and Hirschfelder (1955), and Sternlicht (1964) have obtained rather strange forces in the interaction of conjugate double bond molecules. The energetically best angle between the two molecules is between 60° and 90°, as one would expect from the crystal structure of such molecules. Also, as one molecule is displaced parallel to the other, there is a series of maxima and minima in the interaction energy. In general, $E_{AB}^{(\text{dispers})}$ varies as the fifth power of the length of the conjugate double bond system. Sternlicht (1964) using the method of Tomonaga (1950, 1955) has found that Hückel and free-electron calculations of the $\pi-\pi$ contribution to the polarizability of conjugate double bond molecules is much too large, because of the neglect of the mutual repulsion of the electrons within a molecule. In a similar manner, he finds that the Hückel calculations of Coulson and Davies (1952) and the free-electron calculations of Haugh and Hirschfelder (1955) give too large a $\pi-\pi$ component of $E_{AB}^{(\text{dispers})}$. Thus the $\pi-\pi$ interaction energy dominates at large separations and becomes comparable to the $\sigma-\sigma$ interaction energy at small separations. At close separations, Aono (1958, 1959a, b) has shown that charge-transfer energies between conjugate double bond molecules become much larger than dispersion energies. Much further work will be required to clarify the conjugate double bond molecule interactions.

Dispersion energies are usually considered on the basis of second-order perturbations, and this leads directly to Eqs. (8) and (9). However, recently Linder (1960, 1962), Linder and Hoernschmeyer (1964), Yos et al. (1947), Jehle et al. (1958), Yos (1958), and Jehle et al. (1964) have developed a general type of "reaction-field" technique for considering dispersion energies in terms of fluctuations. Their approach is based on the treatment of Landau and Lifshitz (1958; 1960) and of Callen and Welton (1951). See also Brown (1956). The reaction field of a molecule A is the field produced on it by the moments of the surrounding molecules which have been induced by the moments of molecule A. An idealized model is assumed for the reaction-field response function, which connects the reaction field to the moment that has produced the field. This function determines the dielectric susceptibility and the intermolecular free energy. There are many advantages of the reaction-field technique: (1) All types of electrostatic interactions can be considered simultaneously. (2) Forces resulting from thermal fluctuation of the charge distribution (electron or proton transfers) are also given. (3) The Boltzmann averaging of the interaction energies is included in the calculations. (4) The effects of solvents and three-, four-, etc., body forces are obtained in a rigorous manner. Jehle stresses that the reaction-field technique is particularly well suited to the treatment of biological problems.

IV. Resonance Interactions

Resonance occurs (see MTGL, p. 990) whenever the molecular interaction produces a perturbation which removes an energy degeneracy. The wave function for a resonance state corresponds to a dipole or electric moment, where classically such a moment should not occur. Resonance energies can be either positive or negative—the value of the resonance energy vanishes when averaged over all the quantum states which occur. There are two types of resonance interactions:

1. One-Molecule Degeneracy

Example. Collision proton with an H atom in either $2s$ or $2p$ state.

Under the influence of the proton electric field, the zero-order wave function for the H atom becomes

$$\Psi = \psi(2s) + c\psi(2p_z) \tag{14}$$

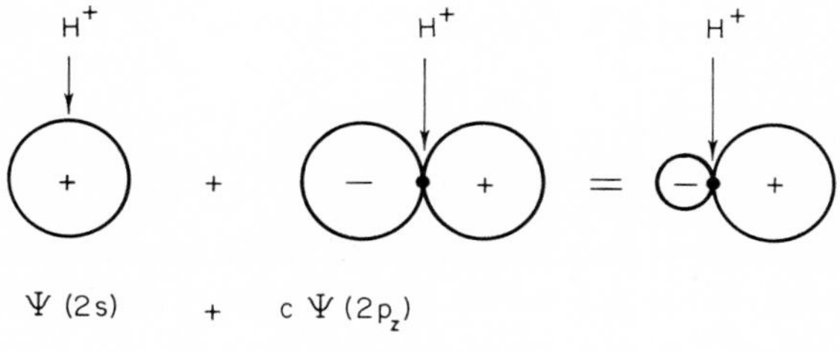

$$\Psi\,(2s) \quad + \quad c\,\Psi\,(2p_z)$$

Fig. 6. H-atom wave function.

As can be seen from Fig. 6, the center of the electronic charge corresponding to Ψ is shifted (the figure shows it shifted toward the right). Therefore the hydrogen atom has a dipole moment! The resulting energy of interaction varies as $1/R^2$ instead of $1/R^4$, as one would expect for a charge-induced dipole energy if no resonance were involved.

2. Two-Molecule Degeneracy

Example. Collision between two like molecules, one in the state 0, the other in an excited state 1, such that the transition $1 \rightarrow 0$ with the emission of a photon is permitted by the selection rules. This example is illustrated in Fig. 7. A photon can be emitted by molecule A and absorbed by B, etc.

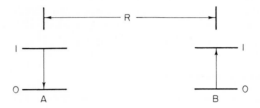

FIG. 7. Two molecule resonance collision stabilized by photon interchange.

The large resonance energy can be attributed to this photon exchange. However, the problem can be analyzed without recourse to photons. The wave function for the two-molecule system can be written in either the gerade or ungerade forms:

$$\Psi_{g\atop u} = \psi_0(A)\psi_1(B) \pm \psi_1(A)\psi_0(B) \tag{15}$$

The square of Ψ contains the product $[\psi_0(A)\psi_1(A)][\psi_0(B)\psi_1(B)]$. This term behaves as though molecule A and molecule B had dipole moments. The resonance energy is given by the expectation value for the interaction potential. Thus,

$$E_{AB}^{(res)}(g) = -E_{AB}^{(res)}(u)$$
$$= -(R^3)^{-1}[\,|\,(\mu_x)_{01}\,|^2 + |\,(\mu_y)_{01}\,|^2 - 2\,|\,(\mu_z)_{01}\,|^2\,] \tag{16}$$

Here

$$\mathbf{\mu}_{01} = \int \psi_0(A)\,\mathbf{\mu}\psi_1(A)\,d\tau = \int \psi_0(B)\,\mathbf{\mu}\psi_1(B)\,d\tau \tag{17}$$

It is equally probable that a collision will result in a gerade or ungerade state. As a result of the resonance, the interaction energy varies as $1/R^3$ instead of $1/R^6$.

Stephen (1964b) has studied the nature of resonance collisions from the standpoint of quantum mechanical field theory. At separations greater than $R = hc/E_{10}(\mathrm{A})$, the problem becomes time dependent rather than stationary. The gerade state, but not the ungerade state, can spontaneously emit a photon to leave both molecules in the 0 state. The concept of intermolecular energy as a function of separation may become ill defined under such conditions.

V. Charge Exchange Interactions

Charge transfer between two molecules may take place at intermediate separations and greatly increase the energy of interaction. Charge transfer is characterized by the (almost) crossing of two potential energy curves, one corresponding to A + B, the other corresponding to $A^+ + B^-$. This is shown in Fig. 8. There are many examples of donor-acceptor charge transfer complexes, such as benzene-iodine, which behave in this manner. Aono (1958, 1959a, b) believes that charge transfers are very important in interactions between conjugate double bond molecules. Whenever

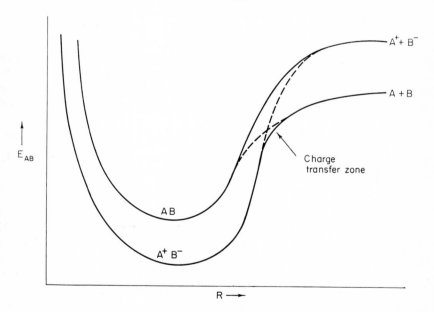

FIG. 8. Charge transfer between two molecules. Here the charge transfer takes place at an intermediate separation. The two potential energy curves (almost) cross in the charge transfer zone.

charge transfer may be important, we should use for the wave function of the two-molecule system the form

$$\Psi = \Psi(\text{AB}) + c\Psi(\text{A}^+\text{B}^-) \tag{18}$$

so that the contribution of the ionic state A^+B^- can be varied by adjusting the constant c. Ionic states are even important in the interaction of two like molecules.

VI. Valence or Chemical Interactions

Valence and chemical interactions are the chemical forces which are familiar in molecular quantum mechanics. They are responsible for the short-range repulsive forces between molecules. For intermolecular purposes, the first-order perturbation "vector model" of Dirac (1929), Van Vleck (1934), Serber (1934), Kimball and Eyring (1932), Pauling (1933), and Bear and Eyring (1935) gives an adequate approximation [see Vanderslice and Mason (1960); Eyring et al. (1944); Hirschfelder (1941); Van Vleck and Sherman (1935); Eyring (1932); and MTGL, p. 939]:

$$E_{\text{AB}}^{(\text{val})} = -\tfrac{1}{2} \sum_{\substack{\text{a,b} \\ \text{orbitals} \\ \text{with} \\ \text{randomly} \\ \text{paired spin}}} K_{\text{ab}} + \sum_{\substack{\text{a,b} \\ \text{orbitals} \\ \text{with} \\ \text{paired} \\ \text{spins}}} K_{\text{ab}} - \sum_{\substack{\text{a,b} \\ \text{orbitals} \\ \text{with} \\ \text{antipaired} \\ \text{spins}}} K_{\text{ab}} \tag{19}$$

Here the K_{ab} are exchange integrals (usually negative) between an orbital a in A and an orbital b in B. All the coulomb, overlap, and multipole exchange integrals are neglected.[4] There are a variety of ways in which these exchange integrals can be estimated. They have the approximate functional form

$$K_{\text{ab}} = -C_{\text{ab}} \exp\left(-\beta_{\text{ab}}R\right) \tag{20}$$

The constant β_{ab} may be approximated by (see Zener (1931); MTGL, p. 26):

$$\beta_{\text{ab}} = [2E_I(\text{a})]^{1/2} + [2E_I(\text{b})]^{1/2} \tag{21}$$

where $E_I(\text{a})$ and $E_I(\text{b})$ are the ionization potentials of a and b, expressed in units of (e^2/a_0), and β_{ab} is given in units of a_0^{-1}. Eyring and Polanyi (1931), Eyring (1931), and Ekstein and Polanyi (1932) approximated the exchange integrals from an empirical knowledge of the binding energy of diatomic molecules.

A further clue regarding K_{ab} is given by Hirschfelder and Eliason (1957), who found that the kinetic theory collision diameter (where $K_{\text{ab}} = kT$)

---

[4] The reader is reminded that the total energy of interaction is taken to be the sum of direct electrostatic, dispersion, . . . , and valence energies. Therefore, the coulombic interaction terms are not required in Eq. (19); they have been considered separately.

is equal to $\bar{r}_a + \bar{r}_b + 1.8$ Å. Here $\bar{r}_a$ and $\bar{r}_b$ are the mean values of the radii of the orbitals a and b, respectively, calculated with the use of Slater orbitals and Slater screening constants. They also found that the equilibrium separation in a diatomic molecule is $\bar{r}_A + \bar{r}_B$, where $\bar{r}_A$ and $\bar{r}_B$ are calculated for the outermost orbitals.

VII. Magnetic and Relativistic Interactions

There are two basic types of energies of interaction—electrostatic and magnetic. Until quite recently, the magnetic forces have been thought to be small and were generally ignored. However, there are good reasons to suppose that the magnetic interactions may be important in some biological problems. As Ampere discovered, a moving charged particle or electric current produces a magnetic field. Thus, the ring currents in conjugate double bond molecules behave like small magnetic dipoles. Two such molecules interact with magnetic dipole-magnetic dipole energy (which varies as $1/R^3$). The magnetic interaction terms tend to be smaller than the corresponding electrostatic interactions by a factor of $(1/137)^2$ or the square of the fine-structure constant. However, the larger the molecule, the more important the magnetic terms can become.

In quantum mechanics, the magnetic terms arise from the relativistic corrections to the Schrödinger equation. In addition to the magnetic moments produced by their motion, the electrons and nuclei possess intrinsic magnetic moments called *spins*. The relativistic corrections to the Schrödinger equation may be expressed in powers of $(1/137)$ and involve spin-spin, spin-orbit, and orbit-orbit magnetic interactions, as well as terms expressing the time lags in the interactions and relativistic corrections to the kinetic energy. For most purposes, the Breit equation [see Bethe and Salpeter (1957); MTGL, p. 1044] can be used to obtain the required energy shifts. But for second-order effects, it may be necessary to use photon annihilation-creation operators to obtain the required accuracy. At the present time, we are examining types of magnetic forces which can occur. An understanding of magnetic coupling terms is essential in the understanding of nuclear magnetic resonance experiments.

A very interesting magnetic interaction term was discovered by Mavroyannis and Stephen (1962). Assuming, in order to simplify the formula, that the molecules are rotating rapidly,

$$E_{AB}^{(\text{opt act})} = -\frac{4}{3R^6} \sum_{i,j}{}' \frac{[\mathbf{u}_{0i}(A) \cdot \mathbf{m}_{0i}(A)][\mathbf{u}_{0j}(B) \cdot \mathbf{m}_{0j}(B)]}{E_{i0}(A) + E_{j0}(B)} \quad (22)$$

Here $\mathbf{m}$ is the magnetic moment operator, $(e/2mc) \sum_k \mathbf{r}_k \times \mathbf{p}_k$. This energy is different from zero only if both molecules A and B are optically active. If B is replaced by its mirror image, the sign of $E_{AB}^{(opt\ act)}$ is changed. The value of $E_{AB}^{(opt\ act)}$ is usually small relative to $E_{AB}^{(dispers)}$; however, it may be important in causing steric arrangements between neighboring molecules.

Mavroyannis and Stephen (1962) used quantum mechanical field theory to derive Eq. (22). However, if we write the interaction Hamiltonian in the form [see Meath (1965)]

$$H = H_0 + \frac{1}{R^3}\left[\mathbf{\mu}_A \cdot \mathbf{\mu}_B - \frac{3(\mathbf{\mu}_A \cdot \mathbf{R})(\mathbf{\mu}_B \cdot \mathbf{R})}{R^2} \right]$$

$$+ \frac{1}{R^3}\left[\mathbf{m}_A \cdot \mathbf{m}_B - \frac{3(\mathbf{m}_A \cdot \mathbf{R})(\mathbf{m}_B \cdot \mathbf{R})}{R^2} \right] + \cdots \quad (23)$$

then Eq. (22) is obtained as one of the interaction energy terms by the use of the usual second-order perturbation procedure.

VIII. Solvent Effects

Up to now, we have considered only the interaction energy between an isolated pair of molecules. Let us discuss briefly the nonadditivity of pair potentials and the effects of solvents.

Dispersion energy is calculated by perturbation theory. The lead term is the second-order term (the usual London–van der Waals energy) which varies as $1/R^6$. There are also second-order terms varying as $1/R^8$, $1/R^{10}$, etc., which are progressively less important. In addition there are small third-order terms which vary as $1/R^9$, $1/R^{10}$, $\cdots$. All the second-order terms are pair-wise additive. It is only the third-order (and higher) terms which lead to three-body forces. Fourth-order terms lead to four-body forces, etc. In order of magnitude, the ratio of the n-body dispersion energy to the $(n - 1)$th is (α/R^3), where α is a polarizability and R is a separation.

Jansen (1964) calculated the magnitude of the deviations from pair-wise additive dispersion energies. In the crystalline noble gases these terms are sufficiently large to make the face-centered cubic lattice energetically favorable as compared to the hexagonal close-packed lattice. However, the three-body energies are quite small. Thus, Ne, A, Kr, Xe satisfy corresponding states equations of state up to 250,000 atm, although their three-body forces are different.

Thus we conclude that the dispersion energy $E_{AB}^{(dispers)}$ between two molecules is essentially unaffected by immersion in a nonpolar solvent.

There is very little evidence at the present time regarding the effect of polar solvents on the dispersion energy. Kestner and Sinanoğlu (1963) and Sinanoğlu et al. (1964) use the same type of calculation as Jansen

(1964) in which they totally disregard the polar nature of the solvents. They obtain reductions in dispersion energy between two polymers in water up to 15–30%. For base-base dispersion energies in water the reduction is only of the order of 5–7%. These calculations are very crude. At the present time we do not even know how to calculate the dispersion energy between molecules in the gas phase to within 10% [see Kingston (1964)].

The effects of solvents on polar molecules are difficult to ascertain. At large separations, the energy of interaction of two polar molecules is reduced by the factor ϵ, the dielectric constant of the solution. However, the more interesting question is, What is the energy of interaction of a single polar molecule with the surrounding solvent?

The simplest treatment is due to Onsager (1936), who regarded the solvent as a continuous medium [see also Bonnor (1951) and Linder (1960)]. He scooped out of the medium a spherical cavity of radius a surrounding the molecule. Here a is regarded as the effective radius of the molecule. The local electric field $\mathcal{E}^{(loc)}$, which acts on the molecule, is the sum of a field C, which would exist in the cavity if our molecule were absent, and a reaction field $\mathbf{G}$, which is produced in the dielectric by virtue of the dipole $\mathbf{\mu}$ of our molecule. On the average, if there is no external field, $C = 0$. Onsager found that

$$\mathbf{G} = g\left[\frac{\mathbf{\mu}}{1 - \alpha g}\right] \tag{24}$$

where α is the polarizability of our molecule and

$$g = \left[\frac{2(\epsilon - 1)}{2\epsilon + 1}\right]a^{-3} \tag{25}$$

The work required to produce the spherical cavity in the dielectric is equal to the energy of interaction of the molecule with the dielectric

$$E^{(\text{solvation})} = -\tfrac{1}{2}\mathbf{\mu}\cdot\mathbf{G} = -\frac{1}{2}\left[\frac{\mu^2 g}{1 - \alpha g}\right] \tag{26}$$

Equation (26) gives good agreement with experiment and can therefore be used on an empirical basis.

Rigorously, however, in Eq. (26) μ^2 should *not* be used as μ^2_{gas}, the square of the molecular dipole moment in the gas. But rather,

$$\mu^2 = \frac{\mu^2_{\text{gas}}}{1 - \alpha g} \tag{27}$$

Substituting Eq. (27) into Eq. (26) gives values for $E^{(\text{solvation})}$ which do *not* agree with experiment. For asymmetric molecules, Wada (1954) generalized the Onsager treatment by scooping out an ellipsoidal cavity. Wada's treatment gives good agreement with experiment.

Onsager is extending his rigorous formalism to consider real dielectric liquids with an arbitrary distribution of solvent molecules surrounding the molecule in question. Also, as stated in Section III, Linder and Jehle are developing a comparatively simple mathematical procedure which (hopefully) should give results equivalent to Onsager's.

The continuous medium model for the solvent is probably satisfactory for hydrophobic molecules. However, hydrophylic molecules are "wetted" by an aqueous solvent. By wetted we really mean that at least part of the molecule is surrounded by rigidly attached water molecules.

Some parts of biologically active molecules are hydrophylic and other parts are hydrophobic. The rigid shell of attached water molecules should be incorporated into any discussion of the molecular properties. Slight changes in pH, temperature, or concentrations can make a profound difference in the attachment of water molecules. For example, the well-known double consulate temperature of nicotinic acid and water solutions has been explained by Eyring as due to a sudden unfreezing of the attached ice layer. Such a change in the nature of solvation is much like a phase transformation. Perhaps such a change in solvation might help to explain the shift from the coiled to the uncoiled structures of DNA, etc. Foam and surface tension studies might reveal a great deal about the nature of the solvation of biologically active molecules. Excellent theoretical work on the hydrophobic stacking of bases and the solvent denaturization of DNA has been done by Sinanoğlu and Abdulnar (1964), but there are many difficult problems which have not yet been solved.

And, lest anyone get the impression that solvation problems are easy, I should mention clathrate compounds such as the hydrocarbon hydrates which result from the energetically easy formation of certain types of cavities in the water [see, for example, McKoy and Sinanoğlu (1963) and Allen (1964)]. The small hydrocarbon (CH_4 or C_2H_6) or gas molecule (O_2, N_2, CO_2, etc.) fills this cavity and is surrounded by a rigid layer of ice. Such clathrate is the very opposite of the continuous medium model of the solvent. From a study of clathrates we learn to appreciate the importance of the detailed molecular geometry of the solvent and its relations to the solute molecules.

ACKNOWLEDGMENT

The author wants to thank Professors Bernard and Alberte Pullman for their encouragement in the preparation and presentation of this paper; also, Debbie Tuan, William J. Meath, and Elizabeth S. Hirschfelder for many valuable suggestions.

REFERENCES

Allen, K. W. (1964). *J. Chem. Phys.* **41**, 840.
Aono, S. (1958). *Progr. Theoret. Phys. (Kyoto)* **20**, 133.
Aono, S. (1959a). *Progr. Theoret. Phys. (Kyoto)* **21**, 217.
Aono, S. (1959b). *Progr. Theoret. Phys. (Kyoto)* **22**, 313.
Bear, R. S., and Eyring, H. (1935). *J. Chem. Phys.* **3**, 98.
Berlin, T. (1951). *J. Chem. Phys.* **19**, 208.
Bethe, H. A., and Salpeter, E. E. (1957). "Quantum Mechanics of One and Two Electron Atoms." Academic Press, New York.
Bonnor, W. B. (1951). *Trans. Faraday Soc.* **47**, 1143.
Brown, W. F., Jr. (1956). *In* "Handbuch der Physik" (S. Flügge, ed.), Vol. 17, p. 1. Springer, Berlin.
Callen, H. B., and Welton, T. A. (1951). *Phys. Rev.* **83**, 34.
Coulson, C. A., and Davies, P. L. (1952). *Trans. Faraday Soc.* **48**, 777.
Debye, P. (1920). *Physik. Z.* **21**, 178.
Dirac, P. A. M. (1929). *Proc. Roy. Soc. (London)* **A123**, 714.
Duncan, A., and Pople, J. (1953). *Trans. Faraday Soc.* **49**, 217.
Ekstein, H., and Polanyi, M. (1932). *Z. Physik. Chem. (Leipzig)* **B15**, 334.
Eyring, H. (1931). *J. Am. Chem. Soc.* **53**, 2537.
Eyring, H. (1932). *J. Am. Chem. Soc.* **54**, 3191.
Eyring, H., and Polanyi, M. (1931). *Z. Physik. Chem. (Leipzig)* **B12**, 279.
Eyring, H., Walter, J., and Kimball, G. E. (1944). "Quantum Chemistry," pp. 214, 240–243. Wiley, New York.
Falkenhagen, H. (1922). *Physik. Z.* **23**, 87.
Feynman, R. P. (1939). *Phys. Rev.* **56**, 340.
Haugh, E. G., and Hirschfelder, J. O. (1955). *J. Chem. Phys.* **23**, 1778.
Hellmann, H. (1937). "Quantenchemie," p. 285. Denicke, Leipzig.
Hirschfelder, J. O. (1941). *J. Chem. Phys.* **9**, 645.
Hirschfelder, J. O., and Eliason, M. A. (1957). *Ann. N.Y. Acad. Sci.* **67**, 451.
Hirschfelder, J. O., Curtiss, C. F., and Bird, R. B. (1964). "Molecular Theory of Gases and Liquids." Wiley, New York.
Jansen, L. (1964). "Stability of Crystals of Rare Gas Atoms in Terms of Three-Body Interactions," Battelle Memorial Institute, International Division, Geneva.
Jehle, H., Yos, J. M., and Bade, W. L. (1958). *Phys. Rev.* **110**, 793.
Jehle, H., Parke, W. C., and Salyers, A. (1964). *In* "Electronic Aspects of Biochemistry" (B. Pullman, ed.), p. 313. Academic Press, New York.
Kestner, N. R., and Sinanoğlu, O. (1963). *J. Chem. Phys.* **38**, 1730.
Kimball, G. E., and Eyring, H. (1932). *J. Am. Chem. Soc.* **54**, 3876.
Kingston, A. E. (1964). *Phys. Rev.* **135**, A1018.
Landau, L. D., and Lifshitz, E. M. (1958). "Statistical Physics," Chap. XII. Pergamon Press, New York.
Landau, L. D., and Lifshitz, E. M. (1960). "Electrodynamics of Continuous Media," Chap. IX. Pergamon Press, New York.
Linder, B. (1960). *J. Chem. Phys.* **33**, 668.
Linder, B. (1962). *J. Chem. Phys.* **37**, 963.
Linder, B., and Hoernschmeyer, D. (1964). *J. Chem. Phys.* **40**, 622.
London, F. (1942). *J. Chem. Phys.* **46**, 305.
McKoy, V., and Sinanoğlu, O. (1963). *J. Chem. Phys.* **38**, 2946.

Mavroyannis, C., and Stephen, M. J. (1962). *Mol. Phys.* **5,** 629.

Meath, W. J. (1965). University of Wisconsin Theoretical Chemistry Institute Report WIS-TCI-89, Madison, Wisconsin.

Onsager, L. (1936). *J. Am. Chem. Soc.* **58,** 1486.

Pauling, L. (1933). *J. Chem. Phys.* **1,** 280.

Pullman, B., and Pullman, A. (1963). "Quantum Biochemistry." Wiley, New York.

Serber, R. (1934). *Phys. Rev.* **45,** 461.

Sinanoğlu, O., and Abdulnar, S. (1964). *Symp. Molecular Mechanisms Photobiology, Wakulla Springs, Florida.*

Sinanoğlu, O., Abdulnar, S., and Kestner, N. R. (1964). *In* "Electronic Aspects of Biochemistry" (B. Pullman, ed.), p. 30. Academic Press, New York.

Stephen, M. J. (1964a). Private communication.

Stephen, M. J. (1964b). *J. Chem. Phys.* **40,** 699.

Sternlicht, H. (1964). *J. Chem. Phys.* **40,** 1175.

Tomonaga, S. (1950). *Progr. Theoret. Phys.* (*Kyoto*) **5,** 544.

Tomonaga, S. (1955). *Progr. Theoret. Phys.* (*Kyoto*) **13,** 467.

Vanderslice, J. T., and Mason, E. A. (1960). *Rev. Mod. Phys.* **32,** 417.

Van Vleck, J. H. (1934). *Phys. Rev.* **45,** 405.

Van Vleck, J. H., and Sherman, A. (1935). *Rev. Mod. Phys.* **7,** 167.

Wada, A. (1954). *J. Chem. Phys.* **22,** 198.

Yos, J. M. (1958). *Phys. Rev.* **110,** 800.

Yos, J. M., Bade, W. L., and Jehle, H. (1947). *Proc. Natl. Acad. Sci. U.S.* **43,** 341.

Zener, C. (1931). *Phys. Rev.* **37,** 556.

Compact Single-Strand Nucleic Acids[1]

HERBERT JEHLE, MICHAEL L. INGERMAN,
AND CARLA G. MESSINA

Physics Department,
The George Washington University,
Washington, D.C.

I. Double- and Single-Strand Nucleic Acids

In the Watson–Crick double-strand helix, the single-strand nucleic acids are paired through hydrogen bonding of complementary bases. This form may be crystallized under appropriate conditions, and X-ray analysis is possible. Consequently, paired nucleic acid structures are well established. Other nucleic acid structures do not readily lend themselves to crystallization. Careful use, however, of space-filling molecule models indicates that there exist only few reasonably possible structures. We would like to report on several such structures here.

Under appropriate ionic conditions of the surrounding medium, single-strand nucleic acids may occur as compact stable configurations on their own. It might also be possible that single-strand forms of nucleic acids may be associated with a protein or several protein chains. This association might, for example, occur through hydrogen bonds between the nucleic acid bases and the protein backbone, or there might be an association of the basic protein side chains with negative phosphates of the nucleic acid

[1] Research supported by the George Washington University Committee on Research, the Research Corporation, and USPHS grant No. CA 04989.

343

chain lying alongside the protein chain. (Or, there might be association of a protein chain with a double-strand Watson–Crick helix—but this is outside the scope of the present note.) In the following paragraphs we shall discuss several of the RNA structures we have built.

II. Single-Strand Nucleic Acid Structures

The ionic constitution of the medium may cause the nucleic acid to open into a random coil configuration, possibly with the bases stretching out alternately from the nucleic acid backbone like the oars of a racing boat. Not much needs to be said about such an arrangement except that the longest monomer spacing, considering a straight section of the coil, is 7.8 Å. The shortest possible monomer spacing of $6.8/2 = 3.4$ Å occurs in the structures in Figs. 1 to 4 to be discussed below. There are many intermediary structures between these two extremes. This note is concerned with compact arrangements of single-strand nucleic acids. Several factors contribute to the stability of structures in this form.

Structure Stabilization

First, we may note the effect of the medium. Small positive ions, in particular magnesium, and basic side chains of proteins or other molecules compensate for the negative charges concentrated on the phosphates of the nucleic acid backbone [cf. Fig. 1(b)]. This compensation makes it possible for the structure to exist in this compact form. Changes in ionic constitution may cause a reversible transition between the compact structure and the loose random coil form of the nucleic acids.

A second factor for stabilization is the general London–van der Waals attraction between all atoms resulting in a preference for structures having no internal cavities. Cavities cause instability, as they cannot be filled because of their smallness or inaccessibility; but pocket or groove-like openings do not cause serious instability should medium molecules and/or water be able to enter.

A third factor is the internal ionic character of the nucleic acid strand. This implies a consideration of all internal hydrogen-bonding possibilities; in this respect RNA and DNA differ substantially. The $C_2'OH$ group on each ribose may hydrogen bond with a base on the same RNA. Such bonding might create considerable stability in single RNA strands. In the present investigation we shall direct our attention to compact single-strand RNA structures.

III. Space-Filling Models

Space-filling models are extremely useful when experimenting with compact structure possibilities. In this investigation we were privileged in

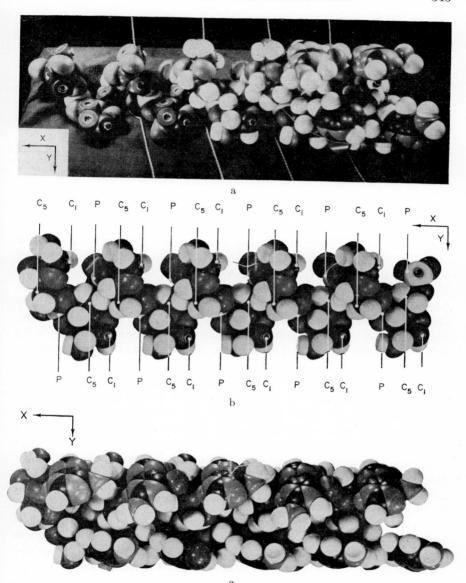

FIG. 1(a)–(c). Single-strand, almost-straight zigzag-shaped RNA (ten monomers per 34 Å). (a) shows, from right to left, four complete monomers, then two monomers with bases off, two with hydrogens off, and the last two monomers with oxygens off, except those on the main chain. The structure receives much stability by virtue of its compactness and through H bonding between the $C_2'OH$ of every ribose and the second next base with which it is in contact. (b) shows only the pentose-phosphate backbone; (c) shows the bases in place.

having access to a set of Pauling–Corey–Marsh molecular models. Their rubberlike elasticity, the friction between their atomic units, and the accurate maintenance of bond angles and distances make them an excellent tool for trying out different structure possibilities. (In the figures, C is black, O is dark gray, N is a lighter gray, and H and P appear as white.) One has, however, to be aware of the fact that there are still hindrances of considerable importance which are not displayed by these molecule model structures.

IV. Prototype Single-Strand RNA Model

Figure 1(b) shows a single-strand RNA 10-monomer segment with bases removed, exposing the "backbone" phosphate-ribose chain. The 10 phosphorus atoms are all almost completely hidden, only small white crescent-shaped parts are visible. The 10 stud attachments (for base groups) at the riboses C_1' are clearly visible. Also clearly visible are the 10 cup-shaped hydrogen donors $C_2'OH$ on the riboses. Figure 1(c) shows the same as Fig. 1(b), with the bases in place. In a compact structure, the backbone has a zigzag shape, so that two consecutive monomers (i.e., a dimer) form the basic repeat unit of the molecule backbone. This structure has five pyrimidines (a random sequence of uracils and cytosines) on the positive y side and five purines (a random sequence of adenines and guanines) on the negative y side, so that the purines and pyrimidines alternate. This choice was made to get as simple a prototype structure as possible. The result was roughly a straight structure in which two monomers of the backbone were considered the repeat unit. (If all the purines were exchanged with pyrimidines, and vice versa, a similar structure could be made only if the pyrimidines were to lie away from the backbone, in contrast to the present compact structure. If a random base sequence were chosen, a modified structure of the kind of Fig. 4 would result.)

In this structure internal hydrogen bonding exists between every base and the adjacent hydrogen donor of the ribose $C_2'OH$ (see Fig. 1). Figure 1(c) shows these hydrogen donors bridging over to the purines. A gap of considerably less than half an Angstrom is visible between hydrogen donor and acceptor, a nitrogen on the purines, but *no* such gap occurs on the pyrimidine side, where an oxygen acts as the hydrogen acceptor.

Another internal hydrogen bond may occasionally occur; a hydrogen from the NH_2 side group of an adenine, if on one side of the chain, may connect with the oxygen in the five-membered ring of the same ribose which furnishes the $C_2'OH$ hydrogen bonding to that same adenine. In this case the NH_2 consequently could not be coplanar with the plane of the adenine.

The structure in Fig. 1(d), and the side view, Fig. 1(e), are related to each other as a top view and a side view would be in engineering drawing practice. The x axes in the two figures are parallel to each other; xyz is a right-hand coordinate system. The same structure is represented in Fig. 1(e)–(g) by drawing only two monomers. Their covalent connections with the adjacent parts of the RNA are indicated by dashed lines; their hydrogen-bonding attachments by dotted lines [cf. also Fig. 1(d)]. The space-filling molecule model actually lies on a surface which is coincident with the xy plane.

The xy positions of specific points on the atom surfaces were obtained by using photographs like Fig. 1(b) and (c) and correcting for parallax. The z components of these points were obtained with a vertical vernier calliper measured from the xy plane level surface. We obtained the locations of the atomic nuclei by three-dimensional graphic methods. Our calculations were based on manufacturing blueprints of the Pauling–Corey–Marsh models.

Some of the subsequent structures involve some bond angle and bond distance deformations. In Fig. 1(a) we tried to build as straight and compact a structure as possible, with virtually no bond angle deformations. Since there are many freely rotating single bonds along the molecule backbone, we found no difficulty in constructing a practically straight model. As noted above, there are, however, gaps of less than half an Angstrom in the $C_2'OH$-purine hydrogen bonding. The dimer repeat distance is 6.8 Å. Different collaborators, working independently, have built this model more than ten times.

Closed-Up Straight Single-Strand RNA Model

We then closed the less-than-half-Angstrom hydrogen-bond gap on the purine side by joining the model together with threads. This produced some bond angle deformations, of the order of one-tenth radian, (i.e., 6°), presumably not larger than the deformations which occur normally. Figure 2 shows that such a structure may still be essentially straight. On the bottom right is a side view showing that the hydrogen bonds are now closed. There is almost no visible difference between the structures in Fig. 2 and Fig. 1(a); the dimer repeat distance 6.8 Å is the same in both cases. In Fig. 2 we are looking along the x axis, whereas in Fig. 1(g) we were looking along the $-x$ direction.

Twisted Single-Strand Structure

A twist is naturally introduced (Fig. 3) when the hydrogen bond gaps on the purine side are closed (see Fig. 1), while permitting no bond angle

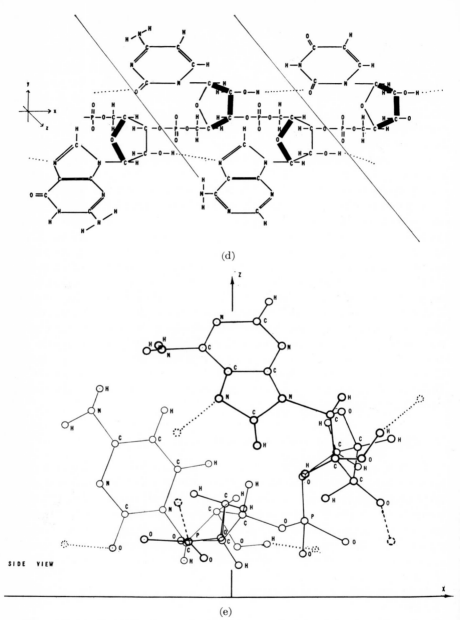

(d)

(e)

SIDE VIEW

Fig. 1(d)–(g). The three line projection drawings of the structure, (e) side view, (f) along $-z$ axis, (g) along $-x$ axis, are hypothetical on the basis of work with the space-filling models, not from X-ray data, and are given only to facilitate the understanding of the structure proposal of Fig. 1(a). The three line projection drawings represent the two monomers between the two fine lines of (d). The two last monomers on the base end of Fig. 1(a) correspond to the two monomers between these two fine lines. There is no correspondence between the ends of (d) and the ends of Fig. 1(a); the bright wires in Fig. 1(a) correspond to the fine lines in (d).

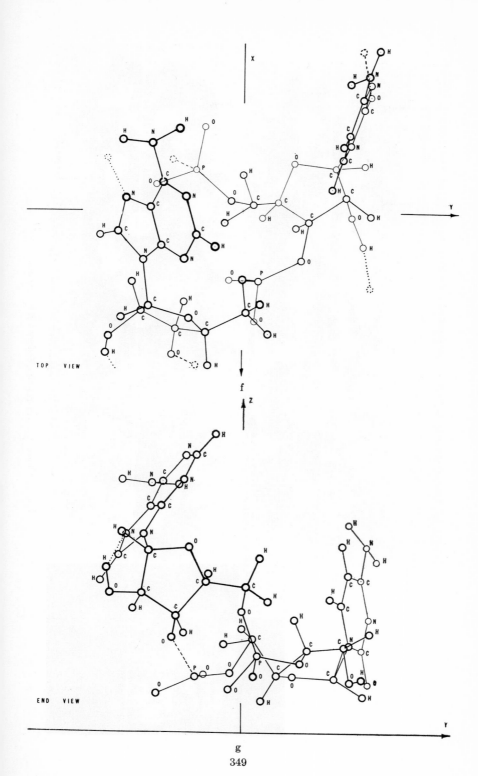

X

Y

TOP VIEW

f

Z

END VIEW

Y

g
349

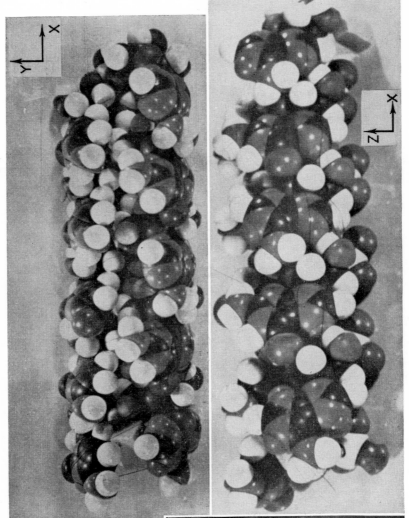

Fig. 2. Closed-up straight single-strand RNA model.

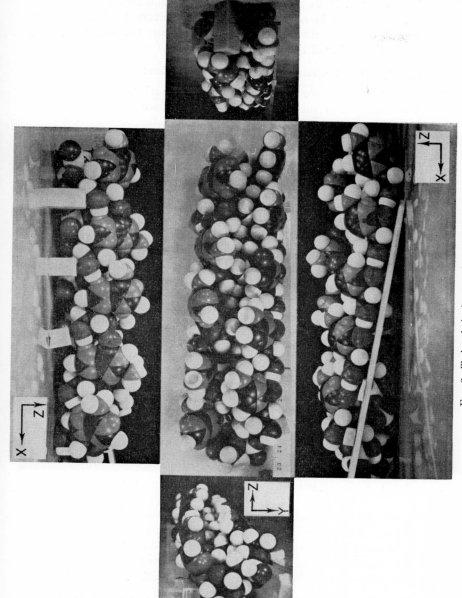

Fig. 3. Twisted single-strand structure.

distortions to occur. This closed distortion-free modification of the structure in Fig. 1(a) resulted in a right-hand-screw structure having the same dimer repeat distance, 6.8 Å. The end views show the bases regularly arranged on either side of the groove.

Naturally Mixed Sequence of Purines and Pyrimidines

In the next structure we shifted the balance of purines and pyrimidines. Instead of alternating purines and pyrimidines, we considered a base

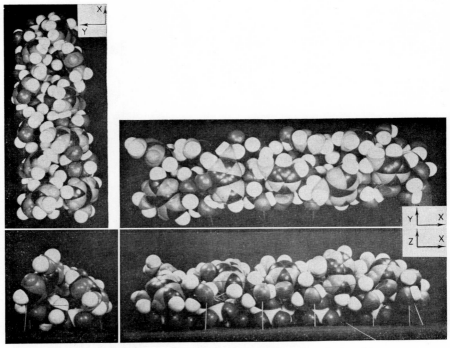

Fig. 4. A base sequence arrived at through a random choice of bases.

sequence arrived at through a random choice of bases (Fig. 4). (This base sequence may structurally resemble a naturally occuring nucleic acid.) In such a random mixture of bases, subsequent dimers do not repeat regularly, nor do their backbone structures. A structure similar to Fig. 4 occurs, with an average monomer spacing of 3.4 Å along the midline.

Possible Attachments of Single Strand Nucleic Acids to Other Molecules

The study of single-strand nucleic acid structures is relevant when attachments between such nucleic acids and other molecules are to be considered, in particular, monomer to monomer attachments. To that effect the monomer or dimer repeat distances of the two molecules should match, and structural and charge complementarity should make such an attachment favorable.

One cannot speculate about such attachments except in relation to a particular situation for which further information is available. Suffice it to remark that a monomer repeat distance of 3.4 Å (i.e., dimer repeat 6.8 Å) in nucleic acids is one of the important factors involved. If an extended protein chain has a structural arrangement of its side chains similar to that of the above described nucleic acid, its dimer repeat distance is 6.8 Å also.

V. Variations of This Structure

It was possible to build structures having a groove between the two rows of five bases on one side and five bases on the other side.

We considered *zigzag single-strand structures* with bases sticking out openly like the pistons of a V-shaped gasoline engine (Fig. 5). We asked ourselves whether such an arrangement might be possible in which there is space between the bases so that another small molecule, like a nucleotide base or an amino acid, might fit in each such space. This structure proposal might achieve such a requirement; its stability can, however, only be understood if it is mounted onto another molecule.

The dimer repeat distance of this straight structure is 8 Å (which is about 1.2 Å longer than the dimer repeat distance of a protein chain whose amino acids are arranged in a similar V-shaped pattern).

Single-Strand RNA with Bases Alternately Sticking out in Opposite Directions

This structure's backbone axis (Fig. 6) is an axis of symmetry, the element of symmetry being a 180° rotation around the axis plus a translation by the monomer repeat distance 3.45 Å, if measured along this axis. It is interesting to note that the bases may be attached in two different ways, one of them implying a firmly locked-in position, the other still permitting considerable rotation around the bond which attaches to the base.

This 180° screw symmetry is, in a crude approximation, even established in the backbone structures of the above models [cf. Fig. 1(b)].

Simple Linear Structures Whose Symmetry Element Is a Translation

Our picture (Fig. 7) shows the backbone in a fairly tight form, with a monomer repeat distance of 6.2 Å, in side view. The end view adjacent to it shows the same backbone with the bases attached like a set of fallen dominoes (or somewhat like shingles).

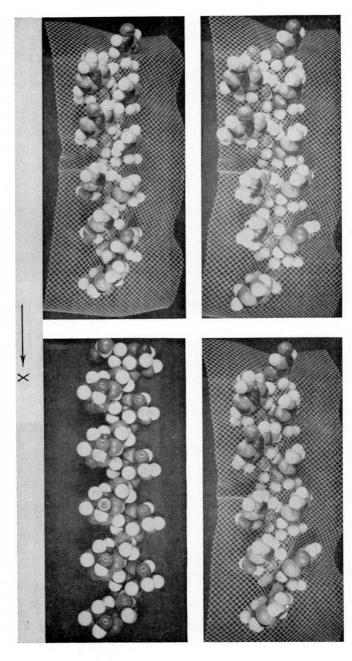

FIG. 5. Zigzag single-strand structures with bases sticking out openly like the pistons of a V-shaped gasoline engine.

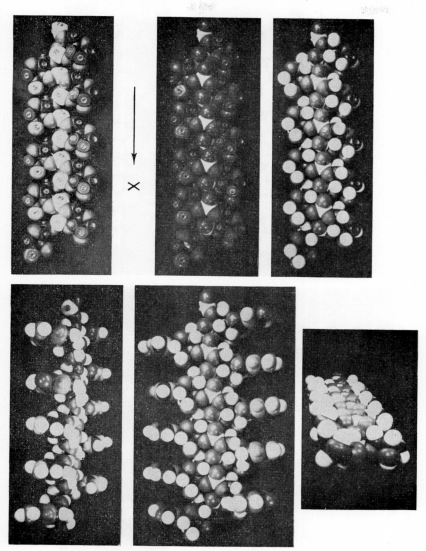

FIG. 6. Single-strand RNA with bases alternately sticking out in opposite directions.

JEHLE, INGERMAN, AND MESSINA

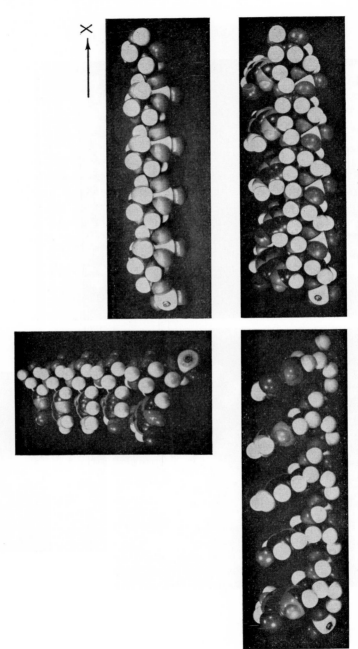

FIG. 7. Simple linear structures whose symmetry element is a translation.

The other two side views with attached bases refer to a 6.8-Å monomer repeat distance RNA backbone to which the bases are attached like a set of fallen dominoes in one picture and more or less perpendicular to the backbone axis in the other picture.

Finally, in what might be called structure type 8 which we have not reproduced, there is the arrangement of a single-strand nucleic acid in the form of *one-half of a Watson–Crick–Wilkins helix*.

VI. Supplementary Remarks

The question naturally arises as to whether the structure of the types represented in Figs. 1–5 may, via a single-strand random coil form, go over into one of the two halves of a Watson–Crick helix. That question is entirely dependent on the possibility of rotating the bases around the bond which attaches them to their C_1' on the sugar without getting into the problem of insurmountable potential barriers. In the random coil configuration there is, as far as the molecule models can give reliable enough indication, a possibility of turning the bases around 360°, under normal thermal excitation. This would mean that the transition from a Watson–Crick nucleic acid to any of the single-strand structures discussed here is possible, if there are no potential barriers beyond the ones built into the space-filling molecule structure models which have been built on the basis of fairly symmetrical van der Waals radii.

Disregarding hydration and disregarding attachment of metal or other ions to the nucleic acid molecule, we determined the crude value for the density of a compact structure of the type of Fig. 4. A five-dimer chain with two guanine, one uracil, three adenine, and four cytosine bases is attached to the backbone in random order. We measured the volume which the model displaced in water with a thin plastic bag surrounding it. The bag's contact with the model was adjusted to simulate the level to which actual hydration molecules would penetrate. The measurements resulted in values for the density close to 2.5 gm/cm³, much higher than the experimental values for naturally occuring hydrated nucleic acids.

ACKNOWLEDGMENTS

We should like to express our appreciation for generous support from the George Washington University Committee on Research and the National Cancer Institute (NIH research grant CA 04989). We are deeply indebted to Mr. Raymond M. Shirven and Mr. William C. Parke for discussions and suggestions.

REFERENCES

Jehle, H. (1959). *Proc. Natl. Acad. Sci. U.S.* **45**, 1360.
Jehle, H., Ingerman, M. L., Shirven, R. M., Parke, W. C., and Salyers, A. A. (1963). *Proc. Natl. Acad. Sci. U.S.* **50**, 738.

Replication of Double-Strand Nucleic Acids

HERBERT JEHLE

Physics Department,
The George Washington University,
Washington, D.C.

I. Introduction

In this note we shall report on a nucleic acid replication scheme (Jehle *et al.*, 1963) based on double-strand nucleic acids providing the immediate source of information for replication. On the one hand, early in 1962, the beautiful work of Swartz *et al.* (1962) brought evidence in favor of single-strand nucleic acids being involved in priming *in vitro* nucleic acid synthesis. On the other hand, evidence was emerging to the effect that the actual biosynthesis of nucleic acids *in vivo* seems to proceed through a replicative stage double-strand nucleic acid—in accord with our 1963 proposal.

The conventional explication of replication of double-strand nucleic acids does not have a very good structural basis. The chemical, kinematic, and dynamic performances which it postulates invoke the following comments:

1. At the Y juncture, accurate synthesis is said to be due to highly selective H-bond complementarity of a parental base with only the correct filial one. Let us consider the status of H bonding at the time and region at which the strands open up. In this instance, the ionic conditions in the immediate surroundings of the Y juncture are such that there is indeed not much difference energetically between either complementary base-pair H bonding or H bonding of bases with the surrounding water or other bases, or some other molecules. It is thus difficult to understand why at that moment a newly opened-up parental base should reach, without fail, for its complementary filial bases.

2. Structural arrangements have been considered for the purpose of helping to bring the appropriate complementary bases into the right positions. The opening-up of the Watson–Crick helix results in strands with many single bonds along the phosphate-sugar chains which do not have

a well-defined structure by themselves, but lack structural stability where it is needed most, i.e., at the Y juncture, where it is supposed to select its complementary nucleotides. Enzymes have therefore been suggested to perform tasks like those of components of a textile machine, i.e., to hold the nucleic acid strands and to guide and even to twist them until the correct filial bases are in place. It is our contention that one should not postulate enzymes to work according to schemes resembling mechanical guidance devices borrowed from engineering, but should rather look for enzymatic mechanisms based on solid structural principles.

II. Accurate Selection of Filial Nucleotides

The principal requirement for understanding nucleic acid replication is that it should account for the extremely high accuracy of replication implied by the faithful preservation of genetic information of nucleic acids. Foremost, an accurately preserved structure of the informational macromolecule, i.e., of the nucleic acid, throughout the replication process seems to be imperative. The naked Watson–Crick helix might be such a one but not while it is being opened up.

The evidence is strong that the findings of semiconservative replication given by Meselson and Stahl's (1958) experiment are to be interpreted in the way that the two complementary strands of one Watson–Crick helix, (rather than two Watson–Crick double-strand helices lying side by side) form the two units of the semiconservatively replicating duplex. Accordingly, replication should imply the opening-up of the double-strand Watson–Crick helix, as is indeed commonly proposed. The desired structural stability during such a semiconservative replication process is most naturally achieved if one postulates that the grooves of the double-strand nucleic acid helix are snugly filled with molecules which fit not only in a structurally but also in a charge-complementary fashion into the grooves of the helix. Presumably these molecules might be proteins, particularly polymerases. In consideration of Wilkins' (1956) work which indicated attachment of basic histones to the grooves (and sometimes folded into them), such a reinforced nucleoprotein helix might be called a Watson–Crick–Wilkins helix. In the case of the polymerases, attachment might be conditional to the presence of cations.

In short, instead of postulating an artificial, machine-tool-like enzyme to perform functions quite alien to what a molecule might do, we consider instead the performance of some polymerase enzymes in assuming that they work essentially by way of being laid along and tightly attached to the grooves of the nucleic acid which is about to replicate. In the form they assume, the polymerases might be specific to the structural and charge distribution on the nucleic acid grooves to which they attach; in some instances there might be much more specificity required than in others. Polymerases might move from one section of the nucleic acid helix to another, going off and on at least at times when and where no replication occurs.

Similarly, in the transcription process of DNA to RNA (i.e., in switching on a particular section of DNA for RNA production), a particular polymerase, which is specific to the section of the information-giving double-strand nucleic acid, might give the signal which makes transcription possible for that section of the genetic message. On the other hand, inhibition may arise through blocking mechanisms which might be much less specific.

We proposed previously that the replication process may proceed as indicated in Figs. 1 and 2. It is interesting to note that three important types of mechanism providing for biological specificity are involved.

First in action is the specificity which favors identical association of individual molecules as nearest neighbors. These London-type charge fluctuation forces tend to give preference to an identical filial nucleotide to be near the parental one (P_{SG} in Fig. 2); Brownian motion shuffles all kinds of filial nucleotides around the surrounding medium. This selective effect is not very strong, but it may help substantially toward a quick selection of the appropriate filial base.

The second step involves the specificity of a lock-and-key type which may permit, because of structural and charge complementarity (Pauling, 1957), only the exact replica of the recently evicted (pried-out) parental base to fit into the cavity. The cavity is formed by the complementary nucleic acid strand together with the two groove-filling protein strands. The condition implied by a tight fit of a filial nucleotide into the cavity is very demanding; charge and structural complementarity may permit only the proper replica base to come in and replace the parental one. The maintenance of a well-defined structure during the process of replication would thus be understood as providing the key for the understanding of the accuracy of the replication process. The enzyme, in *this* instance, would function by virtue of the accurate structural and charge compatibility with the nucleic acid structure.

Third, presumably some time after nucleotide replacement has taken place, normal ionic conditions may be restored. Under such circumstances the H bonds between the complementary bases become important and strongly selective (Watson–Crick complementarity), so that any wrong base would now, again, be discriminated against, because it would prevent the formation of an orderly helical structure. Watson–Crick complementarity is an excellent necessary condition to be satisfied for obtaining a smooth stable structure of a double-strand helix; this H-bond comple-

Sections 5 ---- 5 and 8 — 8

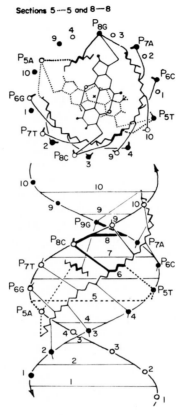

Fig. 1. Side view (lower diagram) and cross section 5–5 and 8–8 through lower diagram (upper diagram) of a Watson–Crick–Wilkins helix, using the Wilkins–Langridge B structure of DNA. The location of the phosphates is indicated by large dots along one helical chain and small circles along the other. The fifth through eighth base layers have their phosphates marked P and a letter referring to its attached base. Those layers are principally involved in the stage of replication shown in the following figure. The pentoses are not specially marked. The two grooves of the nucleic acid are supposed to be filled with two protein chains, whose backbones are indicated by zigzag lines, with the side chains drawn as lines reaching from the protein backbone to the phosphates. In the case of polymerases, the mediation to the phosphate groups and perhaps others is brought about through small cations. For easier legibility, the protein in the wider groove is indicated by a short zigzag line with only the two side chains reaching to the phosphates P_{5A} and P_{8G}. The narrow groove protein has two corresponding side chains reaching to the P_{5T} and P_{8C}. This makes the subunit 5, 6, 7, 8 very stable and compact; a similar statement holds for 6, 7, 8, 9; etc. The top picture shows a cross section of the intact Watson–Crick–Wilkins helix with base-pair layer 5 dotted lines and 8 heavy solid lines (From Jehle et al., 1963); Figs. 1 and 2 reprinted by permission of Proc. Nat. Acad. Sci. U. S.)

but loosening-up the "filial" hybrid DNA-RNA section of the WCW helix. When the process has proceeded so far that the filial end of the hybrid double-strand helix has either been kinked or has temporarily formed some knot or been accidentally attached to something, this loosening-up may actually give rise to some strand separation at the filial end of the structure.

The formerly peeled-off single-strand DNA coil may then readily start base pairing with its complementary DNA on the filial end of the helix, whereas the recently formed RNA, whose separation from the complementary DNA has been initiated by the untwining, may terminate as a single-strand coil (see Fig. 3). The fact that under the circumstances of the first process (Fig. 2) the ribonucleotide triphosphates may successfully compete with the peeling off DNA strand for incorporation into the WCW helix and the fact that, later, under the new circumstances, this same DNA strand successfully competes with the RNA strand for recombination with the complementary DNA strand, would have to be clarified on chemical and energetic principles, but there seems to be no obvious objection to such a mechanism.

The process has to be understood, from there on, as presenting about the same structural picture as in Fig. 3, throughout its entire duration. The material moves, as if sliding, along the channels indicated by the wire model, the RNA growing while the DNA slides in the forward direction in the helical motion indicated by the wires.

IV. Replication of Double-Strand DNA

The replication of a double strand helix should satisfy the Meselson–Stahl experiment. Also, pulse-labeling experiments of Cairns (1963) and of Hanawalt and Ray (1964) have indicated that the two filial chains grow in the same direction, i.e., in opposite polarity, one in the 3–5, the other in the 5–3 direction.

Without attempting to explain these experimentally established facts, we assume that the start of replication of the circular *E. coli* double-strand DNA (whose replicative performance is so accurately known because of Meselson and Stahl) occurs at one locus of the circular DNA, on *both* strands, and that the process continues in one direction. Initially at least, the process described in Figs. 1 and 2 may go with different speeds for the two nucleic acid strands, because the 3–5 and the 5–3 attachments of new nucleotides are expected to present slightly different issues; the process may go at varying rates for the different polarities.

Starting with a parental-parental double-strand DNA-WCW helix section, the section between the two peel-off loci is parental-filial, and the section beyond both peeled-off parental single-strand DNA strands is a

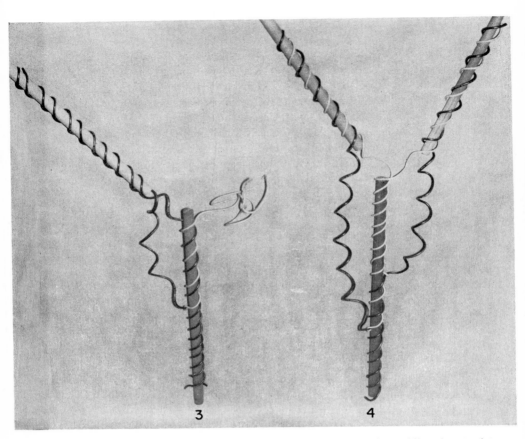

Fig. 3. Ribonucleic acid formation with double-strand DNA providing the template. The difference from Fig. 4 is that, in this instance, only one of the parental nucleic acid strands gets peeled off and replaced by filial ribonucleic acids. These form, together with the other parental strand, a double-strand helix reinforced by proteins, i.e., polymerases. The torque exerted at the synthesis site will tend to unwind the hybrid side of the parental stem and occasionally causes uncoiling which gives a chance to the formerly peeled-off DNA strand to be combined again with its complementary DNA strand. The whole motion is a flow channeled along the helical wires which represent the backbones. The picture at any later time has the same look.

Fig. 4. The process of Figs. 1 and 2 is repeated on both nucleic acid strands of a Watson–Crick–Wilkins helix. Both strands peel off from the stem region of the Y-shaped helix, while filial nucleotides are incorporated as replacement. As far as the stem of the Y-shaped structure reaches, the Watson–Crick helix remains structurally intact as it is reinforced by polymerases in its grooves (not shown in picture). The torque of the peel-off process of these strands causes untwining of the filial section of the helix and formation of two semiconservative helixes. (Wherever the double-strand DNA helixes are intact this is indicated in the model by the wooden rods.) The essential difference of this proposal from the conventional one is that the synthesis region is relegated to the stem (rather than to the Y juncture) of the Y, where a well-defined Watson–Crick–Wilkins helix can assure correct replica formation, according to the scheme of Figs. 1 and 2.

366

filial-filial WCW helix, compact, with both grooves tightly occupied by proteins (presumably polymerases).

The peeling strands might each move easily around the helix without causing topological unwinding problems until they grow to a size which presents so much frictional drag against motion that, instead of the coils, the WCW helix would have to spin around its own axis with a right-hand-screw helical motion driven by the peel-off forces, energy and entropy contributions.

The torque exerted by the peel-offs may, as in the situation described in Fig. 3 (also here, cf. Fig. 4), cause untwining and eventual breakage of the H bonds between the two filial nucleic acid strands. Without giving adequate reason for it, we are assuming that each of these filial nucleic acid strands carries one of the protein strands along with it.

Such a filial nucleoprotein strand may have a good chance of base pairing (in the Watson–Crick fashion) with one of the single-strand nucleic acids (the complementary one) which were previously peeled off from the WCW helix. This may equally well happen for both the filial nucleoproteins which, through untwining, have become separated. Each one would pair up with its complementary parental single-strand DNA (formerly somewhat coiled). The specific attachment of a protein strand to each one of the filial nucleic acid strands might make the Watson–Crick base pairing to the parental peel-offs more advantageous than would be the other possibility—pairing of the two peeled-off parental naked nucleic acid strands with each other. The Watson–Crick pairing would therefore result in the formation of two semiconservative helices forming the arms of the Y. They would each have only one protein strand attached, presumably in one of the grooves.

The specific attachment of a polymerase strand to a single-strand nucleic acid is assumed to enhance the base pairing to a complementary nucleic acid strand, and this same kind of a circumstance may also cause the helices of the arms of the Y to be energetically less advantageous than the exceedingly stable filial-filial WCW helix of the stem, which has *two* protein strands. One may thus understand why the untwining process does not continue all the way backwards toward the peel-off synthesis regions—this would be undesirable indeed.

The complete coiling of the F_1 nucleic acid strands into faultless double-strand helices still needs more detailed attention. Additional study of the occurrence and the repair of eventual breaks in strands and recombinations and crossing over is suggested.

The entire process is proposed to continue, as indicated before, through a sliding type of helical motion (usually called speedometer-cable motion). The picture presented would always look the same as that of Fig. 4, with a forward growth along the channels indicated by the wire models.

The result would then be two complementary semiconservative WC helices, and all further phenomena as regards F_2 in Meselson–Stahl's experiment and as regards Cairn's autoradiographs, would be explained in the conventional way.

On the surface this scheme looks similar to the conventional scheme. The essential difference is the relegation of the synthesis region to the stem (rather than to the Y juncture), where a well-defined WCW helix can assure correct replica formation according to the scheme of Figs. 1 and 2.

ACKNOWLEDGMENTS

I am deeply indebted to many colleagues for suggestions and discussions, and in particular here at George Washington University, to Mr. M. L. Ingerman.

We would like to acknowledge generous support from the George Washington University Committee on Research, and from the National Cancer Institute (NIH research grant CA 04989 BBC).

REFERENCES

Beer, M., and Thomas, C. A., Jr. (1961). *J. Mol. Biol.* **3**, 699.
Cairns, J. (1963). *J. Mol. Biol.* **6**, 208; *Cold Spring Harbor Symp. Quant. Biol.* **28**, 43.
Chamberlain, M., and Berg, P. (1964). *J. Mol. Biol.* **8**, 708.
Freese, E. B., and Freese, E. (1963). *Biochemistry* **2**, 707.
Geiduschek, E. P. (1961). *Proc. Natl. Acad. Sci. U.S.* **47**, 950.
Hanawalt, P. C., and Ray, D. S. (1964). *Proc. Natl. Acad. Sci. U.S.* **52**, 125.
Hotchkiss, R. D. (1962). Dyer lecture.
Jehle, H., Ingerman, M. L., Shirven, R. M., Parke, W. C., and Salyers, A. A. (1963). *Proc. Natl. Acad. Sci. U.S.* **50**, 738.
Kesinski, A. W., Kesinski, P. B., and Shannon, P. (1963). *Proc. Natl. Acad. Sci. U.S.* **50**, 746.
Lipsett, M. N., Heppel, L. A., and Bradley, D. F. (1961). *J. Biol. Chem.* **193**, 265.
Meselson, M. (1964). *J. Mol. Biol.* **9**, 734.
Meselson, M., and Stahl, F. W. (1958). *Proc. Natl. Acad. Sci. U.S.* **44**, 671.
Meselson, M., and Weigle, J. J. (1961). *Proc. Natl. Acad. Sci. U.S.* **47**, 857.
Pauling, L. (1957). *Festschr. Arthur Stoll* p. 597.
Pettijohn, D. E., and Hanawalt, P. C. (1963). *Biochim. Biophys. Acta* **72**, 129.
Pettijohn, D. E., and Hanawalt, P. C. (1964). *J. Mol. Biol.* **8**, 170.
Reich, E. (1964). *Science* **143**, 684.
Rosenberg, B. H., and Cavalieri, L. F. (1963). *Progr. Nucleic Acid Res.* **2**, 2.
Rosenberg, B. H., and Cavalieri, L. F. (1964). *Proc. Natl. Acad. Sci. U.S.* **51**, 826.
Schildkraut, C. L., Marmur, J., Fresco, J. R., and Doty, P. (1961). *J. Biol. Chem.* **236**, PC3.
Swartz, M. M., Trautner, T. A., and Kornberg, A. (1962). *J. Biol. Chem.* **237**, 1961.
Taylor, J. H. (ed.) (1963). *In* "Molecular Genetics," p. 65. Academic Press, New York.
Thomas, C. A., Jr., and MacHattie, L. A. (1964). *Proc. Natl. Acad. Sci. U.S.* **52**, 1297.
Vinegrad, J., Morris, J., Davidson, N., and Dove, W. F., Jr. (1963). *Proc. Natl. Acad. Sci. U.S.* **49**, 12.
Wake, R. G., and Baldwin, R. L. (1962). *J. Mol. Biol.* **5**, 201.
Wilkins, M. H. F. (1956). *Cold Spring Harbor Symp. Quant. Biol.* **21**, 75.

The Binding of Small Molecules to Proteins

GREGORIO WEBER

Division of Biochemistry,
Department of Chemistry and Chemical Engineering,
University of Illinois, Urbana, Illinois

I. Introduction

The interaction of small molecules with proteins has been the subject of extensive research, both theoretical and experimental.[1] Interest in this subject has followed the recognition that the physicochemical basis of biological specificity ought to be exhibited in its utmost simplicity in the interaction of proteins and small ligands. I do not intend to deal here either with the forces responsible for such interactions or with their ultimately expected relation to biological specificity: Before each of these two complex tasks is contemplated in any particular case, one ought to attempt to describe as completely and succinctly as possible the system in question. In this task, we should seek to avoid presuppositions as to the simplicity or multiplicity of the process, as to the homogeneous or heterogeneous character of the population involved, or as to the number of the parameters

[1] General reviews on this subject are given by Klotz (1953), Tanford (1961), and Edsall and Wyman (1958).

required for its description. This may be achieved by introducing a "probability of binding" as the immediate result of the experiments, and by applying to this probability of binding some of the ideas current in information theory.

It is customary to treat the protein molecule as a binding agent to which a definite set of dissociation constants, equal to the number of binding sites, may be attributed. It seems more realistic to consider the protein solution as a system composed of an indefinite number of tautomeric forms in equilibrium, each of them having its own set of constants. The standard free energy change for the binding of a mole of ligand by a system of this type is found to depend upon the mean activities of protein and ligand-protein complexes, and the entropy of mixing of the different forms, besides the usual apparent free energy of binding. Cooperative effects in binding can naturally be expected to arise as a result of the shift in equilibrium among the protein forms brought about by the binding of successive moles of ligand. These effects can also arise in a different way, when as a result of slow equilibria among the protein forms, detailed balance among them is not maintained in the course of binding. The experimental data required to distinguish between these alternatives are imperfect or not yet available. The necessity for acquiring these data in a systematic fashion in the near future has provided the stimulus for the analysis presented in the following pages.

II. Description of the Binding Process

A. The Probability of Binding

In the study of the binding of small molecules by proteins, or in general in the study of any binding process, the direct object of the experiments is the determination of a "probability of binding," which may be defined as the probability that a molecule of protein (or ligand) will be found forming part of a complex, under fixed conditions of temperature, pressure, and over-all chemical composition of the solution under study. We define the probability of binding p as

$$p = \frac{\text{Actual concentration of protein-ligand complexes}}{\text{Maximum possible concentration of protein-ligand complexes}}$$

If total ligand concentration is $[X_0]$, total protein $[P_0]$, and ligand protein complex $[PX]$,

$$p = [PX]/[X_0] \qquad \text{if } X_0 \leq P_0 \qquad (1a)$$

$$p = [PX]/[P_0] \qquad \text{if } P_0 \leq X_0 \qquad (1b)$$

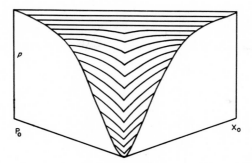

FIG. 1. The $p[X_0, P_0]$ surface giving the probability of binding as a function of total ligand X_0 and total protein P_0 concentration.

The system of free protein, free ligand, and complex is completely determined when the concentrations of all three participants in the equilibrium are given. The function of the concentration of the components chosen to describe the equilibrium, together with the values X_0 and P_0, must define uniquely the composition of the system. If the smaller of the two ratios in Eqs. (1a) and (1b) is alone given, the larger one may be *experimentally* indistinguishable from 1 over a wide range of concentrations. The above definition of p seeks to avoid this uncertainty. A complete description of the system entails the knowledge of p as a function of P_0 and X_0. If all other parameters except P_0 and X_0 are kept constant, p is represented by a surface $p[P_0, X_0]$ defined over the range of values of X_0 and P_0 determined by the experimental circumstances (Fig. 1).

B. Information from Binding Experiments

If we follow the definition of the probability of binding, certain aspects of information theory may be fruitfully applied to the process. The information on binding as a reversible process contained in a measurement of p equals (e.g., Yaglom and Yaglom, 1959; Brillouin, 1962)

$$- I(p) = p \log_2 p + (1 - p) \log_2 (1 - p) \tag{2}$$

Since logarithms to the base 2 are used, the information $I(p)$ is given in binary units or "bits." A plot of $I(p)$ against p is shown in Fig. 2. It is seen that, for $p = 0$ and $p = 1$, $I(p) = 0$. As may be recognized intuitively, such measurements convey no information about binding *as a reversible process*. If a number n of measurements at different p values is made, the total information in binary units obtained is

$$I = \sum_{i=1}^{i=n} I(p_i) \tag{3}$$

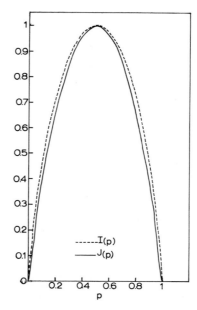

FIG. 2. The functions $-I(p) = p \log_2 p + (1-p) \log_2 (1-p)$, and $J(p) = 4p(1-p)$ plotted as functions of p.

It would appear at first sight that it is possible to increase indefinitely the value of I by simply increasing the number of measurements. This is not really the case, because observations differing by less than twice the standard deviation δp of an individual measurement of p convey the same information. Therefore the maximum information $I_{\max}$ from a given experimental method is limited to

$$I_{\max} = \sum_{i=1}^{i=1/2\delta p} I(p_i) \qquad (4)$$

corresponding to $1/2\delta p$ measurements separated by intervals $2\delta p$, extending between $p = 0$ and $p = 1$. For technical reasons, it is often impossible to obtain values of p below a certain minimum value $p_{\min}$, limiting the information to

$$I = \sum_{i=1}^{i=(1-p_{\min})/2\delta p} I(p_i) \qquad (5)$$

The ratio $I/I_{\max}$ is then the fraction of the potentially available information obtained in the experiments.

C. Presentation of Binding Data

It is clearly a tedious process, seldom attempted, to determine the complete p surface. Almost invariably, the binding properties of the system are examined by keeping either P_0 or X_0 constant and varying the other over a certain range. In this way the values of p corresponding to the intersection of the surface with the planes, $P_0 =$ constant or $X_0 =$ constant, are determined. The general form of the surface $p[X_0, P_0]$ is easy to recognize: For large values of P_0 or X_0 it approaches 1. The experimental significance of this is that, when the concentration of one partner is very high, addition of a small amount of the other results in its stoichiometric binding, with the result that $p = 1$, $I(p) = 0$.

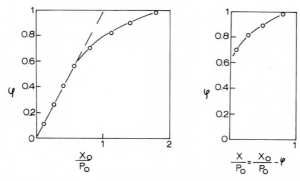

FIG. 3. (a) A plot of φ against X_0 often encountered in the literature. The dotted line is the stoichiometric line $\varphi = X_0/P_0$. The points on it correspond to $p = 1$, $I(p) = 0$. The information content of the plot as defined by Eq. (3) is 1.5 bits. (b) The same values of degree of saturation φ of (a) plotted against free ligand [X]. Evidently no conclusions may be reached as to the reversible process of binding of two-thirds of the sites, since [X] is only known for $\varphi > 0.66$.

Plots of degree of saturation of the protein $\varphi = PX/P_0$ against X_0 have often been used to describe the binding of ligands at a constant protein concentration P_0. This plot is schematically shown in Fig. 3(a). The line $\varphi = X_0/P_0$ is a stoichiometric line. Experimental measurements of φ coincident with it correspond to complete binding of the ligand, or $p = 1$ within experimental error. Of the experimental points shown in Fig. 3(a), only the upper three convey any information. A plot sometimes used is that of φ against [X]. A plot of the preceding type is transformed into this second type by exchanging $(X_0/P_0) - \varphi$ for X_0/P_0 in the abscissa. The ordinate [X] $= 0$ becomes the stoichiometric line, and it is possible to see much more clearly in this kind of plot the range of values of φ for which $p = 1$. Neither of these plots is to be recommended for the presentation of the experimental data. Clearly the best representation is one in which the value $[X] = 0$ is excluded from the graph. This virtually limits us to $\log [X]$ as the function to be plotted on one of the axes, while p itself or a function of p containing no arbitrary parameters is the natural choice for the other. I propose to use the value of p for the abscissa with the proviso that $P_0 \leq X_0$, so that p conveniently represents the degree of saturation φ, as indicated by Eq. (1b).[2]

The advantages of this method of presentation of the data requires little stressing: It does not assume the existence of one or more parameters to which the data could be expected to conform, and it shows immediately the range of p values and, therefore, the fraction I/I_{max} explored in the experiments. A consideration of the form of the $p[X_0, P_0]$ surface shows how the study of the system may be suitably simplified if the object is to obtain the maximum of information with the greatest economy of time and effort: The minimum value of p for a given concentration P_0 or X_0 is found along the plane $P_0 = X_0$. If we select a value of $X_0 = P_0$, at which we measure a high value of $p = p_{max}$ compatible with the techniques of measurement employed, and dilute this solution while keeping the ratio P_0/X_0 constant, we shall pass through the range of values of $p < p_{max}$ and reach p_{min}, already defined. It will be possible, when the solubility of the ligand allows it, to reach the range of values between p_{max} and unity by keeping P_0 constant at the value corresponding to p_{max} and increasing X_0. In those cases in which a molecule of protein combines with n moles of ligand, a solution with n moles of X for each mole of P should be used, or in other words the constant ratio $X_0/P_0 = 1$ must be replaced by the ratio $X_0/P_0 = n$.

It will be noticed that this method, while ensuring the observation of pairs of values p and $\log [X]$, the former comprised between p_{max} and p_{min}, is not sufficient to characterize the whole surface. If concentration-dependent protein interactions of any kind modify the value of p, it is clear that p cannot be a single-valued function of $\log [X]$. In these cases, the mapping of an extensive region of the p surface will be required to characterize the binding process.

D. Stoichiometry

An important part of binding studies is the determination of stoichiometry, which may be defined as the maximum number of moles of ligand bound by a mole of protein over a certain range of ligand concentration. The stoichiometry may be established by a study of the saturation fraction

---

[2] This rule will be followed throughout, p and φ being for us equal under the assumption $X_0 \gg P_0$.

φ as a function of total ligand concentration X_0. The plot of Fig. 3(a) is appropriate for the purpose: If there is a clear linear portion in the plot [the first three points in the plot of Fig. 3(a) are an example], a stoichiometric line is determined. It is apparent that the experimental conditions necessary to establish stoichiometry require $p = 1$ and are thus incompatible with those from which information on the dependence of probability of binding upon concentration may be derived. In practice, it may be difficult or impossible to determine the stoichiometry when the protein has many binding sites of overlapping affinity and structural considerations are not sufficient to fix their number. In this situation, the binding process may be characterized by a plot of $\bar{n}$, the average number of moles of ligand bound at a given value of $[X]$, against log $[X]$ (Scatchard *et al.*, 1957). Such cases are of much lesser interest to us and will not be further discussed.

III. Ligand-Protein Equilibria

We saw in the preceding paragraphs how a description of the binding process may be achieved in terms of purely experimental quantities: the stoichiometry and the dependence of the probability of binding upon the concentration of free ligand. We shall now discuss certain protein-ligand equilibria of interest within this frame of reference.

A. Homogeneous Systems with a Single Dissociation Constant

Many examples exist in which the dependence of the concentration of the partners is described by the relation

$$K = \frac{[P][X]}{[PX]} \tag{6}$$

where K is the dissociation constant of the complex. Introducing the degree of saturation φ,

$$K = (1 - \varphi/\varphi)[X]$$

if $P_0 \leq X_0$,

$$K = (1 - p/p)[X]$$

and

$$\log K - \log [X] - = \log p + \log (1 - p) \tag{7}$$

Equation (7) is the Bjerrum formation function (Bjerrum, 1950). If $P_0 \leq X_0$, the customary plot of ϕ against log $[X]$ is the same plot (of p against log $[X]$) that has been suggested from an argument on information in the last section as being convenient to describe the dependence of binding upon ligand concentration. If Eq. (7) is obeyed, the plot of log $[X]$ against p is

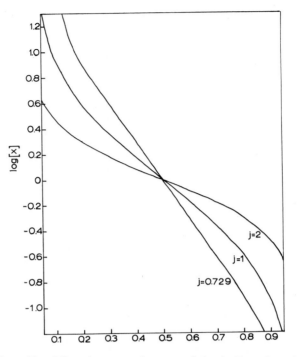

FIG. 4. Plots of log [X] against $p = \varphi$, for cases of simple ($j = 1$), multiple ($j = 0.73$), and cooperative ($j = 2$) binding.

symmetrical about $p = \frac{1}{2}$. Between $p = 0.1$ and $p = 0.9$, a span of 1.908 logarithmic units in [X] is covered (Fig. 4). It is therefore a simple matter to determine in a plot of p against log [X] whether the requirements of an equilibrium with a single dissociation constant are fulfilled.

Applying the usual formula for the propagation of errors to Eq. (6), the relative error in the determination of K equals

$$\frac{\Delta K}{K} \simeq \Delta[PX] \left[\frac{1}{(X_0 - [PX])^2} + \frac{1}{(P_0 - [PX])^2} + \frac{1}{[PX]^2} \right]^{1/2} \quad (8)$$

where $\Delta[PX]$ is the experimental error in the determination of [PX]. If $p = [PX]/P_0$, because $X_0 \geq P_0$,

$$\frac{\Delta K}{K} \simeq \delta p \left[\frac{1}{p^2} + \frac{1}{(1 - p)^2} + \frac{1}{[(X_0/P_0) - p]^2} \right]^{1/2}$$

If $p = [PX]/X_0$, because $X_0 \leq P_0$,

$$\frac{\Delta K}{K} \simeq \delta p \left[\frac{1}{p^2} + \frac{1}{(1 - p)^2} + \frac{1}{[(P_0/X_0) - p]^2} \right]^{1/2}$$

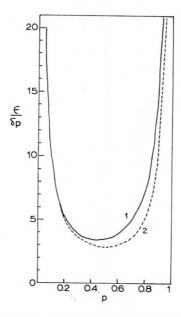

FIG. 5. The error in K, the dissociation constant, plotted as a function of p, according to Eq. (8) (curve 1) and, according to Eq. (9), a function of p alone (curve 2). For all practical purposes, p and δp determine the error in K.

where $\delta p = \Delta[PX]/P_0$ is the experimental error in the determination of p. In either case, the sum of the first two terms in the right-hand side of the last two equations is always larger, often much larger than the third, so that the error in K is practically determined by the quantity

$$\epsilon = \delta p \left[\frac{1}{p^2} + \frac{1}{(1 - p)^2} \right]^{1/2} \tag{9}$$

which depends upon p alone. This analysis shows one of the advantages of the concept of the probability of binding defined by Eq. (1). The small importance of the third term is graphically shown in Fig. 5. $\Delta K/K$ is a minimum for $p = \frac{1}{2}$ or $I(p) = 1$. However, in the determination of K from values in the range of $0.20 < p < 0.80$, ϵ increases over the minimum at $p = 0.5$ by only a factor of two.

B. Binding of Several Moles of Ligand

When the stoichiometry of the system indicates that the ligand-protein complexes involve up to n moles of ligand, the experimentally determined probability of binding is an average $\bar{p}$ to which the various complexes

$PX(1), PX(2), \ldots, PX(n)^3$ contribute individual probabilities $p_1, p_2, \ldots,$ p_n, so that

$$\bar{p} = n^{-1}(p_1 + p_2 + \cdots + p_n) = n^{-1} \sum_{i=1}^{i=n} p_i \tag{10}$$

Thus $\bar{p}$ is the resultant of a probability spectrum, which may appear resolved as regards some or all of its components. Recognition of this resolution is facilitated by the fact that, if this is complete, $d\bar{p}/d \log [X] = 0$ at $p = 1/n, 2/n$, etc., (Fig. 6). In incomplete resolution, the plot of p against $\log [X]$ may show inflections from which some qualitative conclusions

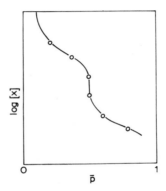

FIG. 6. Complete resolution of $\bar{p}$ into two distinct processes is shown by the presence of a vertical segment ($d\bar{p}/d \log [X] = 0$). The points are placed to indicate the practical minimum required to recognize the existence of two distinct processes and to assign characteristic values of log [X] to each. The information is worth 4.7 bits.

regarding the number and value of the independent dissociation constants may be drawn. A more detailed quantitative test for the recognition of the existence of a plurality of constants and their relative spread is given below.

C. Average Probability and Average Information in Binding

The average information $I(\bar{p})$ obtained from a measurement of $\bar{p}$ is related to the constituting informations $I(p_i)$ derived from the probabilities p_i, by the relation (Yaglom and Yaglom, 1959)

$$I(\bar{p}) \geq n^{-1} \sum_{i=1}^{i=n} I(p_i) \tag{11}$$

[3] $PX(1), PX(2), \ldots, PX(n)$ denotes a molecule of P in which the first, second, $\ldots,$ nth sites are occupied, *not* a molecule of P in which one, two, $\ldots, n$ out of n sites are occupied.

The equality applies when $p_1 = p_2 = p_3 \cdots = p_n$, the inequality when one or more of the p_i's is different from the others. In the first case, no possible distinction may be made among the components, i.e., no resolution is possible. The possibility of resolution increases with the quantity

$$\Delta I = I(\bar{p}) - n^{-1} \sum_{i=1}^{i=n} I(p_i) \tag{12}$$

In a case like ours in which there are only two outcomes (binding and no binding) and therefore two complementary probabilities ($\bar{p}$ and $1 - \bar{p}$, or p_i and $1 - p_i$) the functions $I(\bar{p})$ or $I(p_i)$ may be replaced without sensible error, for our purpose, by the functions

$$J(\bar{p}) = 4\bar{p}(1 - \bar{p}) \tag{13}$$

$$J(p_i) = 4p_i(1 - p_i)$$

The similarity in behavior and value of the functions $I(p)$ and $J(p)$ is shown in Fig. 2. The equivalent of Eq. (12) for the J functions is

$$\Delta J = J(\bar{p}) - n^{-1} \sum_{i=1}^{i=n} J(p_i) \tag{14}$$

A value for ΔJ is easily calculated. Writing $p_i = \bar{p} + \Delta p_i$, we have

$$n^{-1} \sum_{i=1}^{i=n} J(p_i) = (4/n) \sum_{i=1}^{i=n} (\bar{p} + \Delta p_i)(1 - \bar{p} - \Delta p_i)$$

$$= 4\bar{p}(1 - \bar{p}) - (4/n) \sum_{i=1}^{i=n} \Delta p_i^2 \tag{15}$$

and, comparing it with Eqs. (12) and (14), we have

$$\Delta I \simeq \Delta J = (4/n) \sum_{i=1}^{i=n} \Delta p_i^2 \tag{16}$$

Equation (16) shows that the quantities ΔI and ΔJ are directly related to the mean square deviations Δp_i^2 of the component probabilities p_i, with respect to the mean or experimental probability $\bar{p}$. The magnitude of ΔJ (or ΔI) may be rendered evident by plotting $J(\bar{p}) = 4\bar{p}(1 - \bar{p})$ against log [X], or preferably against log ([X]/[X]$_{1/2}$), where [X]$_{1/2}$ is the value of [X] for which $\bar{p} = \frac{1}{2}$. This experimental curve may then be compared with standard curves for any given combination of p_i values. The difference in the areas under the experimental and computed curves (Fig. 7) will be a measure of the over-all discrepancy between computed and observed values.

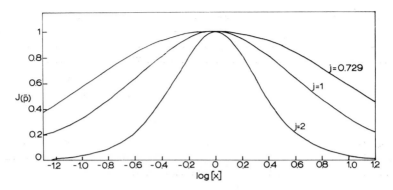

FIG. 7. Plots of $J(p) = 4\bar{p}(1 - \bar{p})$ against log [X] for simple, multiple, and cooperative binding processes, with j values of 1, 0.73, and 2, respectively.

A simple comparison is that of the experimental curve with the curve corresponding to the binding that is due to two independent processes with dissociation constants K_1 and K_2. In this case:

$$p_1 = [X]/([X] + K_1); \qquad p_2 = [X]/([X] + K_2)$$

$$\bar{p} = \frac{1}{2}\left[\frac{[X]}{[X] + K_1} + \frac{[X]}{[X] + K_2}\right] \tag{17}$$

$$\Delta p_1{}^2 = \Delta p_2{}^2 = \frac{(K_1 - K_2)^2}{4} \frac{[X]^2}{([X] + K_1)^2([X] + K_2)^2} \tag{18}$$

The area A_1 bounded by $J(\bar{p})$ and the abscissa log [X] (or log $[X]/[X]_{1/2}$) equals

$$A_1 = \frac{1}{2.302}\int_0^\infty 4\bar{p}(1 - \bar{p})\, d\ln[X] \tag{19}$$

The area A_2 bounded by the curve $\Delta J(\bar{p})$ and the abscissa is

$$A_2 = \frac{1}{2.302}\int_0^\infty (\Delta p_1{}^2 + \Delta p_2{}^2)\, d\ln[X] \tag{20}$$

The value of the integrals is

$$A_1 = \frac{1}{2.302}\left[\frac{K_1 + K_2}{K_1 - K_2}\ln\frac{K_1}{K_2} + 2\right] \tag{21}$$

$$A_2 = \frac{1}{2.302}\left[\frac{K_1 + K_2}{K_1 - K_2}\ln\frac{K_1}{K_2} - 2\right] \tag{22}$$

TABLE I

PARAMETERS A_1, A_2, AND j CHARACTERIZING BINDING WITH TWO INDEPENDENT DISSOCIATION CONSTANTS[a]

m	A_1	$\frac{1}{2}(A_2)^{1/2}$	j
1	1.7372	0	1
1.10	1.7376	0.011	0.9997
1.20	1.7393	0.023	0.9987
1.40	1.7454	0.045	0.995
1.50	1.7490	0.054	0.993
1.75	1.7596	0.075	0.987
2	1.7716	0.092	0.980
3	1.8228	0.146	0.953
5	1.9170	0.212	0.906
7	1.9953	0.254	0.871
10	2.0908	0.298	0.831
15	2.2127	0.345	0.785
20	2.3065	0.377	0.753
25	2.3830	0.402	0.729
30	2.4474	0.421	0.710

[a] $m = K_1/K_2$ is the ratio of the two dissociation constants for independent binding processes. A_1 is calculated by the use of Eq. (21), and $\frac{1}{2}(A_2)^{1/2}$ by the use of (22). j, the apparent order of the binding reaction, is obtained from Eq. (29).

So in all cases $A_1 \geq 1.737$, $A_2 \geq 0$. If there is more than one dissociation constant, the area A_1 increases over that due to a single constant. Table I gives the values of A_1 as a function of $m = K_1/K_2$ calculated from Eq. (21). To recognize the existence of a second dissociation constant, we require A_2 to differ from zero by an amount determined by the condition $\langle \Delta p^2 \rangle_{av} > 2\delta p^2$, where δp is the standard deviation of an experimental measurement of p. This implies that, for a given value of m, δp must be smaller than $(A_2)^{1/2}/2$. The value of this is given in Table I. It is seen that a demonstration of a second dissociation constant differing from the first by 20% requires the determination of $\bar{p}$ within $\delta p = 0.023$, whereas to reveal a difference in K of 10%, a method with $\delta p = 0.011$ must be employed. Precisions of this order are difficult to achieve consistently in the study of protein-ligand equilibria.

When no obvious resolution is observed in the plot of $\bar{p}$ against log [X] but nevertheless A_2 differs significantly from zero, a value of m compatible with the magnitude of the experimental uncertainty δp may be assigned to the system. If the number of constants were greater than two, they would be expected to be distributed over an interval in K of order mK_1. The question of the existence of a spectrum of binding constants has received attention in the study of hapten-antibody reactions. Nisonoff and Pressman (1958) and Eisen and Siskind (1964) have used, in the characterization of the binding process, the two-parameter equation of Sips (1948). This is discussed in the next paragraph. We may remark here that, as descriptive of the binding process, this treatment of the data appears much less satisfactory than the plot of $J(\bar{p})$ against log [X], which permits an easy visualization of the breadth and symmetry of the distribution of the probabilities of binding making up the spectrum.

A related question is the minimum information required to resolve a binding process into a number of separate unitary processes. From a strictly practical point of view, a minimum of three distinct values of $\bar{p}$ would appear necessary for the recognition of a unitary process as distinct, and for the assignment to it of a characteristic value of log [X], *in the case of complete resolution of the probability spectrum* (Fig. 6). In cases of partial resolution, the situation can hardly be expected to be more favorable, and a larger number of distinct $\bar{p}$ values may be required. Thus, the obtention of two to three binary units of information for each expected unitary process might be considered a practical minimum, before any attempt at numerical resolution into the component processes is contemplated.

D. The Order of Binding Reactions: Simple, Multiple, and Cooperative Processes

If there are n independent binding processes taking place simultaneously in our system, and each is described by an equation of the form

$$p_i = [X]/([X] + K_i),$$

then

$$\frac{1}{2.302} \cdot \frac{d\bar{p}}{d \log [X]} = \frac{[X]}{n} \sum_{i=1}^{i=n} \frac{d}{d[X]} \frac{[X]}{[X] + K_i}$$

$$= n^{-1} \sum p_i(1 - p_i) \leq \bar{p}(1 - \bar{p}) \qquad (23)$$

and, comparing Eq. (23) with Eq. (14), we can conclude that in these cases the slope in the plot of $\bar{p}$ against log [X] can never exceed that corresponding to a single process with $p = [X]/[X] + K$. The situation is different if we consider probabilities of binding no longer independent but conditional upon each other. A simple instance of this type is found in the reaction

$$P + 2X = PX_2$$

This would be usually regarded as proceeding in two steps:

$$P + X = PX$$

$$PX + X = PX_2$$

The species PX and PX_2 would both be expected to be present in amounts determined by the dissociation constants for the two steps, a situation discussed in detail in the last paragraph. However, if the binding of the second step depends upon the first in such a way that PX may be considered a reaction intermediate present throughout in negligible amounts in comparison with PX_2, a single dissociation constant K_2 will describe the system:

$$K_2 = \frac{[P][X]^2}{[PX_2]}$$

and from our definition of p,

$$\bar{p} = \frac{[X]^2}{[X]^2 + K_2}$$

Reactions of the same type involving an arbitrary order j may be postulated:

$$K_j = \frac{[P][X]^j}{[PX_j]}; \qquad \bar{p} = \frac{[X]^j}{[X]^j + K_j} \tag{24}$$

It is understandable that in the reactions $P + jX = PX_j$, there will be cases in which the species PX_m $(m < j)$ are present in appreciable amounts. In these the order j of the binding reaction will be nonintegral and less than m, the maximum number of moles of X bound by the protein. Equations (24) may then be considered to describe approximately the binding process, without having a precise physical significance.

The slope in the plot of p against $\log [X]$ is

$$\frac{1}{2.302} \frac{d\bar{p}}{d \log [X]} = [X] \frac{d\bar{p}}{d[X]} = j\bar{p}(1 - \bar{p}) \tag{25}$$

and is therefore j times larger than in a first-order binding reaction. Similarly,

$$A_1 = \frac{4}{2.302} \int_0^\infty \frac{K_j[X]^{j-1}}{K_j + [X]^j} d[X] = \frac{1.737}{j} \tag{26}$$

and the area under the $J(\bar{p})$ curve is reduced by the factor $1/j$, which gives us an integral, and therefore more exact, method of measuring the order of the binding reaction. The usual method is the plot of $\log (\bar{p}/1 - \bar{p})$ against $\log [X]$ (e.g., Roughton et al., 1955). A further way of characterizing the order of the binding reaction may prove of some interest: If an apparent dissociation constant is defined as

$$K_{app} = (1 - \bar{p}/\bar{p})[X] \tag{27}$$

while the binding can be empirically described by Eq. (24), then

$$K_j = (1 - \bar{p}/\bar{p})[X]^j$$

$$K_{app} = K_j/[X]^{j-1}; \qquad dK_{app}/d[X] = -(j - 1)K_{app} \tag{28}$$

K_{app} as calculated for different values of [X] appears to decrease as $\bar{p}$ increases, whereas in the superposition of several independent constants, the opposite is true and in a single process K_{app} remains the same throughout.

The last equation indicates that, if $j < 1$, the effects are qualitatively similar to those due to the presence of several independent dissociation constants. In fact, an equation of the type $\bar{p} = [X]^j/[X]^j + K$ was proposed by Sips (1948) to describe the adsorption of molecules at heterogeneous interfaces. From Eqs. (21) and (26), the value of j that would be needed to describe the effects of two constants K_1 and $K_2 = mK_1$ is given by

$$\frac{4}{j} = \frac{m+1}{m-1} \ln m + 2 \tag{29}$$

and is shown in Table I for a few m values.

Binding reactions may be classified into three types: simple, multiple, and cooperative, according to whether the order of the binding reaction is equal to one, less than one, or greater than one, respectively. This classification does not depend in any way on the number of moles bound per protein molecule: A heterogeneous protein population binding one mole of ligand per mole of protein can be the origin of multiple binding, and the binding of several moles of ligand to the same protein may be of the simple type. Table II indicates the characteristics that permit the experimental distinction among the three types.

The cooperative type of binding is classically associated with the dissociation of oxyhemoglobin, a case that has been extensively studied (Adair, 1925; Roughton *et al.*, 1955; Gibson, 1959; Antonini *et al.*, 1962). Recently, similar behavior has been described in the binding of NADH by several dehydrogenases (Anderson and Weber, 1964). Cooperative binding can be attributed, at least in a descriptive fashion, to the facilitation in the binding of successive moles of ligand once the first is bound. The physical

TABLE II

CHARACTERISTICS OF SIMPLE, MULTIPLE, AND COOPERATIVE BINDING REACTIONS

Reaction	Order j of the reaction	$D = dK_{app}/d\bar{p}$ $K_{app} = (\bar{p}/1 - \bar{p})[X]$	Slope s of plot of $\log (\bar{p}/1 - \bar{p})$ against log X	$A_1 = \int_0^\infty J(\bar{p}) \cdot d \log [X]$
Simple	$j = 1$	$D = 0$	$s = 1$	$A_1 = 1.737$
Multiple	$j < 1$	$D > 0$	$s < 1$	$A_1 > 1.737$
Cooperative	$j > 1$	$D < 0$	$s > 1$	$A_1 < 1.737$

picture proposed in the case of hemoglobin was once one of direct physical interaction of the binding regions in the protein. Recently, the concept of an equilibrium among different protein forms dependent upon the presence of bound ligand has been proposed (Changeux, 1964). This and other possibilities are examined in detail in the following paragraphs.

IV. Binding by Systems in Dynamic Equilibrium

In the preceding paragraphs the protein molecules have been considered a population with fixed characteristics to which one or more enumerable dissociation constants could be attributed. We shall enquire now into the more complex case of binding by a molecular population in which the members, both free protein and ligand-protein complexes, can exist in multiple forms capable of interconversion. In these cases, the dissociation constant computed from the values of $\bar{p}$ is an apparent equilibrium constant K_{app}, the thermodynamic meaning of which differs somewhat from that of the ordinary case.

The large number of degrees of freedom of protein molecules, the weak links among the composing parts, and the rapid fluctuation of electric charges to which they are subject, renders indispensable the assumption that proteins in solution exist in a variety of tautomeric forms in equilibrium. Although the extent to which such tautomeric forms differ from each other under physiological conditions of pH and temperature is unknown, there is every reason to believe that they are capable of introducing large differences in the binding of ligands: The ligand molecule makes contact with a small portion of the protein molecule, and any discrete disruption or modification of the binding region ought to produce a conspicuous change in the binding properties. We shall deal first with the case in which the equilibrium among the different tautomeric forms is maintained in the course of ligand binding. In this way, a given free protein or protein-ligand tautomer exists as a fixed fraction of the total free protein or total protein-ligand population, respectively.

A. The Standard Free Energy Change in Binding by Protein Tautomers

The reactants considered here are the ligand X and the protein tautomeric forms $P_1, P_2, \ldots, P_n$; the products are the complexes $P_1X, P_2X, \ldots, P_nX$. The fractions of the free protein $[P] = \sum_i [P_i]$, in the enumerated forms are $f_i = [P_i]/[P]$. Similarly, the fractions of total complexes $[PX] = \sum_i [P_iX]$ in the different forms are $g_i = [P_iX]/[PX]$. The *reaction itself* may be written

$$P + X = PX \qquad \text{or} \qquad X + \sum_i f_i P_i = \sum_i g_i P_i X$$

The partial molar free energy of the P_i component equals[4]

$$\mu(P_i) = \mu_0(P_i) + RT \ln a_i[P_i]$$

where a_i is the activity coefficient of P_i. The last may be written

$$\mu(P_i) = \mu_0(P_i) + RT(\ln f_i + \ln a_i + \ln [P]) \qquad (30)$$

and, similarly,

$$\mu(P_iX) = \mu_0(P_iX) + RT(\ln g_i + \ln b_i + \ln [PX]) \qquad (31)$$

where b_i is the activity coefficient of P_iX.

The partial molar free energy of X is

$$\mu(X) = \mu_0(X) + RT(\ln d + \ln [X]) \qquad (32)$$

where d is the activity coefficient of X.

At equilibrium the condition,

$$\sum_i g_i\mu(P_iX) - \sum_i f_i\mu(P_i) - \mu(X) = 0 \qquad (33)$$

is obeyed. With the values from (30), (31), and (32), the last equation becomes

$$\sum_i g_i\mu_0(P_iX) - \sum_i f_i\mu_0(P_i) - \mu_0(X)$$

$$= RT \ln \frac{[P][X]}{[PX]} + RT \sum_i f_i \ln f_i - g_i \ln g_i$$

$$+ RT \sum_i f_i \ln a_i - g_i \ln b_i + RT \ln d \qquad (34)$$

The left-hand side of Eq. (34) equals ΔF_0, the standard free energy change in the conversion of reactants to products. In the right-hand side, $[P][X]/[PX] = K_{app}$, the apparent equilibrium constant in the reaction. The term $\sum f_i \ln f_i - g_i \ln g_i = \Delta S_m$ is an entropy of mixing depending only upon the number and proportion of the forms present. In the last term,

$$\sum_i f_i \ln a_i - g_i \ln b_i = \langle \ln a \rangle_{av} - \langle \ln b \rangle_{av}$$

is the difference in the weighted mean of the logarithm of the activity coefficients of reactants and products.

---

[4] The standard states to which the quantities μ_0 refer are "ideal 1 molal solutions," that is, molal solutions in which the thermodynamic properties are those of an infinitely dilute solution in a medium of fixed ionic composition, pressure, and temperature.

B. Entropy of Mixing Effects

Neglecting the term $RT \ln d$, which will be negligible if the activity of the ligand is unity, Eq. (34) may be written

$$\Delta F_0 / 2.3RT = \log K_{\text{app}} + \Delta S_m + (\langle \log a \rangle_{\text{av}} - \langle \log b \rangle_{\text{av}}) \qquad (35)$$

It is seen that the equilibrium constant is determined not only by the standard free energy change in the reaction, but also by the last two terms in Eq. (35). It is known that

$$-\log n < I = \sum_{i=1}^{i=n} f_i \log f_i < 0$$

The maximum absolute value of I is reached when there are equal fractions of all components, and zero is reached when the contribution is from one component alone. If the term $\langle \log a \rangle_{\text{av}} - \langle \log b \rangle_{\text{av}}$ is assumed negligible for the moment,

$$| \Delta S_m | = | (\Delta F_0 / 2.3RT) - \log K_{\text{app}} | < \log n \qquad (36)$$

The maximum difference between $\Delta F_0 / 2.3RT$ and $\log K_{\text{app}}$ is reached when there are n equally probable reactant forms and only one product form, or conversely, one main reactant form and n equally probable product forms. In the first case, $\Delta S_m < 0$ and $\log K_{\text{app}} > \Delta F_0 / 2.3RT$. As compared with the case for which $\Delta S_m = 0$, a decrease in affinity for the ligand or increase in K_{app} takes place. In the second case, $\Delta S_m > 0$ and $\log K_{\text{app}} < \Delta F_0 / 2.3RT$, an increase in affinity or decrease in K_{app} follows. The existence of many observations of the greater stability of ligand protein complexes when compared to the proteins themselves indicates that, in all probability, the number of protein forms is reduced upon binding and that in general we may expect $\Delta S_m < 0$. The case of the binding of ligands by molecules having similar, though in principle distinguishable, subunits deserves special consideration: In this category enter the binding of O_2 by hemoglobin, the binding of NADH by dehydrogenases, and the binding of haptens by antibodies. Consider, as a simple case of this type, that of a molecule AB, where A and B are sufficiently similar to ensure that ΔF_0 is substantially the same for the reactions $A + X = AX$ and $B + X = BX$. Before binding, we have only one kind of molecule present, namely AB, and consequently $\sum f_i \log f_i = 0$. After binding the first molecule of X, we have XAB and BAX as distinguishable forms: $\sum g_i \log g_i = -\log 2$. Thus for the addition of the first mole of X, $\Delta S_m = +\log 2$, and the dissociation constant for this step is

$$\log K_1 = (\Delta F_0 / 2.3RT) - \log 2 \qquad (37)$$

In the subsequent reaction, $\frac{1}{2}(\text{XAB} + \text{BAX}) + \text{X} = \text{XABX}$; the opposite situation obtains. Here there are two forms for the reactants, one for the products. Therefore,

$$\log K_2 = (\ \Delta F_0/2.3RT) + \log 2 \tag{38}$$

From the last two equations $K_2/K_1 = 4$. The presence of the entropy term has resulted in a split of $2.3RT \log 4$ or 0.66 kg-cal in the apparent free energies of binding for the first and second molecules. A careful analysis of the probability of binding by the methods previously described ought to reveal these effects in appropriate cases.

It has already been pointed out that, in some of these cases of binding by polymer molecules, the observed effects are opposite to those just described, that is, the binding has cooperative character. In our example of a dimer molecule AB, the observation of a cooperative effect requires $K_2 < K_1$. If the number of distinguishable forms before binding is n_0, the number of forms after a first mole is bound n_1, and the number of forms after a second mole bound n_2, then

$$K_1 > K_2 \qquad \text{requires} \qquad n_1{}^2 < n_0 n_2$$

If the two parts of the molecule are assumed to be independent, so that the number of forms of one half of it (A or B) is independent of the state (B or BX, A or AX, respectively) of the other half, the condition stated above cannot be fulfilled. For example, with N forms for A or B and M forms for AX or BX, $n_0 n_2 = N^2 M^2 < n_1{}^2 = 4N^2 M^2$. Although the condition $n_1{}^2 < n_0 n_2$ may be fulfilled if the number of forms of each half is made to depend upon the state of the other half, in the absence of specific effects demanding a hypothesis of this kind, this is only one way of introducing intrinsically different dissociation constants obeying the relation $K_1 > K_2$. Within this frame of reference, one ought to conclude that the change in the number of forms upon binding, that is, the ΔS_m term of Eq. (35), cannot *by itself* be the cause of cooperative effects.

It will be noticed that ΔS_m has the form of a difference in information content regarding reactants and products. We may choose to look upon it from two different points of view: From the first, we notice that to evaluate this term we require detailed information as to the number of forms and their probabilities. From another point of view, the change in information content upon binding may be attributed to the molecule itself. We may regard, for example, P as a chemoreceptor capable of existing in several "indifferent forms" and PX as a unique form which by its new properties is able to convey information as to the presence of X in the environment.

C. The Apparent Free Energy of Binding: Concentration Effects

Equation (35) shows two kinds of effects that may lead to differences between the standard free energy change in the binding reaction and the quantity $-2.3RT \log K_{\mathrm{app}}$, which we shall call the apparent free energy of binding ΔF_{app}. Since ΔF_0 is not directly accessible to our measurements, a distinction between ΔF_0 and ΔF_{app} can be established only by an examination of the terms that make up the difference between them. The evaluation of ΔS_m depends greatly upon the refinement of the available methods of analysis, and presently it does not appear possible to determine when the limits of such analysis have been reached. The term $\langle \log a \rangle_{\mathrm{av}} - \langle \log b \rangle_{\mathrm{av}}$ is in principle much more amenable to estimation: The simplest and best known example of the direct conversion of binding free energy into osmotic activity, described by Eq. (34), is found in the erythrocyte, where the correlation of the oxygenation of hemoglobin with the change in volume of the cells and the redistribution of the electrolytes has been known for half a century. In general, a conspicuous difference in the relative activity coefficients of protein and ligand-protein complexes should show itself in changes in the second virial coefficient determined by studies of osmotic pressure or light scattering of the solutions. It is of interest that effects of this type should be greatly dependent upon protein concentration: At sufficiently high concentrations, molecular aggregation phenomena may be the more evident, whereas at low protein concentrations, only small changes in viscosity, light scattering, or osmotic pressure may be observed. Finally, at high dilutions, when all activities tend to unity, no difference between ΔF_{app} and ΔF_0 could be demonstrated. We would in these cases be equally justified in speaking of the protein molecules as producing a change in the binding energy of the ligand by their interactions, or of the energy of these interactions being changed by the binding process.

Cooperative binding demands $dK_{\mathrm{app}}/d\bar{p} < 0$ Eq. (28). Since ΔF_0 is independent of $\bar{p}$, this condition, when introduced into Eq. (35), implies

$$(d/d\bar{p})\,(\langle \log a \rangle_{\mathrm{av}} - \langle \log b \rangle_{\mathrm{av}}) > 0 \qquad (39)$$

This equation shows that, for the appearance of cooperative effects, not only must the activity coefficients of reactants and products be different but also one, or both, of them must show conspicuous change in the range of concentration zero to P_0, the total protein concentration. Apart from the existence of concentration-dependent aggregation or dissociation of the protein, which ought to be easily ruled out by physical measurements of various kinds, the possibility of concentration-dependent interactions among the protein molecules must be taken into account. Without entering into the question of the origin or magnitude of these interactions, it appears necessary for the free protein interactions to be different from those among protein-ligand complexes for a cooperative effect to appear. A simple difference in the quantity ($\langle \log a \rangle_{\mathrm{av}} - \langle \log b \rangle_{\mathrm{av}}$) could show itself in changes in the absolute value of K_{app} with protein concentration, even in the absence of cooperative effects.

D. Cooperative Binding by Protein Tautomers

Perhaps the simplest system in which cooperative binding effects may be expected is that of a protein possessing two distinct tautomeric forms P and P′, and binding two moles of ligand:

$$
\begin{array}{ccc}
\text{P} & \underset{}{\overset{k_0}{\rightleftarrows}} & \text{P}' \\[2pt]
K_1 \updownarrow & & \updownarrow K_1' \\[2pt]
\text{PX} & \underset{k_1}{\rightleftarrows} & \text{P}'\text{X} \\[2pt]
K_2 \updownarrow & & \updownarrow K_2' \\[2pt]
\text{PX}_2 & \underset{k_2}{\rightleftarrows} & \text{P}'\text{X}_2
\end{array}
\tag{40}
$$

In the scheme of Eq. (40), $k_0 = [\text{P}]/[\text{P}']$; $k_1 = [\text{PX}]/[\text{P}'\text{X}]$, and $k_2 = [\text{PX}_2]/[\text{P}'\text{X}_2]$ are first-order equilibrium constants for the two tautomers and the complexes with one and two moles of ligand, respectively. The dissociation constants of the two forms are:

$$
K_1 = \frac{[\text{P}][\text{X}]}{[\text{PX}]} ; \qquad K_1' = \frac{[\text{P}'][\text{X}]}{[\text{P}'\text{X}]}
\tag{41}
$$

$$
K_2 = \frac{[\text{PX}][\text{X}]}{[\text{PX}_2]} ; \qquad K_2' = \frac{[\text{P}'\text{X}][\text{X}]}{[\text{P}'\text{X}_2]}
\tag{42}
$$

Because of the existence of detailed balance in the above equilibria, the following relations obtain:

$$
k_0/k_1 = K_1/K_1' ; \qquad k_1/k_2 = K_2/K_2'
\tag{43}
$$

so that only five of the seven equilibrium constants in scheme (40) are independent. Two apparent equilibrium constants, in which no distinction is made between the forms P and P′, may be defined:

$$
K_\text{I} = \frac{([\text{P}] + [\text{P}'])[\text{X}]}{([\text{PX}] + [\text{P}'\text{X}])} = K_1' \frac{(1 + k_0)}{(1 + k_1)}
$$

$$
K_\text{II} = \frac{([\text{PX}] + [\text{P}'\text{X}])[\text{X}]}{([\text{PX}_2] + [\text{P}'\text{X}_2])} = K_2' \frac{(1 + k_1)}{(1 + k_2)}
\tag{44}
$$

K_I and K_{II} contain the five independent constants and so define the system, completely. The experimental probability of binding is

$$\bar{p} = \frac{1}{2}\left[\frac{[PX] + [P'X] + 2[PX_2] + 2[P'X_2]}{[P] + [P'] + [PX] + [P'X] + [PX_2] + [P'X_2]}\right] \quad (45)$$

so that introducing the relations (44)

$$\bar{p} = \frac{1}{2}\left[\frac{([X]/K_I) + 2([X]^2/K_I K_{II})}{1 + ([X]/K_I) + ([X]^2/K_I K_{II})}\right] \quad (46)$$

As shown by Eq. (46), the order of the binding reaction approaches 2 when $K_I \gg K_{II}$. If to this condition we add the requirement that the dissociation constants for the binding of first and second mole by each tautomer be the same, that is, if

$$K_1 = K_2; \qquad K_1' = K_2'$$

the relations

$$\frac{(1 + k_0)(1 + k_2)}{(1 + k_1)^2} \gg 1; \qquad \frac{k_0 k_2}{k_1^2} = 1 \quad (47)$$

must be satisfied. These relations imply in turn that k_1 must be small compared to unity, whereas either k_0 or k_2 must be large compared to unity. The presence of a cooperative effect depends upon a large shift in the proportion of the tautomers during binding. In the absence of an experimental demonstration of this shift, the above treatment offers no advantage over the treatment of Adair (1925), which describes cooperative binding on the basis of intrinsically different dissociation constants. The general equivalence of Adair's equation with the one that may be derived for n tautomers in equilibrium binding N moles of ligand may be simply shown by the introduction of apparent dissociation constants K_I, K_{II}, ..., K_N similar to those of Eq. (44).

$$K_I = \frac{\sum_1^n [P_i][X]}{\sum_1^n [P_i X]}$$

$$K_{II} = \frac{\sum [P_i X][X]}{\sum [P_i X_2]} = \frac{\sum [P_i]}{\sum [P_i X_2]} \frac{[X]^2}{K_I} \quad (48)$$

$$K_N = \frac{\sum [P_i]}{\sum [P_i X_N]} \frac{[X]^N}{K_I K_{II} \cdots K_{N-1}}$$

The ratios of the protein tautomers present are given by the first-order constants k_{ij} defined by the following equations:

$$\frac{[P_2]}{[P_1]} = k_{01}; \qquad \frac{[P_3]}{[P_2]} = k_{02}; \qquad \frac{[P_3]}{[P_1]} = k_{02}k_{01}; \cdots; \frac{[P_n]}{[P_1]} = k_{0n-1}, \ldots, k_{01}$$

$$\frac{[P_2X]}{[P_1X]} = k_{11}; \qquad \frac{[P_3X]}{[P_2X]} = k_{12};$$

$$\frac{[P_3X]}{[P_1X]} = k_{12}k_{11}; \cdots; \frac{[P_nX]}{[P_1X]} = k_{1n-1}, \ldots, k_{11} \qquad (49)$$

Therefore,

$$K_I = K_{11} \frac{(1 + k_{01} + k_{01}k_{02} + \cdots + k_{01}, \ldots, k_{0n-1})}{(1 + k_{11} + k_{11}k_{12} + \cdots + k_{11}, \ldots, k_{1n-1})}$$

where

$$K_{11} = \frac{[P_1][X]}{[P_1X]}$$

The quantities $K_I, \ldots, K_N$ are true constants independent of $[X]$, if detailed balance among the protein forms is preserved during binding. From Eqs. (48) and (49),

$$\bar{p} = \frac{1}{N}$$

$$\times \frac{([X]/K_I) + 2([X]^2/K_IK_{II}) + \cdots + N([X]^N/K_I, \ldots, K_N)}{[1 + ([X]/K_I) + ([X]^2/K_IK_{II}) + \cdots + ([X]^N/K_I, \ldots, K_N)]}$$

$$(50)$$

Equation (50) is a form of Adair's equation, and it shows that the predicted order of the reaction is always less than N, the number of moles maximally bound.

E. Binding by Protein Forms in Slow Equilibrium

In considering binding involving several forms of protein and protein-ligand complexes, it was assumed that equilibrium among the different forms, as well as of each with the ligand, was maintained at all concentrations of the latter. A more complex situation is encountered if it is assumed that equilibrium among the protein forms is reached much more slowly than the equilibrium of each of them with the ligand. In attempting to decide in the actual experiments whether over-all equilibrium has been reached, we are faced with a paradoxical situation. If after addition of ligand we readily attain stable values of $\bar{p}$, we may all too easily conclude that equilibrium has been achieved. If we possessed methods capable of distinguishing among the different protein forms, we might have observed that a very slow change in their proportion continued to take place and that equilibrium was not yet reached. Proteins in solution do not possess indefinite stability, and the time necessary to reach complete equilibrium among the forms may conceivably exceed the time during which a protein in solution is expected to maintain constancy of its properties.

From the analysis of the last paragraph, it is possible to assert that the condition

$$p = \frac{[X]}{[X] + K_{\text{app}}}$$

is sufficient to establish that detailed balance among the protein tautomers is maintained in the course of binding. In binding reactions of higher order, no such simple criterion exists to determine this property of the system. Cooperative binding may in fact appear as a result of the absence of detailed balance among the protein forms participating in the process. To see this, consider the case of two protein tautomers P and P' and the corresponding protein-ligand complexes PX and P'X. The kinetic analysis of this simple system requires eight different rate constants, and the resulting steady-state equations do not permit easy visualization of the effects resulting when some of them are varied. To render evident the effects that would be expected in the absence of detailed balance,[5] we equate to zero two opposing rate constants in the interconversion of protein forms. In this way our system assumes the simpler form:

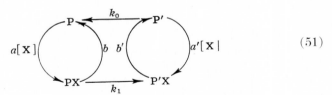

$$(51)$$

in which only six rate constants are involved. Four steady-state equations for the forms P, P', PX, and P'X may be set:

$$d[\text{P}]/dt = -a[X][\text{P}] + b[\text{PX}] + k_0[\text{P}'] = 0 \qquad (52)$$

$$d[\text{PX}]/dt = a[X][\text{P}] - (b + k_1)[\text{PX}] = 0$$

[5] For a general discussion of detailed balance in steady-state systems see Landsberg (1961), pp. 356–398. As shown by Landsberg, the existence of a stationary state does not by itself imply detailed balance.

From these,

$$K_{\mathrm{app}} = \frac{([P] + [P'])[X]}{[PX] + [P'X]} = \frac{[(b + k_1)/a] + (k_1/k_0)[X]}{1 + (k_1/k_0)[(a'[X] + k_0)/b']}$$

Introducing as parameters

$$\alpha = a/a'; \qquad \beta = b/b'$$

$$\gamma = k_1/k_0; \qquad \delta = k_1/b; \qquad K_\infty = b/a$$

we have

$$K_{\mathrm{app}} = K_\infty \left[\frac{(1 + \gamma[X]/K_\infty + \delta)}{1 + \gamma([X]/K_\infty)(\beta/\alpha) + \delta\beta} \right] \tag{53}$$

The observation of a cooperative effect requires $dK_{\mathrm{app}}/d[X] < 0$, or, from the last equation,

$$\frac{\beta}{\alpha} > \frac{1 + \delta\beta}{1 + \delta} \tag{54}$$

In the scheme of Eq. (51), it is implicit that the form P is that observed in the absence of ligand or at high dilution in the presence of it. According to Eq. (54), a cooperative effect will appear if the rate of dissociation of the new form (P'X) is smaller than that of PX, or if the rate of association of P' with X is higher than that of P with X. It is also characteristic of the scheme discussed that P', resulting from the dissociation of P'X, reverts to P after a relaxation time during which combination with the ligand has a chance to occur. Similarly, the conversion of PX into P'X is assumed to occur *after* combination with the ligand. Although in a thoroughly balanced process it is not possible to speak of combination or dissociation being followed by other physical and chemical changes in the protein, but all are to be assumed simultaneous, this language is indispensable in the description of the scheme [Eq. (51)]. It implies that molecular relaxation processes can influence the probability of binding or, in other words, that the molecular hysteresis of proteins is one, or perhaps the sole, origin of cooperative binding. If we define as it is usual, the correlation times of the process as the average times required to observe, respectively, the dissociation of a protein-ligand complex into its components or the combination of a free protein molecule with ligand, we see that effects of the type described would naturally be expected when one of these correlation times is of the order of the molecular relaxation processes postulated for the protein molecule.

The *direct* proof of the existence of a cooperative effect from the causes just discussed requires the demonstration that the ratios P/P' and PX/P'X change as a function of $\bar{p}$, the average probability of binding. A demonstration of such changes or, which is equivalent, a demonstration of the failure of detailed balance in the course of binding has not been achieved, but a very suggestive experiment in this direction has been described by Gibson (1959): When carboxyhemoglobin at pH 9.1 is dissociated by a light flash, the hemoglobin released from the combination differs from ordinary hemoglobin in having a rate of O_2 combination some 15 times higher than the ordinary hemoglobin. This rapid-reacting type decays into the ordinary form of hemoglobin in a time of the order of a millisecond. The significance of this "Gibson effect" is strengthened by the fact that CO-hemoglobin H, which does not exhibit cooperative effects in the binding of O_2, shows after the photoflash a uniform reaction rate corresponding to the faster one for ordinary hemoglobin (Benesch et al., 1964).[6] Either the rapid-reacting photoproduct of CO-hemoglobin is a new form unrelated to the one produced in the course of the dissociation processes that maintain the equilibrium of O_2 with hemoglobin, or the latter differs markedly from ordinary deoxygenated hemoglobin. The failure of detailed balance in this case is further suggested by the observations of Antonini et al. (1962) on the influence of salts upon the oxygen-hemoglobin equilibrium. Light-scattering and sedimentation studies show that at high salt concentration the hemoglobin molecules are dimers instead of the usual tetramers observed at low ionic strength, yet the order of the binding reaction is 2.7 to 3.

In summary, cooperative effects in binding may be thought to arise in three different situations: (1) in equilibria among tautomeric forms of protein when two or more moles of ligand are bound (Section IV, D); (2) in stationary states set up among protein tautomers (Section IV, E); and (3) in cases of dependence of the mean activity of the system upon the probability of binding (Section IV, C). Conditions 1 and 2 presuppose that intermolecular interactions are of negligible, or at most of secondary, importance in giving rise to cooperative effects, whereas according to 3, such interactions are the determining cause of this phenomenon. Since cooperative effects may be observed in $10^{-6}M$ protein solutions at high ionic strength, in which the intermolecular distances are of the order of 500 Å, the latter possibility appears rather unlikely, unless the protein-protein interactions involve time-dependent effects of the kind that are postulated in 2. From the admittedly scanty data at present available, one is drawn to the belief that cooperative effects arise from situations of type 1 or 2. In deciding between them, kinetic arguments like the Gibson effect, and even the anomalous high order of the binding reaction, are not likely to prove decisive, and the direct determina-

---

[6] Other anomalies of hemoglobin reaction rates that may be interpreted as requiring a fast-reacting hemoglobin form are discussed by Gibson (1959).

tion of the proportions of the forms present when $\bar{p}$ is varied remains the final criterion by which detailed balance can be proved or otherwise.

Until recently, the binding of oxygen by various hemoglobins stood as the only well-known example of cooperative binding. The recent observations (Anderson and Weber, 1964) of strongly cooperative character in the binding of NADH by several dehydrogenases should materially help to detect the features common to all these cases. The phenomena in question can only be studied in very dilute solutions of substances of limited stability, and all causes of systematic error must be carefully eliminated before a final verdict is reached. Nevertheless, the demonstration that detailed balance may not be preserved in simple reversible reactions in which proteins participate would materially affect our ideas about the behavior and functions of proteins so that all efforts toward the clarification of this point would seem worthwhile.

ACKNOWLEDGMENT

The author wishes to thank Professor H. S. Gutowsky for discussions of several aspects of binding.

REFERENCES

Adair, G. S. (1925). *J. Biol. Chem.* **63,** 529.

Anderson, S. R., and Weber, G. (1964). *Abstr. 148th Meeting Am. Chem. Soc.,* p. 49C. Also: In the press.

Antonini, E., Wyman, J., Jr., Rossi, F. A., and Caputo, A. (1962). *J. Biol. Chem.* **237,** 2773.

Benesch, R., Gibson, Q. H., and Benesch, R. E. (1964). *J. Biol. Chem.* **239,** PC1668.

Bjerrum, J. (1950). *Chem. Rev.* **46,** 381.

Brillouin, L. (1962). "Science and Information Theory," 2nd ed. Academic Press, New York.

Changeux, P. (1964). *Brookhaven Symp. Biol.* **17,** 232.

Edsall, J. T., and Wyman, J., Jr. (1958). "Biophysical Chemistry," Chapter 11. Academic Press, New York.

Eisen, H. N., and Siskind, G. W. (1964). *Biochemistry* **3,** 996.

Gibson, Q. H. (1959). *Progr. Biophys. Biophys. Chem.* **9,** 1.

Klotz, I. M. (1953). *In* "The Proteins" (H. Neurath and K. Bailey, eds.), Vol. 1, Part B. Academic Press, New York.

Landsberg, P. T. (1961). "Thermodynamics," pp. 356–372. Wiley (Interscience), New York.

Nisonoff, A., and Pressman, D. (1958). *J. Immunol.* **80,** 417.

Roughton, F. J. W., Otis, A. B., and Lyster, R. L. J. (1955). *Proc. Roy. Soc. (London)* **B144,** 29.

Scatchard, G., Coleman, J. S., and Shen, A. L. (1957). *J. Am. Chem. Soc.* **79,** 12.

Sips, R. J. (1948). *J. Chem. Phys.* **16,** 490.

Tanford, C. (1961). "Physical Chemistry of Macromolecules," Chapter 8. Wiley, New York.

Yaglom, A. M., and Yaglom, I. M. (1959). "Probabilité et Information." Dunod, Paris.

On the Mechanochemistry of Contraction[1]

MANUEL F. MORALES[2]

Cardiovascular Research Institute,
University of California Medical Center,
San Francisco, California

In 1939, Engelhardt and Lubimova made two great discoveries in the same experiment; they discovered how to produce contraction *in vitro*, and illustrated how ATP hydrolysis "pays for" cellular work. In the ensuing years, the free energy (Levintow and Meister, 1954) and the enthalpy (Podolsky and Morales, 1956) of hydrolysis have been measured, and the intermediate device for coupling endergonic reactions with ATP hydrolysis is now well understood (see, for example, Klotz, 1957). But the exact role of ATP in true transducers remains enigmatic. Among these enigmas is the mechanism of contraction.

Over two decades Szent-Györgyi, Weber, and many others have shown that myosin and actin are major—if not sole—protein components of the contractile apparatus. It has also been established that Mg^{2+} and traces of Ca^{2+} are essential for normal operation. Especially in the hands of Hugh Huxley, contractile models intermediate in complexity between the "myosin thread" and the living fiber [Szent-Györgyi's ' glycerinated fiber" (1949)] have revealed the organization of myosin and actin into the thick and thin filaments of the living fiber. Finally, Ebashi (1961) has shown that relaxation, or cessation of contraction, is due to an endoplasmic reticular pump which deprives the contractile apparatus of its essential Ca^{2+}. Thus in the years since 1939, many details of the contractile machine have been found, and we are understanding the relation between the Engelhardt model and the real fiber. But we are still speculating about such central questions as: How and where does the contractile force originate? What structures transmit the force? The remainder of this paper is such a speculation, but we hope it is a reasonable speculation relative to contemporary facts.

In the subject of contractility, the whirlpool of dispute is fed by two streams. One stream is morphological, the other is physicochemical; the first says that certain molecular behavior occurs; the second says that such

[1] This research was supported by grants from the American Heart Association and the National Science Foundation. Except for minor additions, this paper will also appear in a volume honoring V. A. Engelhardt, to be published in the Russian language by the Academy of Sciences of the U.S.S.R.

[2] Career Investigator, American Heart Association, and Professor of Biochemistry, University of California School of Medicine.

behavior would be absurd. Any contemporary speculation must mediate between these contentions.

Morphology is now molecular. F-actin (Hanson and Lowy, 1963) appears to be a 2- or 3-stranded "rope"; each strand is a "necklace" of G-actin globules. These ropes may be ca. 80 Å in diameter, but are very long (order of micra). The thin filaments of muscle appear to be identical with the ropes observed in preparations of F-actin. Both hydrodynamic and electron microscopic (Rice, 1961a) evidence suggests that the myosin molecule is a very slender rod, 1300–1500 Å long, one of whose ends is bulbous. This bulb, included in the heavy meromyosin fragment of myosin, contains the ATPase activity and the actin-binding capability. Most of the long shaft is included in the light meromyosin fragment. Since solubility of the light fragment depends upon electrolyte medium in much the same way as solubility of intact myosin, it is likely that the peculiar charge distribution responsible for this dependence resides in the light fragment. Although it has been known for some time that myosin rodlets aggregate laterally, only recently has the electron microscope shown that they may also aggregate end-to-end, and even antipodally (Rice, 1961b). Whether at some point along the myosin rodlet there is flexibility (so that the molecule can be roughly regarded as two "segments" joined by a flexible string) has become an important issue, but it is unsettled. Prevalent opinion is that the heavy meromyosin bulb plus a stem of uncertain length constitute one "segment," and that about 700 Å of rigid shaft (light meromyosin fraction) constitutes the other.

Because thick filaments have not been isolated but only seen in electron micrographs of myofibrillar debris (H. E. Huxley, 1963), their structure is imperfectly known. The filament "surface" is certainly myosin, but whether there is a central core made, say, of tropomyosin is uncertain. Some years ago, H. E. Huxley and Hanson (1955) discovered numerous projections ("bridges") extending radially from the thick filament and seemingly touching six surrounding thin filaments; these projections were absent in the H-zone. Huxley surmised that these projections contained the heavy meromyosin portion of myosin (because heavy meromyosin is known to complex with actin). Recently, Rice and Brady (1964) and H. E. Huxley (1963) have independently suggested that, in the surface "sleeve" of the thick filament, the myosin molecules lie with their shaft axes nearly parallel to the axis of the filament. In each half of the filament the heavy meromyosin bulbs are pointing to the nearest Z-membrane; therefore, at the H-zone, myosin molecules from one side must be joined to myosin molecules from the other side, end-to-end and antipodally. We note here that, if indeed there is a central core (or at least a cylindrical hole), then in the radial sense all molecules would be equivalent, and that, if there is flexibility in the myosin molecule, the segments of the molecules containing heavy meromyosin could all point radially out from the surface sleeves of the filament. In these terms, the filament proper would be constructed from rigid shafts, perhaps 700 Å long.

On the basis of electron micrographs, H. E. Huxley and Hanson (1954) originally proposed that, in the process of shortening, neither thick nor thin filaments suffer any large-scale configurational change, but that the array of thin filaments translates (or "interdigitates") into the array of thick filaments. To this fundamental observation, Elliot et al. (1963) have recently added that, when this shortening occurs, there is a lengthening

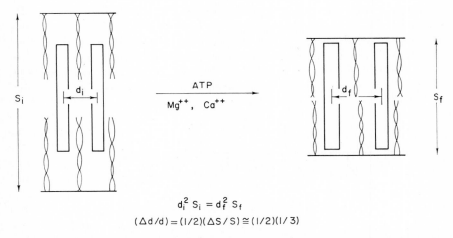

$$d_i^2 \, S_i = d_f^2 \, S_f$$
$$(\Delta d / d) = (1/2)(\Delta S / S) \cong (1/2)(1/3)$$

Fig. 1. Schema to indicate the relative motion of filaments observed in contraction, and the "isovolumic" nature of the process.

in the transverse distance between thick filaments in such a way that the compound array shortens "isovolumically." These morphological observations are schematized in Fig. 1.

The Huxley–Hanson observation has been strongly supported by studies with the interference microscope (A. F. Huxley and Niedergerke, 1954), and by X-ray diffraction work (Elliot et al., 1963), and its wide acceptance has naturally inspired numerous attempts (H. E. Huxley and Hanson, 1954; A. F. Huxley, 1957; Weber, 1958; Davies, 1963) at mechanistic interpretation. A common feature of all these attempts is the assumption that, at fixed positions along the thick filament, there exist tiny impelling devices. For the Huxleys, these were "oars" with unsymmetrical attaching probabilities, for Weber it was an axial array of ATPase sites, and within each site staggered actin and myosin loci, and for Davies these were "springs" instead of oars. Some specific criticisms of these theories as a class appear elsewhere (Morales, 1959; 1964), but their generic weakness is the assumption of large molecules with quasi-intelligent appendages.

When impure antigen artifacts are eliminated, "staining" myofibrils with fluorescent antibodies to the individual muscle proteins is a very powerful investigative method. Using this method, Szent-Györgyi and Holtzer (1963a,b) have shown that, at rest, antimyosin is distributed uniformly over the A-band, whereas after contraction it is concentrated in just one region of the A-band. This important result contradicts the notion that stationary actin-impelling devices exist all along the thick filaments, but it does not conflict with interdigitation. In order to tell whether after contraction the region of concentration of antigen (myosin) was near the center of the thick filaments, or at the ends of the thick filaments, the authors appealed to landmarks deriving from the assumption that myofibrils break along the planes separating I-bands from A-bands. On this assumption, the authors concluded that in contraction the apparent migration of myosin is toward the *ends* of the thick filaments (Fig. 2, left)

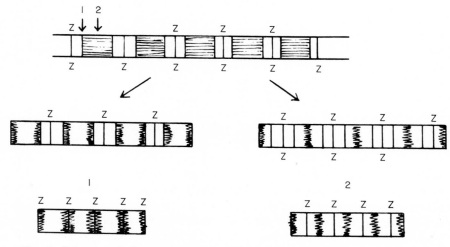

Fig. 2. Schema to indicate expected patterns of labeled antibody bands; "Z" marks the Z membrane. The top line depicts a myofibril at rest (A-bands uniformly stained with antimyosin). The bottom line depicts contracted fragments of myofibril, now showing concentration of antimyosin in narrower bands. (The middle line is a hypothetical intermediate state with the myosin migrated but the fragment not yet contracted.) If myofibrils break at plane 1 (top line), then the concentration of antimyosin into bands indicates arrangement 1 of bottom line; if the break was at plane 2, then the concentration indicates arrangement 2.

Szent-Györgyi and Johnson (1964) have ingeniously suggested that the two surface "sleeves" of the thick filament somehow condense away from one another to the ends of the filament. They speculated that each sleeve was attached to the *contralateral* actin filaments, so that in the condensation process the actin filaments from either side are towed into the thick filament array (as required by interdigitation). Nevertheless, the contralateral attachments between myosin and actin have never been seen, and so the theory has not stimulated wide support. For ulterior motives, we wish to entertain a doubt about the *direction* of the myosin migration inferred in Szent-Györgyi and Holtzer (1963a,b). If breaks in myofibrils occur as well along the plane which bisects the A-band, then the observed changes in the distribution with contraction would indicate that the two "sleeves" of a thick filament condense toward the center of the H-zone (Fig. 2, right). We shall make use of this alternative interpretation below.

Finally, we turn to the descendants of the Engelhardt–Lubimova experiment—to physicochemical studies of the interaction between either myosin B or actomyosin.[3] The contraction of myosin-B threads by ATP in low concentrations (e.g., 0.08 M) of KCl is one of the most dramatic phenomena in biochemistry, and threads do lend themselves to thermoelastic experiments (see below), but dispersed systems (fine suspensions or solutions) of myosin B are more convenient for physical study. When a suspension of myosin B is at 0.08 M KCl and is supplied with trace amounts of Mg^{2+} (e.g., 10^{-6} M), the addition of ATP (10^{-3} M) unquestionably contracts or synaereses the particles. This is indicated by an increase in light scattered at small angles (Fig. 3), and by an increase in the slope of a log (optical density) vs. log (wavelength) plot (Fig. 4), but of course the particles are large enough so that the contraction is also obvious with ordinary microscopy (that is not to say with the naked eye, when the system is in thread form). When a comparable concentration of myosin B is placed in 0.6 M KCl, it readily dissolves, but the addition of ATP still causes structural effects. Although the popular view has been, and perhaps still is, that these effects result from a dissociation of actomyosin into myosin and F-actin, we feel that we have provided ample evidence (Blum and Morales, 1953; Gellert *et al.*, 1959) that, in the heterogeneous population of myosin-B particles, (1) such dissociation as occurs upon ATP addition yields mainly *myosin* as a product, and (2) larger particles do not dissociate

---

[3] There exist certain quantitative differences between the mechanochemical behavior of myosin B and actomyosin, and, in view of Ebashi's recent work (1963), it may be that the former contains an extra component, but for now we shall regard the two systems as equivalent.

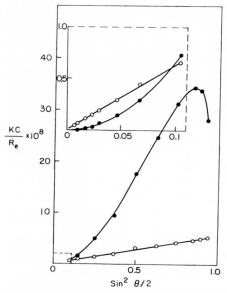

FIG. 3. Zimm plot for a myosin-B suspension without ATP (○) and with m*M* ATP (●). Protein, $0.8 \times 10^{-3}\%$, in 0.06 *M* KCl and 0.02 *M* trismaleate, pH 7.0. Top graph is enlargement of dotted-in area in bottom graph. (From Rice *et al.*, 1963.)

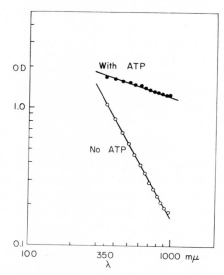

FIG. 4. Logarithmic plot of OD vs. wavelength for myosin B without ATP (○) and with m*M* ATP (●). Protein, 0.01% in 0.06 *M* KCl and 0.02 *M* trismaleate, pH 7.0. (From Rice *et al.*, 1963.)

at all, but only *expand* upon ATP addition (i.e., their radius of gyration increases), as indicated in Fig. 5. Thus the light-scattering method has provided evidence that in a dispersed system the *direction* (contraction or expansion) of the ATP effect on particles of myosin B or actomyosin can be reversed by changes in electrolyte medium (e.g., low or high [KCl]). More detailed knowledge of how myosin or actin participates in these changes, however, can come only from a concerted study by light scattering and electron microscopy (Rice *et al.*, 1963). Whether drawn from a low or high

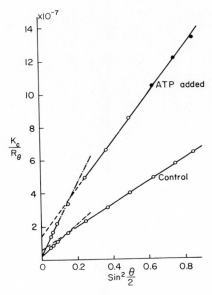

FIG. 5. Zimm plot for a myosin-B solution without ATP (lower curve) and with mM ATP. Protein, 0.01%, in 0.60 M KCl, and 0.10 M histidine, pH 7.0. (From Rice *et al.*, 1963.)

electrolyte medium, specimens of myosin B streaked on a film and examined the electron microscope show a "ladder" structure (Fig. 6), in which the "rails" of the ladder are F-actin filaments, and the "rungs" are end-to-end aggregates of myosin (perhaps five myosin lengths long). These rungs meet each actin rail at a *non*perpendicular angle; along the rung there must be at least one antipodal union between myosin rodlets, since each of the two contacts with the F-actin rails is made by the heavy meromyosin end of a myosin rodlet. When the specimen is made from a solution (high electrolyte concentration) in which light-scattering measurements show the ATP response to have been particle expansion, the electron microscope shows

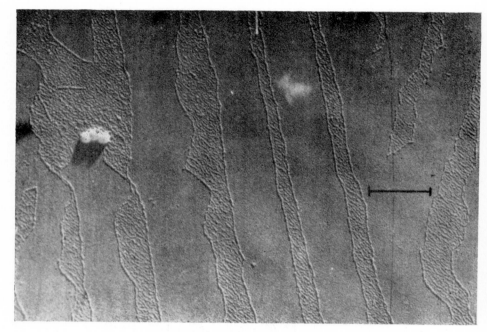

Fig. 6. Ladder-like structures prepared from myosin B in 0.70 M NH_4HCO_3 suspension, $\times 31,900$. Here the scale marker represents 1μ. (From Rice *et al.*, 1963.)

(Fig. 7) that the rungs of the ladders are thinned out, allowing the rails to separate considerably, and revealing here and there some free myosin; thus the detailed changes are neatly consistent with the inferences from light scattering. When the specimen is made from a suspension in which light-scattering measurements show the ATP response to have been contraction

Fig. 7. Expanded ladder prepared from myosin B in 0.70 M NH_4HCO_3 and 10^{-5} M ATP solution, $\times 5300$. (From Rice *et al.*, 1963.)

("superprecipitation"), the electron microscope shows (Fig. 8) that the rungs of the ladders have been severely condensed, thereby drawing the rails closely together. Presumably because the rung-rail junctions were not perpendicular, these movements have obviously contorted the F-actin rails, and it is clear that, if one thinks of the ladder as a contractile structure, one must conclude that it shortens by conformational change; we have never seen indication of any relative translational motion. There is also in this process a thickening of the rails, the nature of which is obscure. That the whole process involves the rungs in their entirety is shown by the fact that both light scattering and electron microscopy indicate that acto-heavy meromyosin (in which the rung-rail unions are made but there

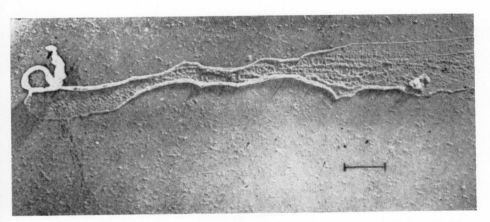

Fig. 8. Contracted ladder prepared by freezing-drying from myosin B in 0.09 M NH_4HCO_3 and 10^{-5} M ATP suspension, $\times 20,600$. Scale marker indicates 1μ. (From Rice *et al.*, 1963.)

are no intact rungs bridging two actin filaments) does not contract, but merely dissociates with ATP addition.

Answering some questions invariably stimulates new questions. In the foregoing behavior of actomyosin, is the force generated in the myosin and transmitted to the actin, or vice versa? Certain experiments do point to myosin as the active partner. First, Szent-Györgyi's surmise that "contractility" follows *myosin* (or even *light meromyosin*) solubility is completely correct. Figure 9 shows contractility followed optically [as the slope of the log (OD) vs. log λ plot] as a function of [KCl]; it bears a striking resemblance to myosin solubility as a function of [KCl] (see, for example, Brahms and Brezner, 1961). Second, with optical methods it has been possible to show that ATP induces reversible (by virtue of the myosin-

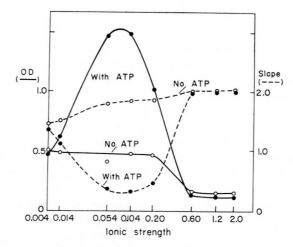

FIG. 9. Left ordinate: $OD_{550\ m\mu}$; right ordinate: logarithmic slope of OD vs. wavelength relation. These ordinates are plotted against [KCl]. Myosin B, 0.01% in 0.02 M trismaleate. No ATP (○); mM ATP (●). (From Rice *et al.*, 1963.)

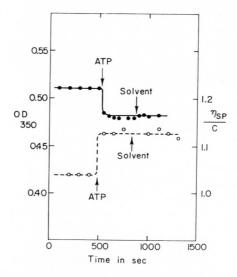

FIG. 10. Changes induced by ca. 2 mM ATP in a 0.21% suspension of myosin in 0.05 M KCl and 0.05 M trismaleate, pH 7.0, 25°C. Left-hand scale and full line: $OD_{350\ m\mu}$. Right-hand scale and dotted line: η_{sp}/c. After sufficient time elapses, these changes reverse, presumably due to the ATPase activity of the myosin. (From Rice *et al.*, 1963.)

catalyzed hydrolysis of the nucleotide) changes in the structure of a concentrated *myosin* solution (Fig. 10).[4]

Another perennial question concerns the physical nature of forces which affect structure. When an Engelhardt-type thread is stretched isothermally, both its entropy and internal energy diminish (Botts and Morales, 1951). This result, plus the observation that ATP can cause oppositely directed structural effects in myosin B, depending on electrolyte medium, led us (Morales and Botts, 1952) long ago to suggest that, when ATP adsorbs on myosin, it cancels preexisting extensile forces which are opposing contractile forces of another kind. The present observations are readily understandable on the basis of this principle, if we suppose the "polyelectrolyte" to be the ladder, the extensile forces to arise from charges on the rungs (either as an electrostatic repulsion or as a massive swelling by solvent), and the "contractile forces of another kind" to be an increase in configurational entropy or whatever forces cause myosin to aggregate, e.g., attraction by specific bonds.

Finally, a structural conciliation must be sought, for at first sight the "ladder" looks, and seems to behave, very differently from the organized myofibril, even though the "mechanical topology" is similar, i.e., in both, the myosin provides a continuous mechanical path from one actin filament to another—in the ladder, through the rungs; in the myofibril, through the thick filaments. Let us agree with Rice and Huxley that the thick filament is a bundle of myosin molecules arranged symmetrically and antipodally to either side of the transverse plane through the middle of the H-zone. Since each thick filament has regularly spaced contacts with each of the six thin filaments surrounding it (H. E. Huxley and Hanson, 1955), we may imagine further that on the "surface sleeve" the locus of points at which the bridge segments bend outward from the straight shaft segments is a helix of diameter 110 Å and longitudinal repeating distance of 435 Å (Fig. 11). In such a helix the straight shafts can be accommodated by having them slightly inclined to the filament axis. From our point of view, the importance of this arrangement is that it permits a dislocation, wherein the helix *shortens* in repeating distance, say from 435 Å to 290 Å, widens in

---

[4] Some years ago Kafiani and Engelhardt (1953) reported that *myosin* threads exhibited a mechanical change in response to ATP. The experiments were disputed by Hayashi *et al.* (1958), who suggested that such threads were contaminated with actin. Experiments illustrated by Fig. 10 are not open to this objection because for actomyosin the OD (λ) response to ATP would be in the opposite direction (increase, not decrease). In retrospect, it seems that basically the original Kafiani–Engelhardt contention may have been correct, but that a macromechanical effect can only be detected when actin is present to link myosin units and to serve as a "mechanical amplifier" (see discussion about ladders).

FIG. 11. Model of a portion of a thick filament and six neighboring thin filaments (straight steel rods); left, relaxed; right, contracted. In this model, a single myosin molecule is a bent white rod arranged so that the bulbous (heavy meromyosin) end projects radially to touch an actin filament, and the shaft (light meromyosin) portion lies almost parallel to the thick filament axis. The bent points of the myosin molecules lie on a helix whose diameter and pitch conform with observed values. At the center of the thick filament is a cylindrical "core" (Plexiglass tube). Contraction is supposed to occur because the array of myosin molecules around the core is rearranged in such a way that the bend points now lie on a helix of reduced pitch and correspondingly increased diameter; the right-hand model illustrates a contraction of about one-third. After the rearrangement, the myosin shafts have been further telescoped into one another (aggregated in an orderly manner), and the translation of the bulb projections has towed the actin filaments. The core has remained of the same length.

diameter, say from 110 Å to 135 Å (the distance between neighboring thick filaments widens correspondingly, of course), *and thereby the lateral interaction between myosin shafts increases.* Put otherwise, this dislocation would result from any environmental change which promotes the aggregation of myosin (cf. "ladder" experiments); it would cause the "migration" of myosin (cf. labeled antibody experiments) from a uniform distribution throughout the thick filament to a condensation near the H-zone. Finally, if in the process the bridge segments have been attached to the six neighboring and (assumed to be) somewhat flexible, F-actin filaments, these would be towed into the thick filament array, while the thick filaments are separating transversely (cf. morphological experiments). Thus the *in vitro* and *in situ* observations would be largely reconciled, and the origin of the force would be understandable in simple terms. A final source of satisfaction would be a *rapprochement* with colleagues who explain contraction of phage tails by a similar dislocation in helically arrayed globules of "subunit" protein (Brenner *et al.*, 1959; Sarkar *et al.*, 1964) of the sheath, as this structure shortens over an inert core.

As is usual in writing a synopsis, one is consciously or subconsciously indebted not only to published work but to many friends with whom the issues were discussed. Of these we would like to cite particularly two scientists who made, from our point of view, highly opportune visits to our laboratory while this paper was in preparation. Dr. Carolyn Cohen of the Harvard Medical School stressed for us the importance of several new structural observations used above. Independently of us, Professor John Marshall of the University of Pennsylvania has made extensive calculations and much deeper thinking than ours on the helical structure of the thick filament, and he generously told us many of his unpublished results.

Addendum. A recent paper encourages the idea that contraction and superprecipitation involve charge cancellation. Bowen and Martin (1964) report that psoas fibers enriched in positive charge (by esterifying carboxyl groups with methyl sulfate) can be contracted with various polyanions (e.g., pyrophosphate, ferrocyanide) in rough proportion to their valence; conversely, fibers enriched in negative charge (by acetylating amino groups with acetic anhydride) can be contracted with cations. Also, recent phase-contrast micrographs of glycerinated arthropod muscle [Gilmour and Robinson, (1964)] show very clearly that contraction is associated with migration of A-substance toward the center of the A-band, much as suggested by the model in Fig. 11.

REFERENCES

Blum, J. J., and Morales, M. F. (1953). *Arch. Biochem. Biophys.* **43**, 208.
Botts, D. J., and Morales, M. F. (1951). *J. Cell Comp. Physiol.* **37**, 27.
Bowen, W. J., and Martin, H. L. (1964). *Biochem. Biophys. Res. Commun.* **16**, 129.

Brahms, J., and Brezner, J. (1961). *Arch. Biochem. Biophys.* **95**, 219.

Brenner, S., Streisinger, G., Horne, R. W., Champe, S. P., Barnett, L., Benzer, S., and Rees, M. W. (1959). *J. Mol. Biol.* **1**, 281.

Davies, R. E. (1963). *Nature* **199**, 1068.

Ebashi, S. (1961). *J. Biochem. (Tokyo)* **50**, 236.

Ebashi, S. (1963). *Nature* **200**, 1010.

Elliot, G. F., Lowry, J., and Worthington, C. R. (1963). *J. Mol. Biol.* **6**, 295.

Engelhardt, V. A., and Lubimova, M. N. (1939). *Nature* **144**, 669.

Gellert, M. F., von Hippel, P. H., Schachman, H. K., and Morales, M. F. (1959). *J. Am. Chem. Soc.* **81**, 1384.

Gilmour, D., and Robinson, P. M. (1964). *J. Cell. Biol.* **21**, 385.

Hanson, J., and Lowy, J. (1963). *J. Mol. Biol.* **6**, 46.

Hayashi, T., Rosenbluth, R., Satir, P., and Vozick, M. (1958). *Biochim. Biophys. Acta* **28**, 1.

Huxley, A. F. (1957). *Progr. Biophys. Biophys. Chem.* **7**, 255.

Huxley, A. F., and Niedergerke, R. (1954). *Nature* **173**, 971.

Huxley, H. E. (1963). *J. Mol. Biol.* **7**, 281

Huxley, H. E., and Hanson, J. (1954). *Nature* **173**, 979.

Huxley, H. E., and Hanson, J. (1955). *Symp. Soc. Exptl. Biol.* **9**, 228.

Kafiani, K. A., and Engelhardt, V. A. (1953). *Dokl. Akad. Nauk SSSR* **92**, 385.

Klotz, I. M. (1957). "Energetics in Biochemical Reactions." Academic Press, New York.

Levintow, L., and Meister, A. (1954). *J. Biol. Chem.* **209**, 265.

Morales, M. F. (1959). *Rev. Mod. Phys.* **31**, 426.

Morales, M. F. (1964). *In* "Cell Specialization" (D. Mazia and D. B. Tyler, eds.), pp. 266–276. McGraw-Hill, New York.

Morales, M. F., and Botts, D. J. (1952). *Arch. Biochem. Biophys.* **37**, 283.

Podolsky, R. J., and Morales, M. F. (1956). *J. Biol. Chem.* **218**, 945.

Rice, R. V. (1961a). *Biochim. Biophys. Acta* **52**, 602.

Rice, R. V. (1961b). *Biochim. Biophys. Acta* **53**, 29.

Rice, R. V., Asai, H., and Morales, M. F. (1963). *Proc. Natl. Acad. Sci. U.S.* **50**, 549.

Rice, R. V., and Brady, A. C. (1964). *In* "Biochemistry of Muscle Contraction" (J. Gergely, ed.). Little, Brown, Boston. In press.

Sarkar, N., Sarkar, S., and Kozloff, L. M. (1964). *Biochemistry* **3**, 511.

Szent-Györgyi, A. G. (1949). *Biol. Bull.* **96**, 140.

Szent-Györgyi, A. G., and Holtzer, H. (1963a). *Biochim. Biophys. Acta* **74**, 709.

Szent-Györgyi, A. G., and Holtzer, H. (1963b). *Biochim. Biophys. Acta* **74**, 722.

Szent-Györgyi, A. G., and Johnson, W. H. (1964). *In* "Biochemistry of Muscular Contraction" (J. Gergely, ed.). Little, Brown, Boston. In press.

Weber, H. H. (1958). "The Motility of Muscle and Cells." Harvard University Press, Cambridge, Massachusetts.

Information Theory and Memory

J. S. GRIFFITH[1]

Department of Mathematics,
Manchester College of Science and Technology,
Manchester, England

I. Information Theory

I want to give an introduction to information theory which, although it follows traditional treatments, is nevertheless oriented clearly toward the biological situation of storage of information. *Information storage* is a term which is used in many ways in the common language, even by scientists, and information theory provides a particular way of assigning numerical values to it. Information theory is usually regarded as a statistical theory. However the conditions which need to be satisfied in such an approach are more restrictive than is acceptable in many biological situations, and therefore we present first that part of the theory which can be treated without assumptions of a statistical nature. (For fuller treatments of information theory, see Shannon and Weaver, 1949; Khinchin, 1957; Brillouin, 1962).

A. Capacity of an Information Store

We lead into the idea of capacity with the example of a valid voting return in an election involving two candidates. Such a return will have been filled in in one of two significantly distinct ways. It records which choice, out of two possible choices, the voter has made. It could be called a two-choice store of information. Similarly, for n candidates, with the possibility of voting for one only, our voting paper forms an n-choice store.

Alternatively, we may think of an n-choice store as something which can be set into one of n possible states. If each of these states is connected with

---

[1] Present address: Department of Mathematics, Bedford College, London, England.

some possible event, then we may set the store in the state corresponding to one of these events as a mnemonic or memory for the event corresponding to that state. A typical example here would be the notices often hung in shop windows which have two possible states, one presenting to the outside world the word OPEN and the other the word CLOSED.

Evidently the capacity of such a finite information store, sensibly, can only be either the number n of states, or at least some function $f(n)$ which increases with n. A suitable form for $f(n)$ is suggested by a consideration of what happens when we put two stores together to form a joint, larger store. If the two constituent stores have, respectively, n_1 and n_2 states, then the combined store has $n_1 n_2$ different states. It is natural to hope that we could define capacity in such a way that the size of the larger store should be the sum of the sizes of its constituents. Thus we require

$$f(n_1 n_2) = f(n_1) + f(n_2) \qquad (1)$$

which is conveniently satisfied by

$$f(n) = a \log_b n \qquad (2)$$

for any constants $a > 0$, $b > 1$. It is usual, although not universal, to choose $a = 1$ and $b = 2$. Then

$$f(n) = \log_2 n \qquad (3)$$

and we shall always use this choice and drop the subscript 2 in Eq. (3). We shall use ln to denote logarithms with base e.

Now consider a store which consists of x switches in a line, each of which may be put up or down. Then the store has 2^x states and hence a capacity of x. On the other hand, if we represent "up" by the digit "1" and "down" by the digit "0," any state of the store gets represented by a number in the scale of two, the number having x digits. Conversely, each such number corresponds to a state of the store. Because of this relation between a store of capacity x and numbers with x binary digits, it is customary to say that any store with n distinct states has an information capacity of $\log n$ bits of information. Here *bit* is the conventional abbreviation for "binary digit."

Important examples of stores are easy to find. A modern digital computer operates entirely with stores of this kind, and one may specify the storage capacity in terms of the number of bits of information. Each bit usually gets stored in a separate position, although it is obviously not necessary that this should be so. A second example is furnished by a DNA or RNA molecule. Here there are normally four significantly different nucleotides in a given molecule, and therefore each nucleotide position can store $\log 4 = 2$ bits of information. So a molecule containing n nucleotides can store $2n$ bits. A nucleotide triplet can store 6 bits. A third example is a polypeptide chain built from, say, 20 distinct amino acids. It can store $\log 20 = 4.32$ bits per amino acid. The difference between the 6 bits of the trinucleotide and the 4.32 bits of a corresponding amino acid could mean that we are mistaken in supposing that all sequences in DNA or RNA are possible. If that were the case, the capacity would obviously be reduced, as, for example, in the commaless codes (Crick *et al.*, 1957). However it is now believed much more likely that the triplet code for the amino acids is redundant, that is, that more than one triplet corresponds to each amino acid and also that at least most triplets correspond to some amino acid (Crick, 1963). If so, we should say that, of the 6 bits stored in a triplet, only 4.32 are relevant for the specification of amino acids.

Now let us note what I think is the most important thing about this definition and approach to information content. It is just that it contains no mention of probabilities. We shall see shortly that the statistical theory of communication leads naturally to the same definition of information capacity. But that approach is more restricted, for it has nothing to say about situations for which probability has no meaning. We may use a traditional example here, popular with philosophers. Let us, at midnight, place a switch in the position "off." Then we arrange that, when the sun rises in the morning, it is switched to "on." If we consult the switch at midday it tells us whether the sun rose that morning. It is acting as a store with a 1-bit capacity. However the majority of statisticians would, I believe, consider that one cannot sensibly talk about the probability of this particular event. It would seem that, at the very least, it is not obvious that all the events in an animal's life can usefully be treated in probabilistic terms, although presumably some may. For this reason it is useful to have a definition of information capacity which transcends the probabilistic situation.

B. Statistical Theory of Communication of Information

1. Uncertainty of the Outcome of an Experiment

The statistical theory is only concerned with events which have definite probabilities, or frequencies. In the simplest nontrivial case we would have two possible events. For example, suppose an experiment is performed which has the possible outcome A_1 with probability p and outcome A_2 with probability $1 - p$. If $p = 0$ or 1, we are essentially certain of the outcome and learn nothing by performing the experiment. If $p = \frac{1}{2}$, we are entirely uncertain beforehand and the experiment is informative. If, say, $p = 0.9$ we are "fairly sure" of the outcome but not certain. In the statistical theory we define a quantity H which gives a useful measure of the degree of uncertainty before the experiment is performed. After it is performed, no uncertainty remains, and therefore H is said to be the information acquired, on average, when the experiment is performed.

As we shall see in a moment, there are a number of conditions one would expect H to satisfy. If these are satisfied, it turns out that the only acceptable definition of H for any experiment with n possible outcomes having respective probabilities $p_1, \cdots, p_n$ is

$$H = -a \sum_{i=1}^{n} p_i \log_b p_i \tag{4}$$

and we shall take $a = 1$, $b = 2$ as before to give

$$H = - \sum_{i=1}^{n} p_i \log p_i \tag{5}$$

When $n = 2$,

$$H = H(p) = -p \log p - (1 - p) \log (1 - p) \tag{6}$$

and this is plotted as a function of p in Fig. 1.

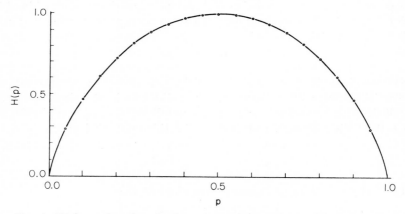

FIG. 1. $H(p)$ as a function of p for an experiment with two possible outcomes.

We now check that H has the right sort of properties. We have $H(0) = H(1) = 0$, and so we acquire no information when we are certain of the outcome beforehand. Similarly, we acquire the maximum amount when $p = \frac{1}{2}$, as would be expected. This latter property may be generalized; that is, for any n, the function H of Eq. (5) attains a unique maximum value when every $p_i = n^{-1}$ (Khinchin, 1957). When p_i has these values, we find

$$H(n^{-1}, n^{-1}, \cdots, n^{-1}) = \log n \tag{7}$$

in conformity with Eq. (3).

Now consider the situation when we have an experiment A followed by another experiment B. Suppose them to be independent, with respective probabilities $p_1, \cdots, p_n$ and $q_1, \cdots, q_m$. Then the joint experiment has nm possible outcomes with probabilities $p_i q_j$, and hence

$$
\begin{aligned}
H(AB) &= -\sum_{i=1}^{n} \sum_{j=1}^{m} p_i q_j \log (p_i q_j) \\
&= -\sum_{i=1}^{n} \sum_{j=1}^{m} p_i q_j (\log p_i + \log q_j) \\
&= -\sum_{i=1}^{n} p_i \log p_i - \sum_{j=1}^{m} q_j \log q_j \\
&= H(A) + H(B)
\end{aligned}
\tag{8}
$$

Thus the uncertainty of the joint experiment is the sum of the uncertainties of the two separate constituent experiments.

If A and B are not independent, this result cannot possibly hold. For example, the outcome of A might determine the outcome of B, in which case one would expect to find

$$
H(AB) = H(A)
$$

whatever the value of $H(B)$. Let us write, then, π_{ij} for the probability of outcome j for experiment B, assuming the outcome i has already occurred for experiment A. Then the joint probabilities are now $p_i \pi_{ij}$. Because, for any i, there must be some outcome for experiment B, we have

$$
\sum_{j=1}^{m} \pi_{ij} = 1, \qquad \text{(all } i) \tag{9}
$$

and

$$
\begin{aligned}
H(AB) &= -\sum_{i=1}^{n} \sum_{j=1}^{m} p_i \pi_{ij} \log (p_i \pi_{ij}) \\
&= -\sum_{i=1}^{n} \sum_{j=1}^{m} p_i \pi_{ij} (\log p_i + \log \pi_{ij}) \\
&= -\sum_{i=1}^{n} p_i \log p_i - \sum_{i=1}^{n} p_i \sum_{j=1}^{m} \pi_{ij} \log \pi_{ij} \\
&= H(A) + \sum_{i=1}^{n} p_i H_i(B)
\end{aligned}
\tag{10}
$$

where

$$H_i(B) = -\sum_{j=1}^{m} \pi_{ij} \log \pi_{ij} \tag{11}$$

is the uncertainty about B after outcome i is known to have been obtained for A. The quantity

$$\sum_{i=1}^{n} p_i H_i(B)$$

is the mathematical expectation of $H(B)$ in the situation that A has been performed first. That is, it is the average uncertainty in B remaining after the outcome of A is known. We write it $H_A(B)$, and then Eq. (10) becomes

$$H(AB) = H(A) + H_A(B) \tag{12}$$

which is intuitively very acceptable. In ordinary language, it may be read: The amount of uncertainty in the joint experiment A followed by B is equal to the sum of the uncertainty in the experiment A and the average uncertainty in B which remains after A has been performed.

The function $H = H(p_1, p_2, \cdots, p_n)$ also possesses two further properties, namely,

$$H \geq 0 \tag{13}$$

$$H(p_1, p_2, \cdots, p_{n-1}, 0) = H(p_1, p_2, \cdots, p_{n-1}) \tag{14}$$

Clearly, it is desirable that H should possess all the properties represented in Eqs. (12)–(14) and also have its maximum for $p_i = 1/n$. It can be shown that the H of Eq. (4), with $a > 0$, is the only function of the p_i having all these properties (Khinchin, 1957). In other words, we have essentially no choice in our definition if we wish H to have reasonable properties. Then H represents the degree of uncertainty before the experiment is performed and therefore also the information obtained by performing the experiment.

2. Communication and Channel Capacity

Suppose now that our experiment A is performed by a first observer who communicates his result to a second observer. It is natural to say that he communicates a quantity of information H. In particular, if the second observer is replaced by a store which has n states and can therefore be set to record which of the n outcomes of experiment A has occurred, the store will then have an average content of information H. The store has capacity

$$C = \log n \tag{15}$$

and is storing an average amount H, where H satisfies

$$0 \leq H \leq \log n = C \tag{16}$$

Thus, from the statistical viewpoint, the capacity of a store is the maximum amount of information which can be stored. However, unless each $p_i = 1/n$, the actual amount stored will be less than this.

The process of transfer of information from the first observer to the store gives an example of a communication channel. In statistical communication theory, such a transfer is regarded as having three components —a source, a channel, and a receiver (Shannon and Weaver, 1949). The source emits a series of symbols according to some probability regime. In our example, the probabilities of successive symbols are independent, but this assumption is not necessary. It is usual, however, to assume that the sequence forms a stationary and ergodic stochastic process (Khinchin, 1957). Essentially, this means that the probability regime is the same all along the sequence, although individual probabilities may depend on which symbols occurred earlier in the sequence. It also denies the existence either of periodicity or of the process breaking down into entirely independent subprocesses. The latter would occur, for example, if the source could emit four possible symbols $A_1, \cdots, A_4$ but in fact, with probability p, always emitted A_1 or A_2 and, with probability $1 - p$, always emitted A_3 or A_4.

The channel carries the symbols and the receiver receives them. In our example the receiver was the store. Clearly, the store is not allowed to register a symbol for long and would get reset each time a new symbol is transmitted. If we wish to have a store which acts as a permanent memory for all the symbols sent in, say, N transmissions in the channel, we need N replicas of our store. Hence the total necessary capacity of store is $N \log n$, and it can store NH bits of information. Evidently,

$$NH \leq N \log n \tag{17}$$

and the capacity of the store is generally more than the information it actually holds.

This brings us to the idea of coding, by means of which, when

$$NH < N \log n \tag{18}$$

we may generally use a store of smaller capacity to store practically the same amount of information.

Before stating a theorem about this, let us consider a simple example. Suppose a source emits three symbols 1, 2, or 3 with probabilities $p_1 = 0.8$, $p_2 = p_3 = 0.1$. Then it emits information at a rate

$$H_e = -0.8 \log 0.8 - 2 \times 0.1 \log 0.1$$

$$= 0.9217 \tag{19}$$

The capacity of stores having two and three states are, respectively, $\log 2 = 1$ and $\log 3 = 1.58$. Obviously the second store will accurately record the transmitted symbols (with erasure before each new symbol, as discussed above). The first store has only two states, A_1 and A_2, say, and might be used in the following way. Set A_1 if symbol 1 is received and set A_2 if symbol 2 or 3 is received. Then we have, in the store,

$$p(A_1) = 0.8; \qquad p(A_2) = 0.2$$

$$H_s = -0.8 \log 0.8 - 0.2 \log 0.2$$

$$= 0.7218 \tag{20}$$

We have lost an amount of information

$$\Delta H = H_e - H_s = 0.1999 \tag{21}$$

because we cannot tell by inspecting the store whether the symbol 2 or 3 was transmitted, in the case that either of them has been.

This gives a simple example of a code. However we could use a different code and set A_1 when 1 or 2 is transmitted and set A_2 when 3 is transmitted. Then

$$p(A_1) = 0.9; \qquad p(A_2) = 0.1$$

$$H_s = 0.4689; \qquad \Delta H = 0.4528 \tag{22}$$

We have lost a much larger amount of information. Evidently our first code is a more efficient one.

Instead of concentrating on the store, we may suppose the channel has only two symbols it can transmit. Then the three emitted symbols must be coded in terms of the two, A_1 and A_2 of the channel. Finally, the channel transmits A_1 or A_2 to the receiver. The channel is now said to have a capacity of $C = \log 2 = 1$. This capacity is achieved if A_1 and A_2 have equal probabilities, for then 1 bit per symbol is transmitted. However in our example, at most 0.7218 bit per symbol passes along the channel.

We can do better than this by coding into pairs of successive symbols as in the following tabulation.

Send	$A_1 A_1$	$A_1 A_2$	$A_2 A_1$	$A_2 A_2$
When i, j is	11	12, 22, 23	13, 32, 33	21, 31
Total probability	0.64	0.10	0.10	0.16

We readily find, for the information content per symbol,

$$H_s = \tfrac{1}{2}\{-0.64 \log 0.64 - 2 \times 0.1 \log 0.1 - 0.16 \log 0.16\}$$

$$= 0.7496 \qquad\qquad (23)$$

$$\Delta H = 0.1721$$

With coding three successive symbols at a time, we can achieve

$$H_s = 0.7896; \qquad \Delta H = 0.1321 \qquad\qquad (24)$$

The information loss ΔH clearly decreases significantly from Eq. (21) to Eq. (24). Does it tend to zero with increasing coding length?

The answer to this is "yes" and is a particular case of Shannon's theorem for information transmission in a noiseless channel. A channel is noiseless if it is possible to reconstruct the emitted sequence from the received sequence. In our example, the channel was noiseless because A_1 is received when A_1 is transmitted and similarly for A_2. For such a channel, Shannon's theorem asserts that, if the information content H of the source is less than the capacity $C = \log n$ of the channel, then, by coding with sufficiently long sequences, the information loss ΔH may be made arbitrarily small. If $C < H$, then this is not possible (although, see Khinchin, 1957, p. 119) and $\Delta H > H - C$, although it may be made arbitrarily close to $H - C$ with suitable coding.

This concludes our introduction to information theory, and we reiterate that the definition of capacity of a store does not depend on statistical considerations. However that capacity coincides with the definition of capacity in the statistical theory. The statistical theory is presumably most useful in discussing constantly recurring events in an animal, such as the firing of nerve cells, or in its environment. Rare events, occurring perhaps once in a lifetime, are more difficult to discuss in this way, especially because of the usual requirement in information theory of stationary stochastic processes. Because of its birth, maturation, and death, the interaction of an animal with its environment can hardly be called a stationary process.

II. Nerve Cells

A typical vertebrate nerve cell consists of three parts—soma, dendrites, and axon. This is shown schematically in Fig. 2. The soma(s) or perikaryon is the body of the cell and contains the cell nucleus. To the left in Fig. 2 is shown a number of thin branching processes called dendrites (d); to the right a single process, called the axon, leaves the cell and may also branch. Typically there are several dendrites and only one axon leaving the soma.

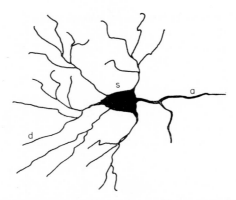

F𝕀G. 2. Schematic diagram of a vertebrate nerve cell; s, soma; d, dendrites; a, axon.

The dendrites may have a hundred branches in all. Nerve cells, however, vary extremely in size, extension of branches, and in form. For example, even the position of the soma in Fig. 2, which suggests a sort of head-quarters into which the dendrites gather and out of which the axon leads, may be somewhat deceptive, for in some cells the soma is off to one side and only connected by a branch to the dendritic-axonal structure (for a review, see Bodian, 1962).

The most important property of a nerve cell is its excitability. The surface membrane is normally semipermeable, resulting in the interior being at about -70 mV relative to the exterior. This is the so-called resting condition. If this potential difference is artificially raised above about -60 mV, the membrane suddenly becomes permeable and the potential is equalized on the two sides. Actually there is a slight overshoot, so that the interior is momentarily positive with respect to the exterior. This process is self-propagating; that is, the electrical breakdown of one stretch of membrane initiates the breakdown of an adjacent piece and the process travels. Shortly after the breakdown, the membrane again recovers and returns to its resting condition. Most of this cycle takes a millisecond or two, but recovery is not complete for 10–100 millisec. This process gives rise to a sequence of measurable potential changes, termed the action potential.

Typically, a mammalian nerve will have excitation traveling into the soma along the dendrites and also directly from end branches of the axon of another (or the same) nerve cell, terminating adjacent to the soma. Joints between neurons are termed *synapses*, and the transmission of excitation across them is mediated chemically. If sufficient excitation reaches the soma, then the nerve cell fires. A wave of excitation then passes out along the axon. A nerve cell is usually, although not invariably, unidirectional (see, e.g.. Fatt, 1958; Roeder, 1963, Chap. 7).

A typical nerve cell thus has a number of inputs and an output. It is believed that the relation between input and output may be described by saying that the nerve cell fires if the number of input excitatory signals reaches a certain threshold value. Thus if $n(e)$ is the number of excitatory inputs and θ is the threshold, then the cell fires if

$$n(e) \geq \theta \tag{25}$$

A cell also usually has inhibitory inputs, and if $n(i)$ is the number of these which are active, then the condition (25) is generalized to

$$n(e) - n(i) \geq \theta \tag{26}$$

Certain things must be said about this simple picture (McCullough and Pitts, 1943). First, the effect of an input is not present at only one moment of time but lasts for a period of the order of a millisecond, decaying thereafter. Thus there is an integration time connected with (26); effects arising from this are termed temporal summation. Second, the simple linear inequality (26) is almost certainly not quantitatively accurate, although it correctly represents the qualitative existence of interaction between a number of excitatory and inhibitory influences which determine when the cell fires. Third, the threshold θ can change for many reasons; in particular, it is infinite immediately after a cell fires, declining after a certain refractory period to its normal value. In thinking about the general behavior of nerve cells, it is often convenient to approximate to this with the assumption that $\theta = \infty$ for a period R after the cell fires, then θ returns immediately to its normal constant value. Fourth, there is evidence that cells fire without receiving an input, at least in the peripheral nervous system (Kuffler et al., 1957). This could be achieved by setting $\theta = 0$ in Eq. (26), although that might not be the best way of incorporating it into a model.

Another interesting point to bear in mind is that the output of a cell may not be completely determined by the input. There could be a random element superposed. In our simple picture this could be introduced by giving θ a probability distribution, rather than a definite value. This would give an intrinsic variability of response which would be, in part at least, transferred to the whole animal (although, see Von Neumann, 1956) and might be regarded as inefficiency in the operating characteristics of the cell. However, remembering from the theory of games (Von Neumann and Morgenstern, 1953) that a certain randomness in response is often a sensible strategy, it may be that evolution favors animals having this property for some, at least, of their nerve cells.

The activity of a nerve cell may be monitored by placing an intracellular, or more usually extracellular, electrode and recording the times t_1, t_2, $\cdots$ at which it fires. This then gives us a time series, and with our approximate assumption about the refractory period, the time series satisfies

$$t_n - t_{n-1} \geq R \qquad \text{(all } n\text{)} \tag{27}$$

III. Information Content of Nerve Cell Firing Sequences

If we suppose, not necessarily accurately, that the time sequence $t_1, t_2, \cdots$ is generated by a stationary stochastic process, we may ask what its information content is.

Such a sequence of pulses may be thought of in one of two equivalent ways. They may be regarded either as the pulses, with their times of occurrence, or as the intervening time intervals between successive pulses. It turns out that the latter is a rather more convenient way for discussing information content.

For reasons which will be apparent shortly, we shall start by supposing that there are only a finite number of distinct intervals possible. Let us label them $\lambda_1, \cdots, \lambda_p$, with p finite. We shall discuss only the case in which the intervals occur independently with probabilities $\phi_1, \cdots, \phi_p$, respectively. This means that the probability of occurrence of a particular interval is independent of which intervals have occurred earlier. Such a process is often termed a renewal process in statistics. First, we consider the information content H_I per interval. This is given immediately by the formula

$$H_I = - \sum_{i=1}^{p} \phi_i \log \phi_i \qquad \text{with} \qquad \sum_{i=1}^{p} \phi_i = 1 \tag{28}$$

The mean length of an interval is

$$m = \sum_{i=1}^{p} \phi_i \lambda_i \tag{29}$$

Therefore the information content H per unit time is given by the ratio

$$H = \frac{H_I}{m} = - \frac{\sum \phi_i \log \phi_i}{\sum \phi_j \lambda_j} \tag{30}$$

Clearly, the value of H depends upon the probabilities ϕ_i. The capacity for the process is defined as the maximum of H for all choices of ϕ_i, that is,

$$C = \max_{(\phi)} H \tag{31}$$

To determine C, we use Lagrange's method of undetermined multipliers, in which we need to satisfy $\delta H = 0$ subject to the condition $\delta \sum \phi_i = 0$.

We have

$$\delta H = \delta \left(\frac{H_I}{m} \right) = \frac{\delta H_I}{m} - \frac{H_I \delta m}{m^2}$$

$$= -m^{-1} \sum (l + \log \phi_i) \delta \phi_i - (H/m) \sum \lambda_i \delta \phi_i \qquad (32)$$

In Eq. (32), $l = \log_2 e$ because the logarithms occurring in Eq. (30) are to base 2 not to base e. We now set

$$\delta H - \mu \delta \sum \phi_i = 0$$

and take the coefficient of $\delta \phi_i$. This is

$$-m^{-1}(l + \log \phi_i) - (H/m)\lambda_i - \mu = 0$$

or

$$l + \log \phi_i + H\lambda_i + \mu m = 0 \qquad (33)$$

We now determine μ by multiplying through by ϕ_i and summing over i. This gives

$$\sum (l\phi_i + \phi_i \log \phi_i + H\lambda_i \phi_i + \mu m \phi_i) = 0$$

or

$$l - H_I + Hm + \mu m = 0$$

$$\mu = -l/m \qquad (34)$$

Using this value of μ, Eq. (33) simplifies to

$$\log \phi_i + H\lambda_i = 0$$

and so

$$\phi_i = 2^{-H\lambda_i} \qquad (35)$$

H itself is determined from the normalization condition for the probabilities, given in Eq. (28). In other words,

$$1 = \sum \phi_i = \sum 2^{-H\lambda_i} \qquad (36)$$

The preceding method is closely related to those used in corresponding situations in statistical mechanics. Section III is based on a discussion given by Wall *et al.* (1956), following a partially incorrect treatment by MacKay and McCullough (1952). See also Rapoport (1955). Another derivation of Eq. (36) was given by Shannon in his classic work on information theory (Shannon and Weaver, 1949). The connection with Shannon's result is most easily seen by setting $y = 2^{-H}$, so that $H = -\log y$. Then Eq. (36) becomes

$$\sum y^{\lambda_i} = 1 \qquad (37)$$

Equation (37) is given in Shannon and Weaver (1949, p. 8).

We have established our result for p finite; then H is finite. It is given by taking that value of y which is the smallest real positive root of Eq. (37). In case we let $p \to \infty$, then H may become infinite, as we show in a particular case in a moment.

We shall now apply our general formulas to some examples.

Example 1. Here we suppose that all the intervals are multiples of a unit τ. Obviously, the value of τ merely sets the time scale, and so to start with we shall put $\tau = 1$. The simplest case obtains when we take all multiples up to a certain value, say p. In other words we set $\lambda_i = i$. In this case, Eq. (37) becomes

$$\sum_{i=1}^{p} y^i = 1 = \frac{y^{p+1} - y}{y - 1}$$

Hence y is a solution of

$$f(y) \equiv y^{p+1} - 2y + 1 = 0 \tag{38}$$

where we reject a spurious root $y = 1$. The solution we are looking for is that y which is real, positive, and as near zero as possible. If $p = 1$, we have $y = 1$ and $H = 0$. This is to be expected, because in this case there is only one distinct length of interval and therefore the information content is zero. If $p > 1$, it is easy to see that there is just one real root in the open interval $(0, 1)$ and that this root satisfies $y > \frac{1}{2}$. Hence $H = -\log_2 y < 1$. It is also easily shown that, as p runs from 0 to ∞, so H runs from 0 to 1. The actual values may be easily computed, and a number of them are given in Table I.

The fact that $H = 1$ for $p = \infty$ is to be expected. because this means that at each point where it is possible to have a pulse we now have a completely free choice of having one or not. Hence there is 1 bit of information per pulse point, i.e., 1 per interval.

If $\tau \neq 1$, the values are the same as before but are now H per interval of length τ. Thus if time is quantized in units of $1/n$ seconds with, there-

TABLE I

VALUES OF H, ALLOWING INTERVALS OF LENGTH 1, 2, ..., p

p	H	p	H
1	0	6	0.988
2	0.694	7	0.994
3	0.879	8	0.997
4	0.947	9	0.999
5	0.975	∞	1

fore, a maximum pulse rate n per second. then $H = n$ per second when $p = \infty$. It is also evident from this, if we allow messages unrestricted in length, that the information carrying capacity is infinite. There is no reason to suppose that the pulse sequences arising from nerve cells actually have their intervals restricted in length. Because of this, the information content of a nerve cell firing sequence is arbitrarily large, depending on the accuracy of our recording technique. However, because of the finite integration time of a nerve cell, the subsequent nerve cells can only interpret the sequence to an accuracy, τ say, of the order of milliseconds. One approximate way of introducing this effect is to say that, since no intervals differing by less than τ are recognizably different, then we should take all messages to be a multiple of τ in the mathematical theory. This gives a convenient model, and we shall call τ the *relevance time* of the sequence.

Example 2. We now consider the case in which all intervals are a multiple of a unit τ but with a minimum possible length $n\tau$ for an interval. This example illustrates the situation when we have a refractory period. Again put $\tau = 1$ at first. Then we have

$$1 = \sum_{i=n}^{p} y^i = \sum_{i=0}^{p} y^i - \sum_{i=0}^{n-1} y^i = \frac{y^{p+1} - 1}{y - 1} - \frac{y^n - 1}{y - 1}$$

which reduces to

$$f_p(y) \equiv y^{p+1} - y^n - y + 1 = 0 \tag{39}$$

where again there is one spurious root at $y = 1$. As $p \to \infty$, the value of y in which we are interested tends to the solution of

$$f(y) \equiv y^n + y - 1 = 0 \tag{40}$$

We shall only consider this equation, which corresponds to the situation when all intervals of length $n\tau$ and over are allowed.

When $n = 1$, we have $y = \frac{1}{2}$ and $H = 1$ in accordance with our previous example. When $n \to \infty$, we find $y \to 1$ and $H \to 0$, as might be expected.

Let us now consider what happens when the refractory period $n\tau = R$ remains constant but the relevance time becomes increasingly small. This will be found by letting $n \to \infty$ subject to R remaining constant. The information content per second is now

$$H' = \tau^{-1}H = -\tau^{-1}\log y$$

$$= -(n/R)\log y \tag{41}$$

We shall obtain an asymptotic expression for H'. This is most conveniently done by setting $y = 1 - \epsilon(n)$. For n large, ϵ will be small. Equation (40) now becomes

$$y^n = \epsilon(n) \tag{42}$$

to which we easily see an approximate solution

$$\epsilon(n) = \ln n / n \tag{43}$$

This gives

$$H' = R^{-1}(\log n - \log \ln n) \tag{44}$$

The next stage in the approximation is

$$H' = R^{-1}\left(\log n - \log \ln n + \frac{\log e \ln \ln n}{\ln n}\right) \tag{45}$$

This shows that, although, if we have a refractory period, the information carrying capacity per second still tends to infinity as the relevance time tends to zero, it does so only very slowly. The capacity is much more sensitively dependent upon the refractory period itself. As an illustration of the dependence of H' on n, we find that, per unit of R, $H' = 1$ when $n = 1$; $H' = 1.39$ when $n = 2$; and $H' = 7.60$ when $n = 1024$. Thus in going from $n = 1$ to $n = 1024$, we only increase the capacity by a factor of 7.6 rather than by the factor of 1024, which would hold if there were no refractory period. Some idea of the accuracy of the approximation given in Eq. (45) is obtained by noting that it gives $H' = 7.61$ when $n = 1024$.

One result of the insensitivity of H' to n is that, from the information carrying viewpoint, there would not seem to be much point in making τ very small compared with R. In fact one might expect τ and R to be of the same order of magnitude. This is in fact the case experimentally, both τ and R being of the order of milliseeonds.

Example 3. We now consider what we may call a Poisson quantized process. At each point 0, τ, 2τ, $\cdots$, $n\tau$, $\cdots$, let us suppose there is a probability p of firing and that the probability of firing at one point is independent of that at all other points. Then the interval of length $n\tau$ has the probability

$$P(n) = p(1 - p)^{n-1} \tag{46}$$

where

$$\sum_{n=1}^{\infty} P(n) = 1 \tag{47}$$

The information content H per unit τ is

$$H = -p \log p - (1 - p) \log (1 - p)$$

This has its maximum at $p = \frac{1}{2}$, when $H = 1$ and $P(n) = 2^{-n} = 2^{-nH}$, which agrees with our earlier results, including Eq. (36).

TABLE II

VALUES OF H FOR POISSON QUANTIZED PROCESS

p	0.5	0.1	0.01	0.001
H	1	0.4689	0.0807	0.0113

Although H has its maximum for $p = \frac{1}{2}$, it is not terribly sensitive to the value of p. We show H for various values of p in Table II (see also Fig. 1). Fairly typical values for p determined experimentally lie in the range 0.01 to 0.001 (see, e.g., Griffith and Horn, 1963; Herz et al., 1964). Hence $H \simeq 10$–100 bits per second, which is, however, considerably less than the theoretical possibility of about 1000 per second based on a relevance time of 1 millisec. Nerve cells are normally capable of firing at rates up to about 1000 per second, and therefore it would be possible for them to make full use of their information carrying capacity of 1000 bits per second. Evidently, considerations other than these simple information-theoretic ones are responsible.

IV. Memory

A. Information Capacity of the Brain

It is not easy to define precisely the information capacity of the brain. However, we should certainly distinguish between instinctive and learned behavior or knowledge. The former is presumably written into the brain, largely genetically, in the form of neuronal thresholds, patterns of connections and similar things. The latter needs a store and if the store has capacity C, this means it can be in any one of 2^C distinct states. We shall not concern ourselves with the first kind of knowledge although, obviously, a considerable amount of information capacity in DNA may need to be used for it. The second kind is not nearly as easy to recognize as might appear at first sight.

For example, suppose an animal has a highly complicated instinctive behavior pattern which is not completely specified at birth. Perhaps the value of a parameter needs to be set at one of x various possible values. Then unless this is realized, the resultant variability of the observed behavior may be taken to mean that it has all been learned. It might then take an external observer many thousands of bits to specify the pattern, and he might suppose the animal can learn and store that number of bits rather than the very few bits which $\log x$ would be.

This consideration is not merely a logical possibility, but is almost certainly very important in practice. Interesting examples occur in the learning of song by birds. Thorpe (1961, especially Chap. 5) summarizes a lot of work in this field. In his own work on chaffinches, he finds that a bird brought up isolated from other birds, and unable to hear them, will nevertheless produce a song but of a much simplified nature. This song is, however, clearly related to the normal song. In other words the bird sings something, but does not get it quite right unless it has the opportunity to listen to other birds and thereby "set a few parameters correctly." The word "correctly," here, means correctly relative to the songs of its fellows. Another example is given by the phenomenon of "imprinting" which is common in many if not all higher animals. Here the animal has a largely instinctive pattern of behavior toward its mother. However it has to learn which is its mother and does this during a short and usually well-defined period of early childhood. That it really learns this is shown by the fact that it can be made to accept a range of alternative "mothers." The ugly duckling was persuaded to accept a duck as its mother, but the modern experimenter can make it accept many other alternatives, even entirely nonliving ones. The existence of imprinting is less certain for humans, although it is well known for monkeys, but it is at least likely. Certainly there is a great range of similar phenomena occurring widely in the animal kingdom, including humans (Scott, 1962).

Another point to bear in mind is that abilities which are present later in life, but not earlier, are not necessarily learned. They can only reasonably be termed "learned" if they can be modified or suppressed by past experience. This would not always seem to be realized; for example, it cannot be deduced that the eye-closure reflex in humans must be learned, because it is not present in the new-born child. It does seem to be learned, but this fact is not in itself sufficient evidence for it.

A related matter is that an animal (or human) may store a fact which, from the human scientist's point of view, seems to be a typical member of a set S consisting of n elements. The scientist might then be tempted to say that log n bits of information were stored. However the brain may be storing according to entirely different principles, according to which the fact is a typical member of a set S' with n' elements. Log n' may be considerably less, or more, than log n. An example of this for a computer is that, if one tried to store the first million primes in a computer with a million-bit memory, there would not be room. Write, however, a program to replace the number x by the xth prime p_x and there would be room. You can "store" the million primes in this way if you recognize that they are primes, i.e., that they belong to a limited class with special properties.

Similarly, when an animal learns a complicated task, it may actually store less or *more* information than you would calculate from a particular classification of the choices needed to define the task.

Of course there are experiments in which it is possible to state a clear lower limit to the information recorded. If one asks a human to learn a sequence of n letters, each of which is chosen at random, it is natural to say that, on average, he has stored at least $n \log 26 \doteq 4.7n$ bits of information. We can only say this "on average," because it is well known from psychological experiments that "meaningful" sequences are learned more easily than "meaningless" ones, and so, perhaps, there is a sense in which we can say that the sequences are coded so that the more frequent, meaningful ones take up a smaller storage space in the brain than the less frequent, meaningless ones. That, of course, is mere speculation but it illustrates a consideration which has to be taken into account in particular cases.

This leads us on to the question: Can we obtain a lower limit of the human information capacity by asking how many books he can learn by heart? I do not know of any precise attempt along these lines; however I suppose the total content of the *Encylopaedia Britannica* would be roughly comparable to a lifetime's work and might at least give an order-of-magnitude estimate. The problem of the information content of written English has been often discussed (see, e.g., Shannon and Weaver, 1949). There is the fundamental problem of whether it should be calculated on the assumption that English is a stationary stochastic process. If one leaves this difficulty aside, there is still the problem of estimating the extent of sequential dependence. If there is none, we have $H \doteq \log 27 = 4.75$ bits per letter or space. If we take into account the letter frequencies, which are of course not all equal, we get $H \doteq 4.1$. Taking into account higher sequential dependence gets us a lower value for H. The lowest estimate I know is about 3.3. This gives us about 10^9 bits for the information content of the *Encyclopaedia Britannica*. Even such a figure is to be regarded with caution in both directions. The information content per letter may be less, although perhaps it is not likely to be much less, but also the brain may or may not have a very efficient coding system. If H is the information content of the *Encyclopaedia Britannica* and C is the capacity necessary to store it, then $C > H$, but it may be that C is much greater than H.

B. Numerical Values

We shall now discuss the magnitude of the information capacity of the human memory, and we shall admit at the start that we do not know what it is. However various methods give orders of magnitude, as our discussion of the *Encyclopaedia Britannica* did, and we shall not try to be more precise than that (for other discussions of this matter, see Von Neumann, 1958; Wooldridge, 1963). If C is the capacity, we shall express our results to the nearest integer as $\mu = \log_{10} C$. Our estimate from books was then, $\mu \simeq 9$ or, if you prefer, $\mu > 9$.

The next method is called the psychological method. Here you measure the rate per second at which information of the type of words or pictures can be stored. Whether they are stored is tested by whether they can be reproduced at the time. Such methods are said to give of the order of 10 bits per second (Quastler, 1956), although there is the usual problem of precisely how much information is presented in such cases. This is then grossed up over a lifetime. A lifetime has 1–3×10^9 sec and hence $\mu \doteq 10$–11. Note, however, that "forgetting" is ignored in this calculation, so if one believes the other premises of it, one would presumably write $\mu < 10$–11.

The next methods are physiological. The largest input is via the visual tract, which has about 10^8 primary receptor cells in the retina and about 10^6 in the optic nerve. We previously calculated 10–100 bits per second per nerve cell, so if all information at the retinal level is stored, we have $\mu \doteq 18$–19. If we suppose information is lost before the optic nerve is reached, we can estimate at the optic nerve and obtain $\mu \doteq 16$–17. It seems extremely unlikely that this much information even gets to the brain, let alone is stored; however this method of estimation has been seriously proposed (Von Neumann, 1958).

Finally, if one supposes the brain stores a full memory of everything that takes place inside itself, one gets a somewhat larger figure still. There are approximately 10^{10} neurons in the brain, so if all their activity is stored we get $\mu \doteq 20$–21.

With the exception of our first estimate, all these values are based on grossing up the most favorable cases and assuming no forgetting. The assumption of no forgetting is usually defended by quoting rather spectacular examples of recall from the distant past, often under the influence of hypnotism or direct electrical stimulation of the cortex. All that such examples, and the reliable ones seem few in number, prove is that detailed accurate memory at the psychological level is possible over long periods, not that it always occurs. It is obviously unrealistic to be dogmatic about this matter at the present time, but my personal perusal of the psychological literature on learning with its normal concomitant, forgetting, makes me feel it is much more likely that these spectacular examples are atypical and misleading.

My personal view is that, with our present limited knowledge, a reasonable estimate of μ at the present time is 9–10. Further, I think it remains to be proved that $\mu > 8$. I think there is no evidence that $\mu > 11$.

C. The Process of Storage and Recall

Experimentally, a distinction appears between short-term memory and long-term memory. It appears that a certain period is necessary for long-term memory to be laid down. The traditional way in which this emerges is through the phenomenon of retrograde amnesia (Russell, 1959). A man who has a severe concussion characteristically cannot remember events for a period, which may be minutes or days, before his concussion. It is believed that this means that, whatever the process of memory is, it takes rather a long time to be "permanently" registered. If the metabolism of the cells is upset during this period, the process is also upset and the memory partially or completely lost. The very long times associated with this might suggest that memory is more likely to be based on a cellular growth process than any simple chemical one, but such an argument is not compelling, of course.

On the other hand, recall is often essentially instantaneous. This might be taken to suggest that the action of the stored memories is permanently to alter cellular parameters, such as threshold or synaptic strength, rather than that they are in some form which necessitates a complex decoding procedure each time they are used.

Finally, it seems likely that memory is distributed, that is, each memory has its trace spread over a large part of the brain. This is indicated by the classical experiments of Lashley on rats, in which they were trained and then regions of the cortex extirpated (Lashley, 1963). The loss of memory is then roughly proportional to the area extirpated. This is to be contrasted with the situation which would hold if each memory were stored in a special localized place, for then extirpation would generally either completely annihilate a given memory or leave it entirely undisturbed. A distributed memory often alarms the biologist, because it implies that memories are all on top of each other, higgledy-piggledy, as if someone were to draw a lot of pictures on top of each other on the same piece of paper. It should not upset the physicist, once he realizes that something akin to a Fourier analysis could easily distinguish the traces. There is no *a priori* reason for supposing the brain would find a Fourier analysis more difficult than a search along a set of localized traces for one having some particular characteristic.

D. Proposals for the Nature of Memory

1. Nucleic Acid

It is very fashionable to try to implicate nucleic acid in memory, although most people who do so are usually careful not to explain in detail how it is supposed to participate. It seems to me that there are three main possibilities here:

1. Memory is coded on DNA or RNA in the same way, or in a similar way, to the coding of genetic information. In this case 4.32 bits per nucleotide can be stored.

2. Memory is stored by the production of a metabolically stable mRNA, which produces one or more proteins which exert some control over the electrical activity of the nerve cell. The sequence of the mRNA is determined genetically from the DNA; only the amount present in the cell at a given time represents the memory trace.

3. Some permanent change in the cell occurs, which gives the basis of the memory trace. This change, in itself, does not involve DNA or RNA, but it can only come about through the mediation of RNA and, perhaps, a temporary increase in the amount of RNA.

On general grounds, the first possibility would seem rather unlikely. As far as DNA is concerned, such a proposal would mean that the DNA of a nerve cell is modifiable by external factors. If such a mechanism were used in nervous tissue, it would be rather surprising that "inheritance of acquired characteristics" does not also occur. For both DNA and RNA, such a mechanism would presumably require a fairly complex coding and decoding mechanism which might be expected to take seconds at least. The speed of recall, in many cases, suggests that there is no such slow decoding mechanism. Then there is the comparative argument. Learning occurs among most, if not all, of the animal kingdom, apparently reaching its highest peak in man. Animals which can learn little and slowly surely do not possess such a sophisticated mechanism. Does the mechanism, then, suddenly appear at some level in evolution? This would seem unlikely. However, none of the preceding arguments are entirely convincing, but they seem to me to be strongly suggestive.

The next thing to consider is storage capacity. If we believe that $\mu \doteqdot$ 16–21, then there is a real problem as to where and how so much information can be stored. This problem would make us view the genetic-type coding with favor. If, however, we believe $\mu \doteqdot$ 9–11, then there is no problem of this kind, as we shall discuss shortly.

Finally, and obviously most important of all, there is the experimental approach. Here there would seem to be no reliable evidence to implicate nucleic acid as the actual store of memory. A great deal of interest has been aroused by the work of McConnell (1962) and his collaborators. It is claimed that planaria can learn conditioned responses and that this training can be transferred to other (untrained) planaria by chopping up the trained ones and feeding them to the others. It is important to note that it is not claimed that the "fed" planaria are now conditioned, but merely that they take less time to learn the conditioning if they are fed on their learned colleagues than if not ("savings" and not "retention" in the psychologist's sense). However this work has been criticized both on general methodological grounds (Jensen, 1965) and also with respect to the specific claim for transfer of learning by cannibalism (Hartry *et al.*, 1964). At present it would certainly seem that McConnell has not entirely proved his case; the reader is referred to the literature for further discussion.

Experimental evidence for the alteration of levels of RNA, proteins, cytochrome oxidase, and succinic oxidase in both glial and nerve cells after stimulation has been provided by Hydén (1961). This work is interesting and important, but it is not easy to decide what it tells one about the nature of long-term memory. (For further references to experimental work and for another recent discussion of the nucleic acid hypothesis, see Dingman and Sporn, 1964.)

The present position seems to be that possibility (1) has no solid experimental evidence in its favor, and seems most unlikely. Possibility (2) implies the presence of a metabolically stable mRNA. Otherwise, either (2) or (3) seems to be perfectly plausible.

2. Circulating Impulses

It is necessary to mention the circulating impulse model of memory, although it is now in disrepute. By analogy with certain computer storage procedures, it was suggested that memory might occur by streams of pulses passing continually around closed cycles of neurons. Such a self-excitatory process could, obviously, last indefinitely. Perhaps the strongest argument against this is that neither general epilepsy nor electroconvulsive therapy have much effect on long-term memory. If the latter were based on circulating impulses, one might expect the patterns to be completely disrupted and all long-term memory to disappear. Short-term memory is quite a different matter and, if not based necessarily on cycles, might very well be based on a potentiated reverberating firing activity in the nerve cells.

3. Other Possibilities

It was remarked by Beurle (1956) that any permanent change in the characteristics of nerve cells or their interactions would really serve as a basis for memory. Until we have experimental evidence of what basis is used or, at least, have a decent theoretical model of the nature of thought, including memory, we can hardly distinguish between various possibilities in this category.

What sort of permanent changes are possible? There are many but the most obvious are that there is a change in the threshold θ of a cell (or even in its randomness of response, see Section II), dependent upon use, or a change in the connectivity of pairs of cells, depending on the number of times they fire together. The specification of the threshold to a significant accuracy might need 10 bits, so we could get $\mu \doteq 11$ by this method. A change in connectivity from one cell might involve anything between 10^2 and 10^4 connected cells, and each connection might need 1–10 bits to specify its strength. This gives a possible $\mu \doteq 12$–15. Such methods would seem to give sufficient capacity.

It has been remarked that in the brain, as well as in nerve cells, there are other cells called glial cells which surround and nourish the nerve cells (see, e.g., Schmitt, 1961). It is possible that the glial cells store the memory and that the nerve cells are merely passive participants. The glial cells might control the thresholds of the nerve cells by providing more or less nourishment. There are probably 10^{10}–10^{11} glial cells in the brain, so this type of store might yield $\mu \doteq 11$–12.

The mechanism of these changes could be due to growth of the cell. It could be due to the production in the cell of a metabolically stable compound, X say, which either catalyzed or inhibited one or more reactions which controlled the activity of the cell. Of course, X could be mRNA, although it could equally be some totally different kind of compound, such as a phospholipid. For a discussion of a promising experimental approach to these problems, see Bennett et al. (1964).

Let me conclude by summarizing my rather negative and dull view. I believe there is no evidence even to suggest seriously that the information capacity of the human brain lies outside the range 10^9–10^{11} bits. It seems to me most unlikely that memory is stored on DNA or RNA in the way in which genetic information is stored. It seems quite unnecessary to postulate any exotic mechanism whatever, nor, apart from the fact that we do not know exactly how it is stored, does there seem to be anything paradoxical or magically mysterious about the nature of the memory trace. On the other hand, there seems to be considerable experimental difficulty in determining its nature and considerable theoretical difficulty in the overall organizational problem involved in its laying down and, especially, recall.

REFERENCES

Bennett, E. L., Diamond, M. C., Krech, D., and Rosenzweig, M. R. (1964). *Science* **146,** 610.

Beurle, R. L. (1956). *Phil. Trans. Roy. Soc. London* **B240,** 55.

Bodian, D. (1962). *Science* **137,** 323.

Brillouin, L. (1962). "Science and Information Theory." Academic Press, New York.

Crick, F. H. C. (1963). *Science* **139**, 461.

Crick, F. H. C., Griffith, J. S., and Orgel, L. E. (1957). *Proc. Natl. Acad. Sci. U.S.*, **43**, 416.

Dingman, W., and Sporn, M. B. (1964). *Science* **144**, 26.

Fatt, R. (1958). *Rept. Progr. Phys.* **21**, 112.

Griffith, J. S., and Horn, G. (1963). *Nature* **199**, 876.

Hartry, A. L., Keith-Lee, P., and Morton, W. D. (1964). *Science* **146**, 274.

Herz, A., Creutzfeldt, O., and Fuster, J. (1964). *Kybernetik* **II**, 61.

Hydén, H. (1961). *In* "Macromolecular Specificity and Biological Memory" (F. O. Schmitt, ed.), p. 55. M.I.T. Press, Cambridge, Massachusetts.

Jensen, D. D. (1965). *Animal Behaviour*, Supplement, in press.

Khinchin, A. I. (1957). "Mathematical Foundations of Information Theory." Dover, New York.

Kuffler, S. W., Fitzhugh, R., and Barlow, H. B. (1957). *J. Gen. Physiol.* **40**, 683.

Lashley, K. S. (1963). "Brain Mechanisms and Intelligence." Dover, New York.

McConnell, J. V. (1962). *J. Neuropsychiat.* **3**, Suppl. 1, S42.

McCullough, W. S., and Pitts, W. H. (1943). *Bull. Math. Biophys.* **5**, 115.

MacKay, D. K., and McCullough, W. S. (1952). *Bull. Math. Biophys.* **14**, 127.

Quastler, H. (1956). "Information Theory" (C. Cherry, ed.), p. 361. Butterworth's, London.

Rapoport, A. (1955). *Bull. Math. Biophys.* **17**, 15.

Roeder, K. D. (1963). "Nerve Cells and Insect Behavior." Harvard University Press, Cambridge, Massachusetts.

Russell, W. R. (1959). "Brain, Memory, Learning." Oxford University Press, London and New York.

Schmitt, F. O. (ed.) (1961). "Macromolecular Specificity and Biological Memory". M.I.T. Press, Cambridge, Massachusetts.

Scott, J. P. (1962). *Science* **138**, 949.

Shannon, C. E., and Weaver, W. (1949). The "Mathematical Theory of Communication." University of Illinois Press, Urbana, Illinois.

Thorpe, W. H. (1961). "Bird-Song." Cambridge University Press, London and New York.

Von Neumann, J. (1956). *In* "Automata Studies" (C. E. Shannon and J. McCarthy, eds.), p. 43. Princeton University Press, Princeton, New Jersey.

Von Neumann, J. (1958). "The Computer and the Brain." Yale University Press, New Haven, Connecticut.

Von Neumann, J., and Morgenstern, O. (1953). "Theory of Games and Economic Behavior." Princeton University Press, Princeton, New Jersey.

Wall, P. D., Lettvin, J. Y., McCullough, W. S., and Pitts, W. H. (1956). "Information Theory" (C. Cherry, ed.), p. 336. Butterworth, London.

Wooldridge, D. E. (1963). "The Machinery of the Brain." McGraw-Hill, New York.

Author Index

Numbers in italics refer to pages on which the complete references are listed.

Stapleton, R., 61, 66, *75*
Steele, R. H., 207, 238
Stent, G., 73, *79*
Stephen, M. J., 331, 335, 337, 338, *342*
Stephenson, M. L., 5, 6, 7, *76*
Sternlicht, H., 248, *267, 324,* 332, *342*
Stevens, A., 37, *79*
Stevens, K. W. H., 194, 196, *202, 203*
Stevenson, R. W. H., 192, *203*
Stodolsky, M., 49, *80*
Stone, A. L., 144, *189*
Strauss, N., 63, *79*
Streisinger, G., 409, *410*
Streitwieser, A., 102, 110, *115*
Stretton, D. W., 35, *79*
Strominger, D., 192, *203*
Struck, W. A., 168, *189*
Suard, M. 105, 106, 109, *113, 115,* 124, *189*
Sueoka, N., 6, 17, *79*
Sugano, S., 194, *203*
Sundararajan, T. A., *57, 77*
Suskind, S. R., 11, *79*
Sutton, L. E., 136, *187, 189*
Swartz, M. M., 359, *368*
Sypherd, P. S., 63, *79*
Szent-Györgyi, A. G., 397, 400, 401, *410*
Szent-Györgyi, A. L., 207, *238*
Szer, O. W., 39, *79*
Szybalski, W., 135, *189*

T

Takanami, M., 33, *79*
Tanabe, Y., 194, *203*
Tanaka, K., 7, 8, *74*
Tanford, C., 369, *396*
Taylor, A. L., 13, 14, *79*
Taylor, J. H., 16, *79, 368*
Tener, G. M., 8, *74*
Terenin, A. N., 247, *267*
Tessman, I., 179, *186*
Thomas, C. A., 17, *74, 80, 368*
Thomas, D. D., 315, 318, 320, 321, *324*
Thomson, C., 237, *238*
Thorpe, W. H., 428, *435*
Timasheff, S. N., 31, *79*
Tinkham, M., *238*
Tinoco, I., Jr., 123, 136, 137, 140, *185,* 281, 282, 283, 284, 285, *291*
Tissières, A., 6, 19, 22, 23, *79, 80*
Tocchini-Valentini, G. P., 49, 50, *75, 78*

Toebert, G., 52, *79*
Tomasi, J., 303, 308, *309*
Tomita, K. I., 132, *189*
Tomlinson, R. V., 8, *74*
Tomonaga, S., 332, *342*
Townes, C. H., 294, 298, 300, *309*
Townsend, J., 321, *324*
Trambarulo, R. F., 298, *309*
Trasciatti, M., 161, *187*
Trautner, T. A., 359, *368*
Tridgell, E. J., 57, *77*
Trupin, J., 41, *78*
Ts'o, P. O. P., 19, 25, *75, 80,* 135, 152, 154, 155, *185, 186, 189*
Tubbs, R. K., 144, 145, *189*
Turner, J. D., 315, *324*
Turro, N. J., 207, *238*

U

Urnes, P., 285, *291*

V

Vänngärd, T., 198, *202*
Van Der Kaa, J. M., 148, *185*
Vanderslice, J. T., 336, *342*
van der Waals, J. H., 209, 225, 231, 233, 234, 236, 237, *238*
Van de Vorst, A., 170, 171, *189*
Van Vleck, J. H., 95, *115,* 336, *342*
Van Winkle, Q., 144, 145, *189*
Vasilescu, D., 148, 150, *187*
Vaska, L., 198, *203*
Veillard, A., 123, 136, *189*
Villée, F., 170, *189*
Vinograd, J., 14, 17, 19, 25, 75, 80, *368*
Vladimirov, I. A., 207, *238*
Vogel, H., 55, *80*
Vogt, M., 14, *75*
Volkin, E., 36, 37, *80*
Von Ehrenstein, G., 9, 41, *74, 80*
von Hippel, P. H., 401, *410*
Von Neumann, J., 421, 430, *435*
Vosick, M., 407, *410*

W

Wacker, A., 173, 174, *189*
Wada, A., 339, *342*
Wahba, A. J., 35, 40, 41, *79, 80*
Wahl, A. C., 91, 97, *115*
Wake, R. G., *368*

Subject Index

A

Absorption, of polarized light by polymers, 269
Actin, 397–409
Actinomycin, 52, 164, 165
Actomyosin, 401, 403
Adenine
    dipole moment, 138
    electron-donor properties, 160
    interaction with actinomycin, 165
        with 3,4-benzopyrene, 156, 157, 159
    ionization potential, 150, 169
    polarizability, 154
    resonance stabilization, 129
    spin densities in free radicals, 172, 173
Adenine-thymine pair
    dipole moment, 138
    electron donor-acceptor properties, 144
    electronic charges, 126
Adenosine
    absorption spectrum, 271
    optical rotatory dispersion, 280
Adenylic acid, 282
Alanine, 19, 38
Alloxan, 167, 168
Amino acids
    coding units, 40
    specificity of incorporation, 38
Aminoacridines
    electronic characteristics, 147
    intercalation in DNA, 144
    mutagenic activity, 146
2-Aminopurine, 165
Aminopyrazolopyrimidine, 165
5-Aminouracil, 175, 176, 177
Antimyosin, 400
Arginine, 38, 54
Aromatic hydrocarbons, interaction with nucleic acid bases, 155, 156, 157, 159
Aspartic acid, 38
6-Azathymine, 175, 176

B

Barbituric acid, 167
Base-base interactions, 152

Base pairs, 121
    dipole moment, 138
    electronic charges, 125, 139
    energy characteristics, 124
    interactions between, 135
    resonance stabilization, 130
Benzene, 105, 237
Benzimidazole, 165
3,4-Benzopyrene, 156, 157, 159
Biphotonic processes, 248
Binding process, 370
    of several moles of ligand, 377
    by systems in dynamic equilibrium, 385

C

Caffeine, 156, 157, 159
Carcinogenesis, 155, 162, 179
Charge exchange interactions, 335
Charge transfer complexation, 141, 323, 335
Chromosome, 11
Contraction, mechanochemistry of, 397
Coronene, 237
Cyclobutadiene, 105
Cysteine, 38
Cytosine
    dipole moment, 138
    electron donor properties, 160
    interaction with 3,4-benzopyrene, 156, 156, 159
    ionization potential, 150, 169
    polarizability, 154
    spin densities, 172, 173, 175, 176, 177
    tautomeric forms, 260

D

Deoxyribonucleic acid
    possible implication in memory, 431
    presence of linkers, 15
    ring configuration, 14
    transcription of RNA from, 364
2,6-Diaminopurine, 165
Dichroism, 273
6-Dimethylaminopurine, 156, 157, 159, 165

449